# Recognizing Patterns

# Recognizing Patterns

## *Studies in Living and Automatic Systems*

EDITORS

Paul A. Kolers
Murray Eden

CONTRIBUTORS

Shin-Ho Chung
Jon K. Clemens
Murray Eden
Morris Halle
Samuel Jay Keyser
Paul A. Kolers
Samuel J. Mason
William M. Siebert
Joseph Weizenbaum

The M.I.T. Press
*Massachusetts Institute of Technology*
*Cambridge, Massachusetts, and London, England*

*Set in Times New Roman and*
*printed and bound in the United States of America*
*by the Colonial Press Inc.*



*Library of Congress catalog card number: 68-14443*

*for Nira and Pat*

# Preface

Engineers usually detect or measure things, but until recently the things were hardly to be called patterns. Psychologists, physiologists, linguists, and other students of living systems, in contrast, have been working in the field of pattern recognition for a very long time but until recently had not called it that. The development of the computer as something more than a calculating machine marks the true birth of the area of study we now call pattern recognition, for the computer gave engineers the opportunity to measure things in terms of multiple properties, and finer properties, than they could before; it gave students of living systems a name for their inquiry; and it established a common ground of interest between engineers and students of living systems.

There is a significant conceptual difference between making a machine that will detect a specific wavelength of light, a specific frequency of sound, a voltage, or a weight, and making a machine that will detect objects on the basis of a number of their features, as engineers now attempt to do. In contrast, perhaps the reason that students of living systems never bothered to call their study "pattern recognition" is that it was too obvious a name. Recognizing patterns (and taking action on the basis of the recognition) is the principal thing that all living systems do—a frog flicking its tongue at a fly, a man reading a newspaper, or a scientist studying the frog or the man. In fact, the only serious data on pattern recognition come from the behavior of living systems. Living systems, and people in particular, are the most flexible, efficient, and versatile pattern recognizers known. The real problem of pattern recognition, however, is to generate a theory that specifies the nature of objects in such a way that a machine could identify them. This problem has not yet been solved. Anyone seriously interested in developing automatic pattern recognizers, or working on the theory, can nevertheless learn much from a study of the way living systems operate. This book is a collection of essays with a strong empirical bias that describe various approaches to the problem. The bias is not only empirical, it emphasizes a concern with phenomena found in living systems and explores the common ground.

It may be argued of course that machines are not living systems and that consequently they need not, for they cannot, perform in the same way. The extension of this argument is that the machine is a thing unto itself with its own rules and regularities, so that the development of automatic pattern recognizers can proceed without reference to the successes of living systems. One might say that a bird, for example, is sufficiently different from an airplane that studying the one can contribute nothing to an understanding of the other. To bolster the argument one can point out that early attempts to fly ended in disaster *just because* they were attempts to imitate birds, to have men flap their arms, or "wings" attached to their arms. Airplanes, on the other hand, became possible when inventors gave up the idea of flapping wings and developed the "unnatural" form of propulsion provided by a whirling propeller. But even though this kind of argument is wrong, it is not empty, and in one form or another has been proposed as the basis for ignoring living systems in the design of automatic pattern recognizers. A few words will show why it is wrong.

In the specific case of bird flight and human flight, the argument is wrong because it ignores certain essentials. The early imitators of bird flight made a false analogy. They selected a single attribute of the bird, its flapping wings, and tried to transfer that attribute to men without realizing that it is not its flapping wings alone that enable a bird to fly. It is the wing as a source of lift and thrust moving a body of a certain mass and configuration in a particular medium that describes bird flight. Merely appending flaps to a man's arms does not provide him with the same aerodynamic properties the bird has, and lacking them, necessarily he cannot then fly. Furthermore, as it turns out, he does not have the power in his arms to move flaps of a large enough size rapidly enough to give him the necessary lift, and it is for this reason that the inventor had to look for other sources of power. The basic principles that govern bird flight are not violated by an airplane; the identical principles are preserved in the two cases and only the means by which they are manifested are different. If more had been known about the mechanisms that actually govern a bird's flight, no man would have tried waving his hands or flapping his wings in order to fly. The intelligent study of any successful system can supply principles applicable to another, though their realization in the two cases is likely to be different. The differences in form only serve to demonstrate the reality of the underlying principles. An understanding of how biological systems recognize patterns can only facilitate the development of automatic devices.

The influence of course is not in one direction only. Realization of a successful machine illuminates principles whose operation may be sought in living systems. A machine's operation tends to make starkly clear a principle which in a living system is just one of many and so increases the visibility of that principle in a complex living system. Of course, sometimes the influence is bad. The history of the biological sciences is full of poor analogies taken from machines. It has become almost a truism in psychology and biology that every successful machine becomes a "model," however inappropriate, for understanding living systems. In the past there have been "Galilean theories" of humans (advanced not by Galileo but by Hobbes and LaMettrie), and more recently, "telephone theories" of hearing and "switchboard theories" of the nervous system. Now of course we have "hologram theories" of memory and "computer theories" of the brain.

In the past, engineers erred by taking biological phenomena literally and trying to apply the facts of biological phenomena (such as a flapping wing) to other systems. At present, many people err by taking the facts of a computer and applying them literally to people. The brain is not a computer, nor does it work the way a computer works. Cells are not vacuum tubes, or transistors, or even integrated circuits. Certain measurements made on electronic components can, of course, also be made on brain cells, such as measurements of voltage, impedance, resonant frequency, and the like. But this similarity does not make cells into electronic components. On the other hand, concepts such as coding, feature analysis, parallel processing, and the like, can be applied usefully to living systems. Thus, in both directions—from living systems to automatic ones and the reverse—the discovery of principles facilitates the common endeavor and the application of empty facts does not. We would hope therefore that life scientists and engineers will benefit from this collection, which discusses the operations of some living systems and of some automatic ones.

Our interest in this book is in pattern recognition considered broadly. Some writers on the subject restrict the term to mean the recognizing of two-dimensional visually presented arrays. At this stage of our endeavor, such a restriction serves no conceptually useful purpose; it is, rather, an arbitrarily narrow delimiting of the field. We are using the term in this collection in a far broader sense than that of two-dimensional visual patterns; we mean it to comprise the detection, perception, or recognition of any kind of regularity or relation between things. Both things and the relations between them are patterns; there is little justification for restricting the objects of study to things. Indeed, the recognition even of things requires some formulation of the abstract structure that characterizes them, which is already a formulation of the relations between their identifiable parts. Perhaps the reason that successes in automatic recognizing of patterns have been so few is that the "recognizing" has been built upon the identification of templates (things) rather than upon the principles that guide their construction and of the contexts in which they are found. As there is little logical justification for arranging abstractions dimensionally (that is, in saying that one abstraction is more abstract than another), we have followed the course of taking any relational regularity as an instance of a pattern. Therefore this volume ranges from electrophysiology to the perception of speech in living systems, and from contour-tracing algorithms to the identification of semantic patterns and medical diagnosis by machines.

The volume represents a sampling of interests of the several authors. It is by no means exhaustive of the topic of pattern recognition, of all of the interests of the authors, and certainly not of the institution where most of them work. The volume grew out of a summer session course on pattern recognition at M.I.T. in which the various authors participated. The papers they have since prepared for this volume represent either reviews of a field or descriptions of an approach to problems of pattern recognition. As we make no claims for completeness, at least we have tried for continuity. Thus, as an aid to the reader, we have prefaced each of the chapters with a brief note telling what it is about and what its author usually does to earn his way in the world. The reader will find that the various authors do not always agree with each other. From these disagreements, and from those any reader may feel, will come the syntheses we all work toward.

We acknowledge with gratitude the support for compiling this volume provided principally by the National Institutes of Health (Grant 1 PO1 GM-14940-01) and in part by the Joint Services Electronics Program (Contract DA-28-043-AMC-02536(E)) to the Research Laboratory of Electronics of the Massachusetts Institute of Technology.

PAUL A. KOLERS AND MURRAY EDEN

*Cambridge, Massachusetts*
*June 1967*

# Contents

# PART I: LIVING SYSTEMS

*We lead off our collection with a description of some of the perceptual phenomena psychologists have paid attention to that are relevant to the study of pattern recognition. In the course of describing the issues and the phenomena, the author takes some pains to dismiss one of the analogies from physical systems applied to the psychological: the analogy that one can profitably discuss the brain's functioning in terms of wiring diagrams, or psychological aspects of pattern recognition in terms of template matching. The alternative he illustrates is that human pattern perception is characterized by generative, constructive routines the perceiver applies to inputs that he selects for attention. Some of these depend upon the timing and geometrical arrangement of the inputs, others on more cognitive variables involving conceptions, ideas, wishes, and plans.*

*Paul A. Kolers is a research psychologist whose experimental work is in visual perception and in language. He teaches the psychology of the higher mental functions (cognitive processes) in the Department of Electrical Engineering, where he is a research associate, and conducts his experiments in the Research Laboratory of Electronics at M.I.T.*

# 1. Some Psychological Aspects of Pattern Recognition

*Paul A. Kolers*

Recognizing patterns and visual targets occupies a large part of the daily activity of most humans. Pattern recognition, in this sense, may range from the straightforward identification of a familiar object of everyday use to the detection of trends in a set of data or to finding one's way about a strange environment. The computer scientist interested in developing pattern-recognizing machines sometimes tries to make a machine that will emulate a human perceiver; since humans are, by far, more sophisticated pattern-recognizing devices than even the best of contemporary machines, some knowledge of how humans perceive may aid the engineer in his search. This chapter is a report of experimental findings on the diversity of human pattern recognition. The focus will be on evidence that emphasizes the synthetic, constructive, rule-following aspects of human perception; for it is these features that make human perceiving the flexible, powerful process it is.

First I shall summarize briefly some of the anatomical facts of the visual system in order to point out that their very complexity rules out of serious consideration certain kinds of theories. Following that, I shall describe certain coding operations that characterize human perception of two-dimensional arrays, and then describe phenomena illustrating the temporal course of the formation of simple perceptual experiences. The final sections deal with more complex kinds of pattern perception relating to serial organization of inputs, reading, and exploration of the environment.

## Anatomy

We know definitely only a small portion of the anatomy of the normal human visual system. We know a good deal about the eyes and about the nerve pathways that get signals to the brain, but little about where they go once they reach that complex structure or how they interact with other impulses from within the brain to modify and direct behavior. To make an analogy to the computer: We know a good deal about the various input devices and their operation, but very little about the program. Nevertheless, one fact that stands out with clarity is that human perceiving cannot be adequately understood, if understood at all, as the passive transmission of impulses from physically defined stimuli; rather, perceiving is an active, selective process that often entails a significant

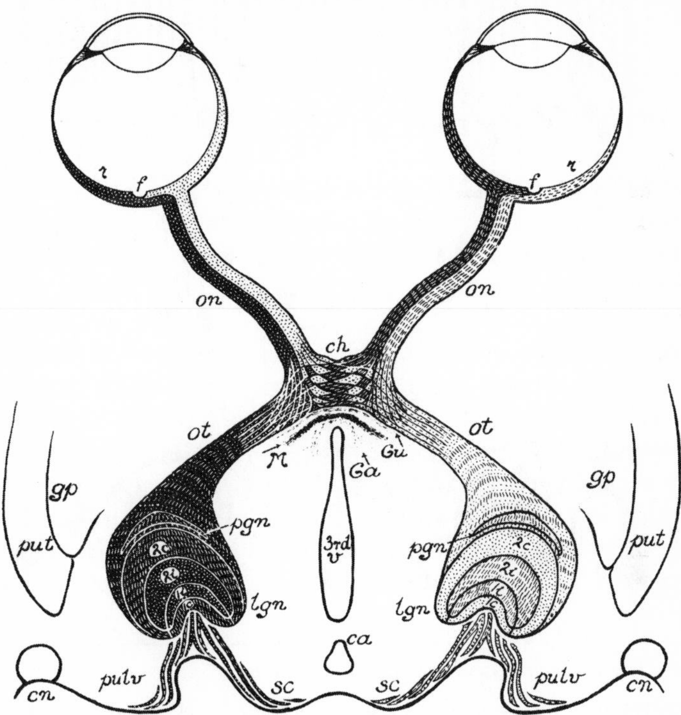


**Fig. 1.1** The visual pathways in Rhesus monkey.

Optic nerve fibers originating from the retinae (r) of both eyes are assembled in the two optic nerves (on). After a partial crossing of nasal fibers in the chiasma (ch), they continue as optic tracts (ot) and terminate in the subcortical visual nuclei: laminated lateral geniculate nuclei (lgn), pregeniculate gray nuclei (pgn), superior colliculi of the midbrain (sc), and possibly also in the pulvinars of the thalami (pulv). No other nuclei of the brain, such as the globus pallidus (gp), the putamen (put), and the caudate nucleus (cn) of the striate bodies, or the commisures of Gudden (Gu), Meynert (M), and Ganser (Ga) are directly related to the visual system. The cerebral aqueduct (*ca*), central fovea (*f*), and third cerebral ventricle (3rd v) are also shown. (From Polyak, 1957, p. 302.)

amount of problem-solving, and depends upon various recoding mechanisms in the perceiver.

Although the physiological basis of perception is not the main interest of this chapter, it is still useful to point to a few facts from physiology that are relevant to visual perception. The large-scale schematization of a primate visual system in Fig. 1.1 shows the eyes and the principal fiber tracts from the eyes to the lower regions of the brain. Notice that fibers from each eye separate at the optic chiasma and go eventually to both hemispheres of the brain. The sensory surface of the eyes, the

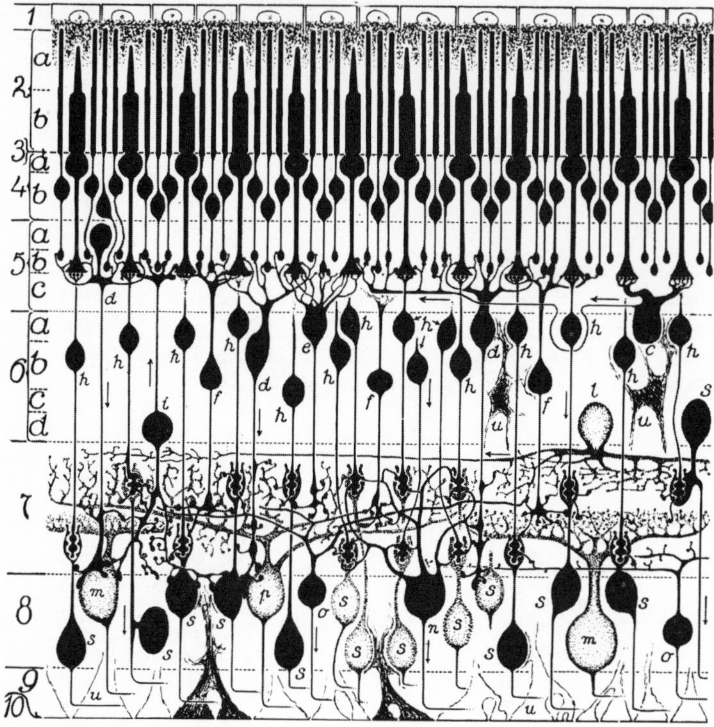


**Fig. 1.2** The nervous structure of a primate retina.

In the upper part of the diagram are photoreceptors, both rods (a) and cones (b), the bacillary parts sticking into the pigment layer, the inner fibers of the rods terminating with round spherules, and those of the cones, with conical pedicles, which form zone 5-b of the outer plexiform layer. Here the synaptical contacts are made with upper or dendritic expansions of horizontal cells (c), along which the impulses spread in adjoining parts of the retina, and with the bipolars of centripetal varieties (d,e,f,h), along which they pass to the inner plexiform layer, where synaptical contacts are established with the ganglion cells (m,n,o,p,s). From the ganglions arise nerve fibers which, as the optic nerve, enter the brain. Other types of neurons, called "centrifugal bipolars" (i), may condition photoreceptors under the influence of the ganglion cells, hence in a direction opposite to that of the centripetal bipolars (d,e,f,h). There may be still other neuron varieties whose connections are lateral, spreading in the inner plexiform layer (l). This indicates that the primate retina is a complex organ whose function is not only to react to physical light as an external stimulus but also to sort the generated impulses in many ways before they are further transmitted to the brain. (From Polyak, 1957, p. 254.)

retina, is shown in another schematic drawing in Fig. 1.2. There one may see the two kinds of transducers of light into nerve impulse, the rods and cones, along with the bipolar cells and the ganglion cells upon which they terminate, and the laterally branching nerve networks that modulate their effects.[1] The late Stephen Polyak (1957), from whose work these figures are taken, has indicated ten separately identifiable layers to the retina, the last the bundle of fibers that leave the eye as the optic nerve, shown at the bottom of the figure. Not included is the dense network of blood vessels that furnish nutriment to these cells; also not included is an arrow to show direction. Such an arrow would show that light enters from the bottom in the figure while the sense receptors are at the top. As a consequence, it is not possible to form a perfect image on the retina of even so simple a target as a point source of light. Given the medium the light must penetrate, blurring necessarily occurs (Fry, 1955); nevertheless, human visual acuity is such that the offset between two stationary vertical lines (vernier acuity) can be detected when it subtends about 10 seconds of visual angle, a distance which is actually less than that between two cones on the receptor mosaic (Riggs, 1965). It follows that a perfect retinal image is neither achieved nor needed for good vision.

A few other facts from physiology are also relevant here. There are about 120,000,000 receptors in each eye, but only about 1,000,000 or so fibers in the optic nerve leaving the eye, a reduction of about 120:1. Nevertheless, there is a point-for-point mapping of the retina on the cortex; that is to say, every point on the retina will, when properly stimulated, elicit a response from some point on the cortex. One might therefore initially assume that the image on the retina is preserved as an image in the brain; such an assumption would be wrong, however, for the topological arrangement of an image on the retina is preserved neither in the nerve fibers leaving the eye nor on the cortex. Figure 1.3 shows, again in schematic form, how an image on the retina would be represented in the optic nerve and on the visual cortex. Tracing through the diagram will show the reader that the projection of the retina onto the cortex is discontinuous.

Even this very brief summary should indicate that there is no straight-

[1] The cones are represented most densely in the center of the eye, and the rods most densely in the periphery. There is good reason to believe that the two kinds of transducers concentrate upon different functions, for detail vision is most acute in the central part of the eye, while sensitivity to light itself is most acute in the periphery. This twofold organization is referred to as the Duplicity Theory of Vision. What is not known, however, is whether these two functions, of light sensitivity and acuity, are best performed in different parts of the eye because of the way the eye is organized or as a result of an inherent property of the transducers themselves. As Fig. 1.2 shows, the cones tend to have their own "lines," while many rods converge upon a single ganglion cell. The likelihood that a ganglion will fire is increased when a number of impulses reach it rather than only one; multiple impingement enhances the ability to detect light, but reduces the ability to resolve contours. Thus it may be that functions differ in different parts of the eye because of the way the transducers terminate upon ganglion cells rather than because of the inherent structure of the transducers.

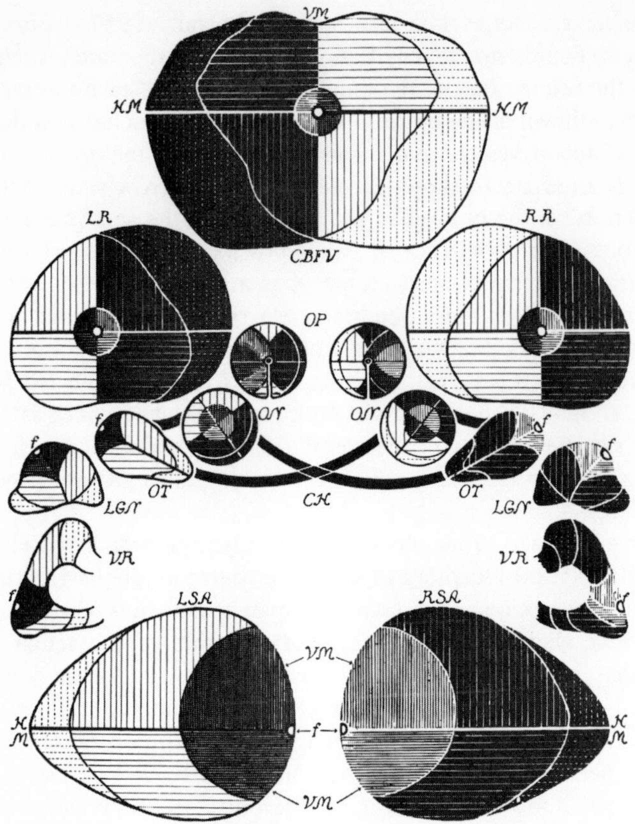


**Fig. 1.3** Projection of the eyes onto the brain.

Topographic representation or "projection" of the common binocular field of view (CBFV, above), and of the left and right retinal surfaces (LR, RR) in the visual pathways and centers of the brain, in Man and in other Primates. The two monocular fields of view, superimposed over each other as in normal binocular vision, are divided by a vertical meridian (VM) into a right and a left half, and again each half is subdivided by a horizontal meridian (HM) into an upper and a lower quadrant. A small white circle in the very center indicates the point of fixation. The next circle surrounding it, divided into four small quadrants, represents the central fovea (relatively much enlarged). The largest complete circle represents the extrafoveal parts of the binocular field of view. It is flanked on each side by the monocular temporal crescents. Each half and each quadrant are marked in the same way throughout the entire scheme: in the two retinae (RR, LR), optic papillae or disks (OP), optic nerves (ON), chiasma (CH), optic tracts (OT), lateral geniculate nuclei (LGN), visual radiations (VR), and the striate areae of the brain (RSA, LSA). The position of the fixation points (f), vertical and horizontal meridians, their approximate orientation in each locality, and the relative size of each quadrant are also indicated.

forward transmission link that conveys an exact image of the physical stimulus from the peripheral receptor to the brain. Rather, the convergence of receptors upon ganglion cells, with a consequent reduction in transmission lines, and the absence of topological fidelity between the retinal image and its cortical representation, indicate that the cortical representation and, necessarily, the perceptual experience, are highly recoded abstractions from the retinal image. At each of the several stations in the visual system, operations occur that make the output something other than a mere relaying of the input, operations which are selective for certain figural properties such as brightness, contour, color, or motion; and which may be affected by nonvisual factors such as attention and motivation as well.

Finally, it has been estimated that about three million sensory nerve fibers enter the brain. At any moment, any fiber may be either conducting or quiet, with a refractory time after firing of about 0.5 msec before it can fire again. Thus, in any one second there are about $2000 \times 2^{3,000,000}$ states possible for this network of sensory fibers. The enormous size of this number makes it obvious that perception could not stand in any simple relation to the firing of nerve cells following the impingement of physical stimuli upon sensory receptors. The understanding of perception must look to principles and rules that give structure and organization to this input. Such rules create a system that is more complex than those suggested by models based upon electrochemical conduction along well-mapped networks.[2]

## Organization of Visual Figures

### *Background*

In the early days of experimental psychology, students of the mind took their task to be the identification of the elements of sensation and the laws of association by which they combined. Three premises guided this work: the information of interest existed in the stimulus; the action of the peripheral nervous system was to decompose complex physical

[2] The networks in fact are not that well mapped. The most extensive electrophysiological analysis of visual perception has proceeded only to the fourth or fifth synapse beyond the retina, in the region immediately surrounding the primary projections in the visual cortex (Hubel and Wiesel, 1962; 1965); yet it is possible to find responses to visual stimulation in many other cortical regions, and damage to virtually any part of the brain will, in the human, interfere somewhat with visual perception (Teuber, Battersby, and Bender, 1960). Effects in other sensory modalities are sufficiently similar to support the in-group joke that the brain is a big hand, a big nose, a big eye or ear — depending upon which sensory system the experimenter is interested in. Certainly for the visual system, one cannot assume that the pictorial aspects of perception — the picture in the head — stand in any simple relation to the physical environment or to an "image" in the brain. In fact, that selfsame "picture" may be produced entirely in the absence of any light rays, as in the case of dreams and willed images. (The perceptual experience in dreaming seems to be as real as that from a response to light.) Light rays focused on the eye, that is to say, constitute neither a sufficient nor even a necessary condition for perception — they constitute only the most studied condition.

stimuli into their sensorial elements; and the brain combined these sensorial elements or sensations into a perception, passively, according to the laws of association.[3] This associationistic point of view has a long history, especially in British empiricistic philosophy, and in one form or another dominated experimental psychology generally. "Experiments" conducted in the early years were introspectionist in form, the task of the experimental subject or observer being to describe analytically the sensations he experienced on the presentation of various stimuli. While producing fundamental data on the perception of hue and contour, this style of investigation eventually ended in a scandalous disputation over the reproducibility of experimental results. The particular issue concerned the role of images in mental life. One school of observers held that at least thoughts and ideas and, perhaps, many perceptions were not based on sensory images, while another school held that images played a fundamental role in perception and cognition. E. B. Titchener, the leading proponent of the American variety of analytical introspection, insisted that images and their sensory attributes were the basis of perception and cognition. Endowed with a brilliantly vivid sense of his own body (one which, incidentally, often led him to involve kinesthetic imagery as an important component of perceiving), he once asserted that images characterized not only individual items but abstract ideas as well; for him, the concept of triangularity was "a flashy thing, come and gone from moment to moment: it hints two or three angles, with the red lines deepening into black, seen on a dark green ground. It is not there long enough for me to say whether the angles join to form the complete figure or even whether all three of the necessary angles are given" (Titchener, 1909, pp. 17–18). There is not much that an automatic pattern-recognizer or mathematician could do with such an idea of triangularity.

Not all investigators thought this way nor was all work concerned with examining the content of consciousness, however. The discovery of visual illusions in two-dimensional space (for example, Necker,

[3] The laws of association asserted that events were called to mind merely by virtue of their relation to other events. The strength of associations — the likelihood that one event would remind a person of another — was said to be based on contiguity, similarity, frequency, intensity, and similar properties of stimulation, some of which were regarded as primary and others as secondary. There is, however, no proof that associations are formed passively by virtue of their stimulus properties. An alternative view is that the observer classifies or categorizes events in various ways, and that semantic properties of the categories define the combination that appears as an "association." Compare M. Wallach (1959), and Miller, Galanter, and Pribram (1960), especially Chapter 10, for examples. A fourth premise of the early investigators was that the trained mind could observe its own workings fully; this was perhaps the fundamental assumption of introspectionism and one of the easiest to disprove.

1832) stimulated some workers to new lines of thought; Mach's interest in illusions (1890, translation, 1959) and in the development of ideas and knowledge (Ratliff, 1965) suggested to others that the nervous system, as any transducer must, transforms its inputs in characteristic ways. Although it was sometimes implied, incorrectly, that the transformations could be accounted for as linear operators on the input, the important point is that at least some attention came to be paid to the ideas of transformation and operation — of what we now call coding.[4] Nevertheless, the renowned German psychologist Külpe (1895) writing near the turn of the century could still argue that perceptions are ultimately in essential agreement with objective reality, and described illusions as "subjective perversions of the contents of objective perception." It remained for Max Wertheimer (1912, 1923) to refute the thesis that perceptions are sensory analysis plus association and to introduce in systematic form the idea that the nervous system contains unique organizing principles as one of its inherent properties. One consequence of his work is the contemporary assertion that there is, in fact, nothing in a perception that testifies to its accuracy or "reality": all perceptions are recoded versions of an input which in principle *cannot* map 1:1 into a perception.

### *Gestalt discoveries*

The thesis Wertheimer rejected can be called, as some of its adherents called it, "mental chemistry." The name implied that the mind worked first to isolate the various sensations the nervous system was able to respond to, and then combined them according to the laws of association into mental compounds or perceptions. Wertheimer rejected the idea of association as the basic combinatorial activity of mind and also rejected the idea that objects were perceived in terms of the sensations they produced. He noted especially that there was no principle in the sensations themselves that would guide their combination; there was not even a mechanism for deciding how many of the potentially infinite sensations a visual array might elicit would be effective in a given perception. He argued, rather, that one sees objects, organized wholes (*Gestalten*), not sensations:

I stand at the window and see a house, trees, sky. I might then on some theoretical basis try to count out and say that there, there are 327 brightnesses and hues. Do I experience the 327? No, only sky, house, trees; experiencing the 327 as such cannot be achieved. And even were there, in this particular

[4] An argument about reaction time, near the turn of the century, assumed that the increments in time to respond that occurred as the task was complicated were direct measurements of the mental operations of choice and judgment.

> computation, 120 for the house, 90 for the trees, and 117 for the sky, I am still obliged to say that they are organized in this particular way and not as 127, 100 and 100; or 150 and 177 (Wertheimer, 1923, p. 301, my translation).

This concern with what is perceived and experienced is called phenomenology; the early Gestalt theory emphasized the casual, naïve, unanalyzed approach as the normal one people use, and contrasted it with the highly artificial analysis of subjective sensations elicited by stimuli in the laboratory. Wertheimer, who initiated the Gestalt movement in psychology, emphasized the fact that inputs are actively organized by the nervous system, not passively detected. He succeeded in identifying organizing principles (or coding strategies) that characterize the perceiving of two-dimensional arrays. I will illustrate a few of them.

He began with arrays of dots, lines, and figures, such as are shown in Fig. 1.4. Most people, on casual inspection, see columns of *x*s and *o*s

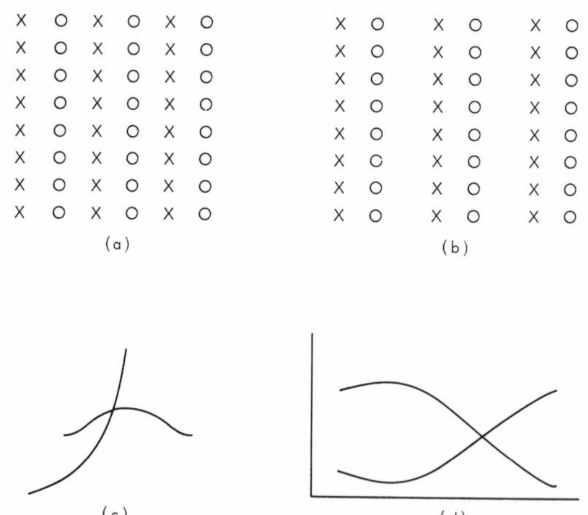


**Fig. 1.4** Some examples of perceptual grouping.

in Fig. 1.4a and only after considering the matter do they also see rows of alternating symbols. Wertheimer called the former "grouping by similarity." Many people describe the example shown in Fig. 1.4b as pairs of columns; in this instance, grouping by proximity is more powerful than grouping by similarity. Figure 1.4c illustrates the principle of good continuation, which is especially interesting when considered with reference to Cartesian graphs. The curves of Fig. 1.4d are not usually seen as two V-shaped forms that abut, but rather as two smooth curves, one accelerating and the other decelerating. From these simple examples we may infer that perception is not the result of a mere point-for-point transmission from the receptor organ to the brain. Some parts of an array are seen as belonging with others, and the whole array is perceived as organized.[5] From the point of view of mathematical logic, of course, any array can be organized in an infinite number of ways. The fact that a few stable organizations are achieved by the observer indicates that they must be imposed by him rather than reside in the stimulus. Our perceptual world is a world of objects, whole figures, and relations, not a simple integration of dark and light patches on the retina, or of sensations.

An important addition to Wertheimer's work on grouping was an elaboration of the role of contour in the perception of forms. Wertheimer showed that arrangements of rows, columns, and lines of simple objects could be perceived in different ways; Gottschaldt (1926) used closed figures and studied the role the outline or contour of a simple two-dimensional figure played in its being perceived. In the process, he elaborated some very important principles of visual camouflage. Figure 1.5a shows a simple contour; Fig. 1.5b shows the same contour with

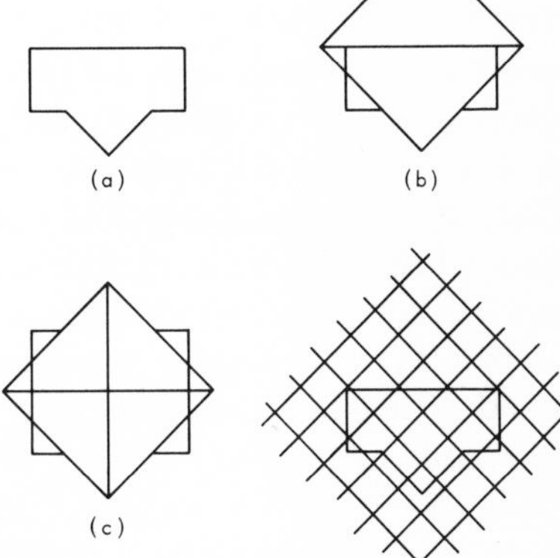


**Fig. 1.5** Successful and unsuccessful camouflage of a contour.

some lines added to it; and Fig. 1.5c adds still more lines. Figure 1.5d shows the same initial contour overlaid with a grid. What is demonstrated here is that interfering with the contour of a figure by extending or elaborating it is a very powerful way of hiding it from adult human perceivers. On the other hand, merely overlaying the basic figure with a network of visual noise does not necessarily affect its perceptibility. Thus contour provides basic visual information, and a "good" contour (for example, a continuous figure) resists interference from extraneous factors.

[5] Although past experience and training affect what is seen in these examples, they do not offer a sufficient explanation of grouping. Even unfamiliar displays would be grouped in *some* way.

Contrast the perceptibility of Fig. 1.5d in normal, adult humans and in computers. Any pattern-tracing or contour-tracing pattern recognizer would be thrown into a random walk by Fig. 1.5d, yet normal adult humans are not. Perhaps this means that pattern-recognizing machines are defective, which may be true; more powerfully, it suggests that human pattern perception is *not* based on edge-tracing or even template-matching. Thus, for humans, if some haphazardly chosen pattern interferes with the perception of another, it is likely to do so by interfering with its contours.

*Related discoveries*

A second contrast with Fig. 1.5c may be made with children and with adult humans who have received some injury to their brains. Children, because they have not yet developed the ability, and injured adults, because they have lost it, find it difficult to locate the target contour. Ghent (1956), for example, found that some of Gottschaldt's figures create extremely difficult perceptual problems for children younger than 6 years. They often cannot trace out the target figure when its contours are shared; but they have far less difficulty in identifying drawings of objects when their contours merely overlap. Results of a similar kind are obtained from adults who have had some damage inflicted to "non-visual" parts of their brain, that is, areas other than occipital cortex, the primary projection areas of vision (Teuber and Weinstein, 1956). The normal observer seems to be able to achieve a kind of parallel processing in looking at such figures, separating signal from noise or figure from ground (Rubin, 1921). That kind of visual abstraction is lost to some traumatized adults and is not yet available to young children.

Still another demonstration of the active encoding that characterizes human pattern recognition is found in the work of Bartlett (1932). He noted that reproducing a figure was far easier when one located the rule guiding its construction than when one merely tried to draw the pattern from memory, and he noted also that prediction played a role in detection. One of his subjects remarked that "when you have a straight line, you know where it must go, and if you have an impression that the figure was symmetrical, and notice two or three straight lines, you can join them up and make something of what you have seen. But curves might go anywhere. You never can tell" (Bartlett, p. 25). Following up on this work, Attneave (1954) elaborated two new organizing principles. In one experiment a number of naïve observers were required to locate markers on a contour in a way that conveyed the essence of the irregular figure they were shown. Attneave found that regions of curvature were the places most likely to be indicated; that is, the inflection points on a contour are its informationally richest parts, so that connecting them with straight lines will still preserve the essence of a contour. An illustration is given by the drawing of a cat constructed by connecting regions of curvature with straight lines. The cat, as Fig. 1.6 shows, is easily recognized despite the distortion.

**Fig. 1.6** A sleeping cat, drawn by connecting the points of maximum curvature in its outline.

(From Attneave, 1954.)

In addition to demonstrating the important role curvature plays in defining contours, Attneave's work also implies that in looking at a pattern, the observer makes predictions about what he is going to see and has assumptions about what should follow what. He anticipates continuity rather than merely detecting it. Assumptions and predictions characterize most human perceiving and, though often more difficult to measure and thus more challenging to the experimenter's ingenuity, play as real and powerful a role as the more readily quantified properties of dot density, luminance, contrast, and so on. Attneave, and Hochberg and McAlister (1953) have tried to use information theory to account for some of the simpler kinds of human pattern perception, but the effort has not led very far. An interesting variation on this attempt was made by Ryan and Schwartz (1956), who measured the length of time for which a target had to be presented in order to be recognized correctly. Caricatures, which distort crucial elements of a display, were recognized far more rapidly than accurate photographs of the target, usually because there was too much detail, too much redundant information, in the photographs. Information theory, however, has proved to be of limited applicability in understanding psychological processes in which concepts, categories, and meaning play important roles. (See Green and Courtis, 1966, for a recent critique.)

Among these cognitive organizing principles are the roles of needs, values, assumptions, and motivational states generally. While our perceptions tend to be in some accord with physical reality, they are very sensitive to momentary subjective states. We may see the flash but misidentify what is shown or be selectively attuned for certain sounds or voices (Broadbent, 1958). Food is more readily seen when one is hungry and less readily when he is not; new sights stand out to the recently arrived traveler, but with too much viewing he may fail even to see them; well-known and expected patterns are more readily recognized than unfamiliar ones, and so on. These variables, and the dependence of perception upon transitory existential states, are studied less intensively now than in the past (Blake and Ramsey, 1951; Bruner and Krech, 1950), but their existence should be borne in mind in any discussion of pattern recognition lest one assume incorrectly that because a pattern can be described in precise physicalistic language, it is therefore perceived in the way it can be described.

Other conditions also affect the perception of two-dimensional configurations. While light is neither a sufficient nor even a necessary condition for perceiving (as in dreams and images, for example), it is necessary for the perception of physical objects in ordinary viewing. The role of physical parameters — luminance, wavelength, contrast ratio, dot or figure density, and the like — have not been mentioned here because standard descriptions are available in several places (for example, Graham, 1965; and Boynton and Bush, 1956, for an interesting study of figure perception); instead, the direction taken has been to show that even so simple a configuration as a two-dimensional array is perceived by means of organizing principles that act to convert the physical stimulus into a coded form, which may itself be transformed in the course of transmission. A particularly elegant demonstration of the role of certain constructive factors in perceiving is provided by research on stabilized images.

### *Stabilized images*

Under normal circumstances, the eyes of an awake adult are in constant motion. The motions are of four kinds: (1) low-amplitude, high-frequency nystagmus motions; (2) moderate-amplitude, low-frequency drift motions; (3) regular saccadic motions; and (4) pursuit movements. Nystagmus and drift movements are involuntary; saccades and pursuit movements can be voluntary or involuntary. (1) The most determined efforts to maintain fixation on some single point are inadequate to eliminate nystagmus motions completely; they are a property of the awake normal human, disappearing only in deep sleep. Nystagmus motions subtend a few minutes of visual angle at frequencies averaging about 70 cycles per second (Ratliff, 1952). (2) As one fixates a target determinedly, the eye will actually drift off course, sometimes by as much as half a degree of visual angle. After it has reached some limit of tolerable drift, the eye snaps back rapidly to its fixation point, only to drift off course again (Cornsweet, 1956). The occurrence of the drift is usually not represented in conscious perception; the observer is unaware that his eye has either drifted or jumped back. One basis for this ignorance is the absence of kinesthetic feedback from moderate motions of the eye. That is to say, the direction of gaze of the eye is known only by virtue of the objects the observer is looking at and certain other conditions affecting his perceived orientation in space. It is not known "automatically" by virtue of the movements themselves that the eyes make. (3) When examining a target, the eye moves about it at a seemingly regular rate, somewhere between 2 and 5 times per second. This is best illustrated in reading a page of text, where the eye moves at about 3 to 4 times per second. (The difference between fast and slow readers is not in the speed with which their eyes move but in the nature of the material they take in at each fixation.) The various forms of saccadic motion are usually involuntary but may be brought under voluntary control. (4) Finally, pursuit movements are those manifested typically when the observer visually tracks an object moving through space.

The fact that the eye is in continuous motion during waking hours makes it difficult to study the effect of a stimulus presented to a single area of the retina for a protracted period. For example, we know that if a moderate stimulus is applied to the skin and left there undisturbed for some moments, as happens, say, with a wrist watch or the clothes we wear, the subject will very quickly lose perception of it. It is true, of course, that perception of the stimulus can be recovered by a proper directing of attention to the stimulated area, but that is a special consideration. (See Basmajian, 1963, for some extraordinary experiments on the directed nature of attention and Pritchard, 1958, on the selective perception of stimulus properties.) Several investigators sought to learn what happened when the visual system was similarly stimulated for a protracted period. To counteract motions of the eye, a contact lens was made to adhere firmly to the eyeball. Attached to the lens were appropriate optics that aided in compensating for the normal relative motion between eye and visual target. One system, developed by Riggs, Ratliff, Cornsweet, and Cornsweet (1953) works as follows. A large contact lens fits over the cornea of the eye and has attached to it a small optical flat. An image projected onto this mirror is reflected to a screen at which the observer looks. In this situation, a motion of the eye through angle $\theta$ produces a motion of the viewed image through an angle $2\theta$; therefore a compensating optical path is introduced which, by increasing the path length of the viewed image, reduces its apparent excursion. Proper settings of the compensating path then produce a target image which moves with, and for a distance exactly equal to, the movements of the eye in a lateral plane. The target therefore remains stationary with respect to the retina. Because the mirror is not on the visual axis, however, the system does not compensate perfectly for movements not in the lateral plane.

The principal effect observed when simple targets such as straight lines or grids are viewed in this way is that they quickly disappear, the latency to disappearance varying with intensity of the stimulus, contrast, size, and similar variables. Virtually identical effects are achieved with a system developed almost simultaneously by Ditchburn and Ginsborg (1952), which mounts a small telescope and the visual target itself on the contact lens. Thus, with respect to its inability to respond to continuous stimulation, the eye is like the skin, the ear, the nose, and other sensing organs; in fact, variation in sensory input appears to be a minimal condition for normal consciousness itself (Fiske and Maddi, 1961).

This important technical achievement for stabilizing retinal images has been exploited in a number of studies of the perceptual processing of two-dimensional figures. In one set of studies, for example (Pritchard, Heron, and Hebb, 1960), simple two-dimensional arrays were observed one at a time. The discovery was rapidly made that the targets did not disappear haphazardly; rather, the observer tended to preserve certain figural properties of the target and sometimes even added parts to a figure that was disappearing. That is to say, parts of the visual system rapidly lose their ability to respond to a continuous input, but the variations in perception that follow this process maintain a semblance of order and organization. Often the figures disappear in a way that tends to maintain lines, planes, contours, and even, in some cases, the meaningfulness of the perception. A few of these effects are shown in Fig. 1.7. The largely qualitative observations illustrated there have

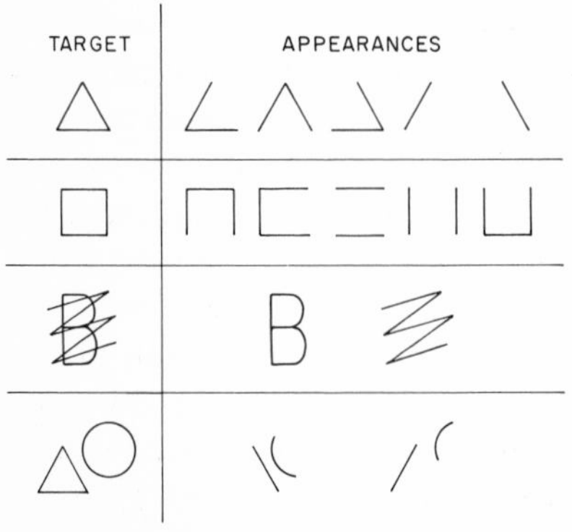


**Fig. 1.7** Examples of a target form and some of its appearances when it was presented as a stabilized retinal image.

(From Pritchard, Heron, and Hebb, 1960.)

been confirmed with more quantitative work (for example, Evans, 1965). Evans confirmed the earlier finding that acutely angled figures are more prone to disappear than rounded ones (Z, for example, is more likely to disappear than S), but the nearness of the parts of the target cannot by itself explain this. These results, as well as those described in the following discussion, indicate that more is involved than mere fatigue or adaptation of local retinal regions.

An important variation on these experiments was carried out by Krauskopf (1963). He arranged a green disk to be a stabilized image, while a red annulus concentric with the disk was stabilized only in the region of the disk's contour and was unstabilized at a distance from it. The results of earlier experiments suggest that the green disk will disappear, as in fact it does; however, its disappearance does not leave a hole in the visual scene, or a gray or black region surrounded by a red ring. Rather, the region of the disappeared disk is reported to fill in and become red, so that the subject sees one large red disk. The process here is somewhat analogous to the perceptual filling in or impletion of the blind spot, the region of the retina in which the optic nerve exits from the retina and which therefore lacks sense cells: only under special testing conditions can the blind spot be located, for normally people see a filled or completed visual field. We will return to these impletion phenomena later in connection with the description of certain visual illusions. They play an important role in perception as instances in which the observer supplies himself with information not present in the physical array.

### *Depth*

The images on the two retinas are two-dimensional, while most people see the world in three dimensions. One component of this perception is the disparity of the retinal images when the two eyes are fixated on a single target. The existence of this disparity has been known for a considerable time, and intensively investigated since Wheatstone's description of his stereoscope in 1838. The perception of depth is an especially dramatic demonstration of the constructive operations involved in seeing: it is impossible to account for depth, even if one wanted to, as a passive transmission of images along the optic paths, for the images on the retinas are in two dimensions, not three. The perception of objects in three dimensions is a simple proof of the occurrence of operations in perception other than mere image transmission.

A number of hypotheses have been offered to account for stereoscopic depth perception. One hypothesis frequently advanced is that a perception of depth results from the combination in the nervous system of the disparate images of identical contours that come from each eye. Recently, however, Julesz (1960, 1964) and following him Kaufman

(1965), have been able to show that the perception of depth occurs in the absence of uniocular contours.

The method for demonstrating their depth effect consists of presenting random arrays of dots or letters separately to each eye. The arrays viewed individually are without any macrostructure (contour or figure) within their borders and have only what appears as random microstructure. When a pair of such arrays is viewed stereoscopically, a depth effect occurs: one part stands out before or behind the remainder. The construction of the arrays can be schematized as follows: a random distribution of dots, *b,* is surrounded by another random distribution, *a,* in one array. The distributions are preserved almost intact in a second array except that the *b* distribution is displaced slightly. For example, to the left eye one presents *xxxaaaxx* and to the right eye *xxaaaxxx*. Combined stereoscopically, the *a*s of the matrix, by virtue of their disparity, will appear either in front of or behind the plane of the *x*s.

Nothing in either half-image would make this result predictable; a prediction based on the assumption of simple binocular summation of the two uniocular patterns would be a perception of two clear *x*s at either end, two clear *a*s in the middle, and a smudge pattern separating the *a*s and *x*s. The depth effect, which resolves the "predicted" smudge, is a construction by the nervous system. The mechanism for depth hypothesized as a point-by-point difference field has not been supported by subsequent research; an alternative, that of similarly signed brightness values whose relative rank orders are computed by the nervous system, has also been offered (Kaufman and Pitblado, 1965). There is some similarity between this suggestion of signed brightness values proposed for depth perception and Land's speculations (1964) regarding ranked brightness values as the cue for color perception. However, neither of these abstract models has been critically tested yet. It should be noted also that depth responses can be obtained from uniocular presentations that are disparate in time rather than space (Kolers, 1963); thus, it may be possible to produce depth with Julesz-Kaufman displays that are flickered to a single eye. Such a result would demonstrate an equivalence for perception between spatial and temporal disparity.

Given the importance of disparities, it is easy to see how movement of a stimulus would play a role in the perception of depth; a moving stimulus presented to a fixated eye would create slightly disparate images on a single retina in a brief interval. The kinetic depth effect, elaborated by Wallach and O'Connell (1953), illustrates uniocular depth perception. Shadow figures, any one of whose instantaneous images is seen as two-dimensional, are readily perceived as three-dimensional configurations when the object whose shadow is seen is made to rotate at a proper rate.

Other conditions also produce a perception of depth; one of them, recently studied by Eden (1962), is a variation on an illusion discovered by Mach in the latter part of the last century. Mach discovered that a piece of cardboard folded into a V-like shape was an ambiguous visual target (1886; 1959 recent edition): its apparent orientation varied as one stared at it. Eden has discovered a more interesting property of this illusion. If the cardboard is folded into a W-like shape and the observer rocks his head slowly back and forth while staring at it, both the figure and nearby objects appear to move in the direction *opposite* to head motion, as would be expected. However, when the illusory figure appears to have reversed its orientation, nearby objects continue to move in the opposite direction, but the target itself appears to move *with* the head. That is to say, apparent motion of the figure conforms to its apparent orientation and not to the physical geometry. An experiment described by Mach himself extends this finding to show how apparent motions depend on the perceived framework.

> An oil-cloth of simple pattern is drawn horizontally over two rollers . . . in uniform motion by means of a crank. Across the oil-cloth and about thirty centimetres above it is stretched a string with a knot [in it]. . . . Now if the oil-cloth be set in motion in the direction of the [observer] . . . , and the observer follow the pattern with his eyes, he will see it in motion, himself and his surroundings at rest. On the other hand, if he gazes at the knot, he and the whole room will presently appear in motion in the contrary direction to the [motion of the oil-cloth] . . . while the oil-cloth will [seem to] stand still. This change in the aspect of the motion takes more or less time . . . but usually requires only a few seconds. If we once get the knack of it, the two impressions may be made to alternate with some rapidity and at will. Every following of the oil-cloth brings the observer to rest, every fixation of [the knot] . . . sets the observer in motion (Mach, 1959, p. 143).

These striking phenomena, in some respects similar to the well-known waterfall illusion, have not yet been studied analytically; their occurrence makes it clear that the orientation of objects in the environment is perceived with respect to a larger-scale spatial-coordinate system. The perception of depth, therefore, depends on far more than disparity of two images, more even than on the algebraic relations of the retinal images. It involves what is apparently a constructed system of spatial coordinates as well. The following discussion of experiments on the system of spatial coordinates will show how the recognition of visual objects presupposes the perception of their spatial framework.

### *Space coordinates*

The visual system appears to lack proprioceptive feedback regarding the position of the eyes. The way one usually knows where he is looking is to know what he is looking at. In the absence of a structured informational field, the observer rapidly loses the sense of direction of his gaze (Miller and Ludvigh, 1958). Consider a commonplace illusion. If you sit in a room that is totally dark except for a small point of light at which you stare, the light will appear to move about after a few moments. An equivalent effect can be obtained on a starry night: looking up at a bright star, preferably from a supine position, you soon see a segment of the starry field appear to move. Matin and MacKinnon (1964) have conducted an experiment which demonstrates the dependence of these illusory movements — called autokinetic movements — upon unrecorded motions of the eye. When a subject looks fixedly at a point source in a dark room, he will report that it moves *k* times in the vertical plane, *n* times in the horizontal, and so on. Matin and MacKinnon's subjects looked at the source under two conditions: as a stabilized retinal image and again as a freely observed object. For the stabilized condition the subjects wore a contact lens similar to that described earlier. This device kept the image on the retina stationary for movements of the eye in the lateral plane. When the subjects used this apparatus, movements of the point source remained the same or increased slightly in the vertical plane; but movements in the lateral plane were no longer reported. (See also Marshall, 1966.)

These results suggest that under free viewing conditions the observer *attributes* motion to the stationary light whose image is displaced on his retina in the course of eye movements that occur without his awareness. But contrasted with this condition are the observations of daily life, in which movements of the eye (saccades or voluntary pursuit movements) are made with only negligible amounts of apparent displacement of objects in the environment. In the latter case, apparently, a command signal to the eye goes also to a record-keeping system that takes account of motions of the eye in interpreting the relative changes of position of eye and retinal image. Involuntary motions of the eye while it is under the command to fixate, which may be due to aperiodic changes in muscle tension, are apparently not recorded, and so the record-keeping system continues to "believe" that the eye has not changed its position. Consequently, the displacement between eye and object is interpreted as a movement of the object. (See Gregory, 1966, for a similar treatment.) There is no question, then, that one component of the recognition of objects in space is the information in the record-keeping system about the position of the eye. This information may be regarded as Stage I in a complex process of object location.

Many kinds of stimulation irrelevant to the properties of the object being viewed can affect its perception, however. For example, a subject who can align a luminous rod to the gravitational vertical in a dark room will offset the same rod by a few degrees if, while he is aligning it, a loud tone is presented to one ear or if his chair is tilted, say, thirty degrees from the vertical (Wapner, Werner, and Chandler, 1951). In these cases auditory or kinesthetic information acts to change the apparent location of the perceived vertical. These changes are obviously not at the level of image motion or relative ocular position. In fact, the amount and direction of displacement have been found to change in an orderly way with age, from childhood through adulthood (Wapner and Werner, 1957). These changes, therefore, may be taken to imply that the information in Stage I is transmitted in terms of absolute displacements of the retinal image, or local signs, in a coordinate system; but a coordinate system whose axes themselves can be translated. The location of the axes may be assumed to depend on information integrated from several independent sources — the eye, the ear, the gravitational sense, and so on. The integration of these diverse sources that fix the axes of the coordinate system of Stage I we may call Stage II.

Compare an analogous case for audition. Sound localization — the perceived position of an auditory target — is based in part upon the difference in time of arrival of sound waves at the two ears. That information corresponds to Stage I. But whether the target is perceived as above or below, left or right, depends in part on the tilt of the head, whose position would have to be taken into account by the auditory record-keeper in order for correct localization of the target to take place. That alignment of space coordinates is also labile. The head also tends to depart from the normal vertical when one sits for long periods. In the dark, the location of sounds would be misperceived if the tilt of the head had gone unrecorded. The unanchored quality of Stage I coordinate systems itself implies the existence of a hierarchically higher system that establishes perceived position in space from the balance of several inputs.

Normally, intense "extraneous" stimulation can disrupt perception drastically: spinning or centrifugal rotation are examples. Unlike most people, the ballerina who spins rapidly is not made dizzy by spinning. One may note a difference in the way she spins: from the shoulders down, her body moves continuously; but her head moves saccadically, for she fixates an object in front of her while her body moves through about 180 degrees, then snaps her head through 360 degrees to restore fixation while her body moves through another 180 degrees, and so on.

In this case, as in many others, certain cognitive activities control sensory inputs to keep a perceptual configuration stable in a wildly changing environment. This third kind of informational control may be regarded as Stage III. The three stages are brought together in Fig. 1.8. In

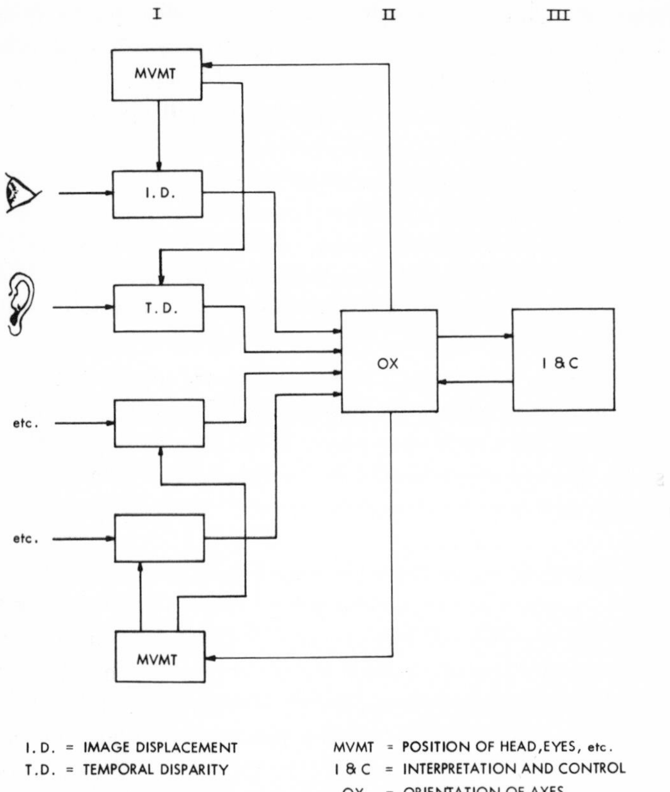


**Fig. 1.8** Three stages of perceptual orientation and recognition.

all cases, the way a particular input is organized seems to depend upon the existence of assumptions and control regarding the spatial coordinate system. Such coordinate systems, in turn, appear to be relatively high-level cognitive achievements of the observer, as the experiments described in the next section will show.

*Adaptation to displacement*

The principal method of studying the organization of the systems of spatial coordinates has its history in one of the more heroic and courageous psychological experiments. It has been known for over three hundred years that the image on the retina is inverted with respect to the physical environment; a question of some interest was the manner by which such images were represented "pictorially" in consciousness as right-side-up.[6] At the end of the nineteenth century, the psychologist G. M. Stratton (1897) inquired into this question experimentally by reinverting the retinal image. He accomplished the task by mounting a small telescope in a frame that otherwise completely covered his eyes; he wore the device for about a week during all his waking hours. In addition to reinverting the image, the telescope reversed right and left. Immediately upon putting the device on, Stratton found that his perceptions were of an upside-down world in which left and right were exchanged. His experiences with the device are impressively described: initially he was very confused, made inappropriate motor adjustments, bumped into objects, reached incorrectly, perceived the world to move when he moved his head, and so on. But during the course of the week, he achieved a fairly stable orientation to his new visual environment, and by the end of the week, Stratton claimed, the world looked right again. After this period, upon removing the telescope, the world again looked strange and appeared to move when he moved his head, requiring that he go through a period of relearning before it again appeared normal. The readjustment to normality seemed to take less time than the adjustment to an upright image.

The problem of adaptation to optical transformations and the rectification of visually distorted objects has come in for considerable study since then. Stratton's procedure is cumbersome and complicated; further, it transforms two spatial coordinates simultaneously, right-left and up-down. Other workers have simplified the situation, either by using prisms that produce a lateral shift or mirrors that produce a shift in the vertical dimension only. The universal finding is that humans and monkeys adapt readily to optically transformed arrays. However, the conditions necessary and sufficient for this adaptation have not yet been spelled out unambiguously. At the present time it appears that one essential requirement is that the subject engage in some kind of action that carries him about the environment, either physically or cognitively, and that he be aware of the consequences of his actions. For example, if he is to reach for an object whose image is displaced laterally by means of prisms, he must be able on successive tries to identify the location of his hand with respect to the target. Mere alignment of hand and target are not sufficient, however. If the experimenter moves the subject's passive hand,

[6] The question is "of interest" only if we assume, as many investigators did, that the image on the retina is what is seen. But as Helmholtz noted, the question is trivial; inasmuch as we do not see our retinas, it is in a certain sense irrelevant how the images on them are formed.

little or no adaptation to the displacement occurs; active, willed movement by the subject is necessary in many conditions in order for adaptation to take place (Held and Freedman, 1963). This active movement is alleged to produce a motor outflow signal in some comparator system whose task it is to keep the visual signal and the appropriate motor adjustments correlated (analogous to the record-keeper of Stage I). In other cases, orientation may be achieved purely by symbolic means, as when one is driven about in a car in a strange city: some people can maintain a good sense of their orientation in space even though their overt behavior is passive. Illustrations of this kind introduce a principle of substitutability between action and thought, identified by a number of psychologists; that is, thought may substitute for action in achieving certain adjustments.

The role of awareness of the consequences of action is illustrated by comparing the behavior of the human or monkey with that of the much more primitive frog. In the visual system of the frog, when the optic nerve is cut it regenerates its original connections, which suggests that each nerve fiber has its own tag. Taking advantage of this fact, Sperry (1951) cut the optic nerves of frogs, rotated the eyes 180 degrees, and then permitted the fibers to regenerate. Thereafter, the frog's visual system coded objects in the physical lower left as being in the upper right, and vice versa. Unlike higher animals, the frog failed to adapt to the rotation; it continued to respond to the apparent rather than the physical location of objects. An analogous experiment makes the same point: a fly mounted on a pin inserted into a stick will, when it is moved about in front of a frog, cause the frog to flick its tongue at the fly. Doing so lacerates the tongue; nevertheless, the frog will continue to respond in this primitive stimulus-response fashion for as long as the moving fly is present, eventually reducing its tongue to shreds. The point of these illustrations is to identify an evaluative mechanism that is present in higher animals for assessing the consequences of actions, and its near-absence in lower ones. Presumably such a mechanism that compares performance and result is necessary for adaptation to spatial distortion and, perhaps, for all active learning.[7]

An important component in the learning of spatially transformed patterns is the interplay between perception and action. Merely looking at a transformation, it has been claimed, is insufficient to achieve an adaptation to it, at least for the case of orientation in three-dimensional space.

[7] This does not mean that the frog is altogether incapable of learning, but rather that the range of conditions from which it can learn is severely restricted. See Maier and Schneirla (1935) for a review distinguishing stereotyped from modifiable behavior and describing the emergence of modifiability with progression up the phylogenetic scale. Compare also the role of TOTE units in human information-processing suggested by Miller, Galanter, and Pribram (1960).

A point at issue is whether the system of touch acts to modify the visual system, or whether the visual system acts to transform the implicit coordinates of space — the position sense of the body. One argument holds for a rigid position sense and a plastic visual system; another holds the opposite (Walls, 1951; Harris, 1965). Under certain conditions, in fact, both systems seem to be plastic. The 30-inch-long arm of the adult is a different system from the 18-inch-long arm of the child, yet in some fashion the mapping of the latter is transformed into that of the adult.[8] Similarly, the variety of illusory visual perceptions and the lability of the entire spatial system of vision (for example, the Mach-Eden illusion) argues for a plasticity in the coordinate system of visual space. Some other attributes of these systems in responding to distortion and maintaining perceptual stability are discussed in the following section, where we begin with the description of still another illusion.

### *Orientation and stability*

A simple arithmetic ("Archimedes") spiral will appear to undergo great changes if it is stared at as it rotates at about 3 times per second. It changes in size and, for some observers, appears to develop tridimensionality. On turning one's gaze to another object after looking at the spiral for about a minute, one perceives an equally great but opposite effect. If the spiral had earlier appeared to expand, objects looked at subsequently appear to contract, and vice versa. This much has been known for some time. Now let a "contracting" spiral be viewed that subtends about 4 degrees of visual angle, and then let the subject look at a large regular matrix of squares (about 20 × 20 degrees). A region of the matrix subtending about 4 degrees will appear to enlarge and, for some observers, to approach; yet at no place does one see any curvature of its lines or any discontinuity with the remainder of the matrix (Kolers, 1966b). This logical paradox — that part of a figure seems to change its size and position without creating a discontinuity with the remainder — implies that different attributes of a stimulus array are processed selectively in different parts of the nervous system. The illusion demonstrates also, what has been known from other investigations (for example, Köhler and Wallach, 1944), that although our perceptual experience is of a whole scene, this whole is composed of a large number of parts that are separately processed by the visual

[8] This mapping is not a simple dilatation, for while the adult's body is larger than the child's, two-point thresholds on the surface of the adult's body are smaller than on the child's. Thus the increase in body size is accompanied by an increase in resolving power, not the decrease implied by simple dilatation. An excellent critical discussion of the problem of adaptation to "transformed space" is given by Howard and Templeton (1966, Chapter 15).

system and which can undergo local perturbations. That is to say, only the part of the system actually stimulated by the spiral undergoes subsequent distortion although a much larger part is involved in perceiving the matrix. While our perceptions usually are consistent and free of paradox, this fact seems to be the result of the way we sample the world rather than a necessary property of perception.

Although this illusion demonstrates a paradox between perception and reason (that is, part of a contour cannot reasonably change its size and position without undergoing some discontinuity with the remainder), most such perceptual illusions are not of this kind. In the main, perceptual experiences rationalize and code the physical array into a meaningful or comprehensible pattern. The distortions imposed then are just opposite in effect to the distortion produced by the spiral. The typical distortion rationalizes our perceptions, while the spiral makes them paradoxical. To achieve the rationalization, the observer supplies himself with information the physical array lacks; many examples of this are known in the literature, obtained from experiments using brief exposures of stimulus objects as targets (for example, Bartlett, 1932). The typical finding is that the subject, unless carefully instructed otherwise, reports seeing what he assumes is there, rather than exactly what is there. He reports what is actually an inference or impletion — a perceptual construction — based on cues. He behaves "intelligently," as a problem-solver, not a passive detector. The context in which the presentations occur and the frame of reference the subject adopts in the situation "pretune" him for these constructions. While often leading to faulty reports in the experimental laboratory, contextual generalization, prediction, and impletion, the processes that lie at the heart of such phenomena, perform a profoundly useful task in everyday life, where often a glance is enough to let us perceive and describe what is important to us in a complex situation.

Among the more notable achievements of this kind are the so-called constancies, the perceptual mechanisms that act to maintain some invariance in object perception despite transformations of the array. The constancies have been described for most stimulus domains: size, shape, color, speed, brightness, and so on. As an example, consider the fact that for nearby objects (say, within 20 feet) the angular size of the retinal image almost doubles as the distance from the eye to the object is halved; yet a man does not appear to be twice as big at a distance of 10 feet as he does at 20. Rather, the perceiver maintains a constancy of apparent size that is virtually independent of the absolute angular size of the image on the retina.

In order for object constancies to be achieved, the perceiver must be in an informationally rich environment. Normally the perceiver computes or evaluates a number of properties of the environment before giving his best guess about an object. The computations are the result of the normal working of the perceptual machinery and need not, although they can, be the result of conscious guessing by the perceiver. In the absence of information regarding distance or scale, however, his judgments of size can be based only on the visual angle subtended by the object. The perceiver typically does the best job he can under the circumstances to keep himself oriented in a world of changing objects. Unfortunately, little is known about the specific perceptual mechanisms that achieve the space constancies. It is not known whether displacements in one dimension of space, for example the vertical, are more likely to be rectified than displacements in another; whether certain perceptual transformations are more likely to be "disambiguated" than others (inversion versus mirror reflection, for example). It is known that perceptual space is anisotropic and is clearly non-Euclidean (Koffka, 1935); it is known also that various animal species differ in their ability to recognize two-dimensional shapes whose orientation has been varied (Sutherland); and that the human visual system is spatially polarized: the threshold for horizontal lines is lower than for verticals, which is in turn lower than that for diagonals. But of actual mechanisms, little more is known.

One approach to these problems has required literate young adults to learn to read connected English discourse that has been transformed geometrically (Kolers, Eden, and Boyer, 1964), as illustrated in Fig. 1.9. The upper set of four texts are all rotations in three-dimensional space; the lower set of four repeat the upper set with the addition that each letter is rotated on a vertical axis through itself. In each sample the asterisk shows where to begin reading. When the amount of time is measured that college students need to read a page in each of the transformations on each of eight successive days, differences between the transformations rapidly emerge (Fig. 1.10). Two observations may therefore be made: mathematically identical transformations (for example, rotations in space) impose different loads on the decoder; and the additional transformation of letter reversal (r) does not have a constant additive effect (for example, rRo > R, but rI < I). Thus, whatever the operators are that are involved in decoding these distortions, they clearly are nonlinear in combination. The perceiver varies in his ability to adapt to or learn to decode different kinds of spatial transformation. The problem now is to establish the nature of the operators that will account for the data, and their relation to adaptation to optically induced distortion and the maintenance of object constancies. One may note incidentally that the adaptations just described occur in the absence of any sensory feedback and so differ in that respect from those described in the preceding section.

Perceptual space is obviously non-Euclidean: the same target viewed alternately by the two halves of a single retina, for example, may appear to differ by several per cent in apparent size or shape (Brown, 1953); further, protracted observation of a single target induces an apparent spatial displacement of subsequently viewed targets (Köhler and Wallach,

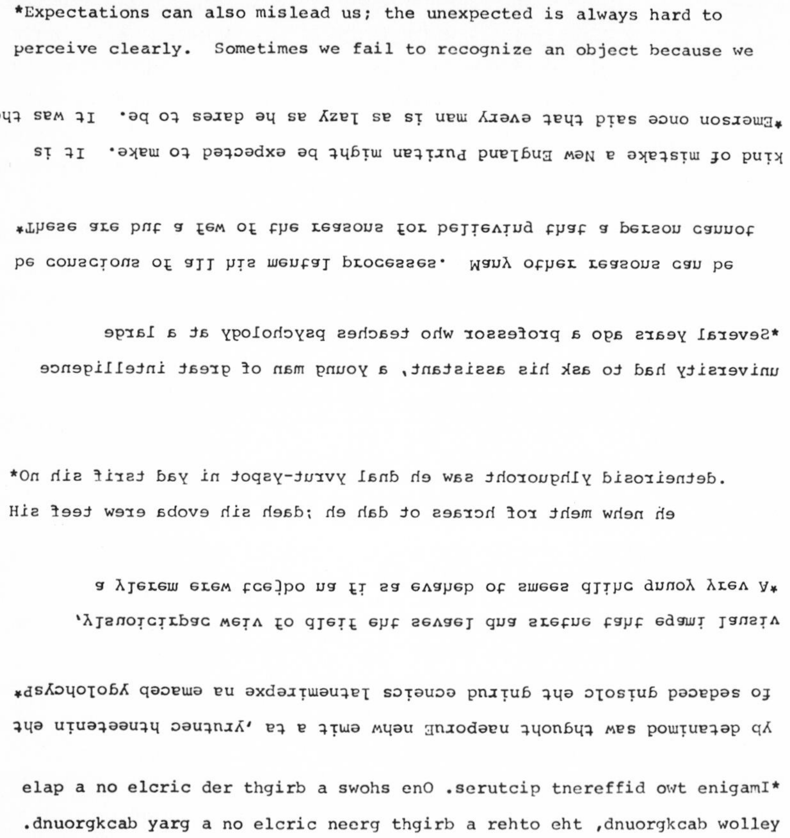

*Expectations can also mislead us; the unexpected is always hard to
perceive clearly. Sometimes we fail to recognize an object because we

*Emerson once said that every man is as lazy as he dares to be. It was the
kind of mistake a New England Puritan might be expected to make. It is

*These are but a few of the reasons for believing that a person cannot
be conscious of all his mental processes. Many other reasons can be

*Several years ago a professor who teaches psychology at a large
university had to ask his assistant, a young man of great intelligence

*On his first day in topsy-turvy land he was thoroughly disoriented.
His feet were above his head; he had to search for them when he

*A very young child seems to have as its objects merely a
visual image that enters and leaves the field of view erratically,

*Psychology became an experimental science during the closing decades of
the nineteenth century, at a time when European thought was dominated by

elap a no elcric der thgirb a swohs enO .serutcip tnereffid owt enigamI*
.dnuorgkcab yarg a no elcric neerg thgirb a rehto eht ,dnuorgkcab wolley

**Fig. 1.9** Examples of geometrically transformed text.
The asterisk shows where each pair of lines begins.

1944). The latter effect suggests that the coordinates of visual space may themselves be plastic. The argument is akin to that in physics between absolute and relative space: Is visual space determined by the objects that fill it, or do the coordinates of visual space respond to stimulus events independently of the objects that fill it? While several answers to this question have been suggested, none has enough support to warrant full discussion.[9] There is no inherent reason, however, to discourage

[9] The concept of local signs alluded to earlier as a basis for object location has recently been examined by Matin, et al. (1966). See Jammer (1960) for the concept of space in physics.

exploring the notion that the coordinates of visual space are processed as a perceptual event independent of the processing of the objects that appear to fill it; and that, consequently, some of the perceptual distortions noted may be due to alterations induced in the coordinate system itself.

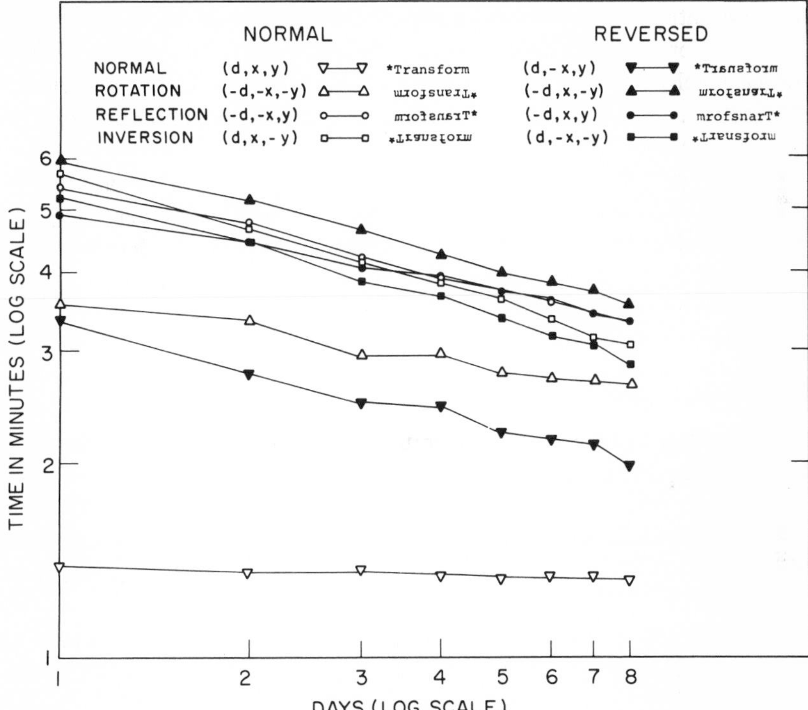


**Fig. 1.10** The time needed by 32 subjects to read pages of text in the transformations shown in Fig. 1.9.

The inset legend defines the orientation of the characters of each sample in the $(x,y)$ plane, and the direction of reading $(d)$.

Perceptual space has another meaning for the human pattern recognizer: the spatial framework in which he finds himself and in which he ambulates. As Lynch (1960) has shown, moving about a well-structured environment involves a number of perceptual and cognitive processes, the latter particularly having to do with memory, intentions, plans, and goals. The image of the environment that the traveler develops, or the use of nodes and other points of maximum information that direct his observation and affect his recognition, have not been much studied quantitatively; yet they identify a level of pattern recognizing that occupies a large part of most people's lives. It is important to realize that ambulation typically is performed with respect to an internalized map of the environment. This is shown by the fact that even with their eyes closed most people can get around quite well in a familiar environment. The source of this internal map is not necessarily a visual memory. People born blind also have good cognitive maps of their familiar environments, in the absence of visual memories.[10] The human constructs a representation of the environment in which he does his recognizing, a construction which usually has to compensate for bias in his orientational mechanisms. These constructions go far beyond the capacity that any passive-detection, energy-exchange, or template-matching theory has to explain them.

One approach to studying some of these phenomena quantitatively takes the view that the human acts more as a puzzle-solver than as a template-matcher; he uses rules to get from A to B rather than matching responses to stimuli. A discussion of this view follows the next section on temporal phenomena.

## Temporal Phenomena

It is obvious that physical stimulation is continuous. A fundamental question concerning the construction of perceptual experience asks, what acts to segregate the continuity into discrete objects and events? Why, given a continuously varying input, do our perceptions not blur and smear into each other? Why do we see a stable world? The Gestalt psychologists and others have identified the object-based character of perception. What is of equal importance is to identify the mechanisms that produce the discreteness of perceptible objects in a continuous stimulus flux.

In the awake adult the eyes are in perpetual movement; not in smooth, but in saccadic movement, alternating pauses with rapid jumps. Experiment shows that the eye is somewhat less sensitive during voluntary movement (Volkmann, 1962); in fact, the decrease in sensitivity occurs *before* the onset of the movement, suggesting that it is not due to the movement itself, but to a signal associated with the command to move (Zuber and Stark, 1966). In general, the eyes move about three times per second, and given the velocity they attain, it is unlikely that they take in much detail during the movement. Most of the input probably occurs during the pauses.[11] The continuity of visual experience therefore

[10] With respect to such ambulations, there is some evidence to indicate that lesions of particular parts of the brain interfere selectively with orientation to and interpretation of maps and similar patternlike structures (Semmes, et al., 1955).

[11] The issue is complicated, however. Whether or not inhibition occurs seems to depend upon whether the eye movement is voluntary or involuntary. Apparently,

may be regarded as constructed by the nervous system from a series of static displays processed at the rate of about three per second. Investigations have considered both the segregation of continuous physical stimulation and the maintenance of continuity from discontinuous inputs, their concatenation, and their naming and deposit in memory. Earlier we discussed some phenomena of stability in the presence of change; now we will discuss some phenomena associated with change in the presence of continuity. A number of problems are associated with the perception of discreteness among objects.

Two approaches have been taken to these questions. One is based on the assumption that the visual system has a fixed-frequency internal scanning mechanism that operates in the region of 10 cycles per sec. On this assumption, all the stimulation occurring within one 100-msec interval is thought to be processed together in one percept. The interval of 100 msec thus would define a "psychological moment" or "temporal quantum" or "informational scanning rate" (Lindsley, 1952; Stroud, 1956). The analogies here are to a raster in one case and to motion-picture cameras in the other. The former assumes a fixed frequency point-by-point scan in the visual system whose integration produces a percept. The latter assumes a shutterlike mechanism that opens and closes at a fixed frequency; all of the elements that arrive during one cycle would be processed together. Experimental facts, however, are more complicated than these conceptions can accommodate.

In the first place, we find that stimulus-analyzing mechanisms are selective for different attributes of a percept: color, contour, brightness, motion, depth, and certainly "meaning" seem to be processed in different places in the visual system. The perceptual experiences of people who have suffered damage to the brain (Teuber, Battersby, and Bender, 1960) and certain kinds of analytical experiments (for example, Kolers, 1963) show that perceptual attributes can be interfered with selectively. These facts argue against any simple scanning or framing mechanism in which all aspects of a stimulus are processed together. Again, it is found that the detection of sequence — which one came first? — can be segregated from the detection of number — were there one or two? — and from the estimation of numerousness — how many were there? — (Hirsch and Sherrick, 1961; White, 1963). It may be impossible to reconcile these different perceptions with a fixed-frequency scanning or framing mechanism. But more telling is the fact that if there is a temporal quantum, it seems to vary in size with the task the subject is required to perform (Kolers, 1962; Kahneman and Norman, 1964), so that at the

no inhibition of seeing occurs during involuntary eye movements. See Krauskopf, Graf, and Gaarder (1966) and Matin, et al. (1966).

least one would have to say that there are several different "sizes" of quanta. It would be better still to say that there are not quanta at all, but that different perceptual processes take different amounts of time to occur and that some of them run off somewhat in parallel.

The second approach has been to study the role of time in visual perception, or the trade-off between time and intensity or time and task. The earlier investigations along these lines analogized from the Bunsen-Roscoe relation of photochemical reactions: in many physical conditions time and intensity are reciprocally related so that $I \times T = C$. This constant relation is found to hold in the visual system over brief durations; but the size of these so-called critical durations is found to vary with the task the subject is performing. When the stimulus is a single flash of light presented to the dark-adapted eye, the critical duration varies between 50 and 80 msec, depending upon the intensity and angular size of the light (Graham and Kemp, 1938). When the subject is required to say which of two patterns was flashed, in one experiment, or to compare their brightness, in another, the critical duration for brightness is again near 80 msec, while that for identifying the stimulus extends to about 300 msec (Kahneman and Norman, 1964). Earlier, Hunter and Sigler (1940) had shown that a trade-off between intensity and duration also occurs for the detection of the number of dots on a card; but there, too, it was far longer than the 50–80 msec Graham reported. In principle, there is reason to believe that a reciprocity between intensity and time would be found for any perceptual task involving light; but its range would vary with the nature of the task. Such variations make it unlikely that these effects can be interpreted completely and only in biophysical terms relating to energy exchanges. In fact, if any principle has emerged in this field in the last few years, it is that perception is to be understood in terms of the processing of information, not of energy.

The range of basic visual functions also varies with time. Measurements of such "simple" processes as visual acuity, the detection of motion, the fusion-frequency threshold, brightness, size, and the so-called constancies all may take duration of exposure as a variable (Riggs, 1965; Brown and Mueller, 1965). It is usually found that time is important as a variable in these tests only through about the first 100–300 msec of stimulation, the precise value varying with the task the subject is performing. Furthermore, the processes that occur in these intervals are not always continuous, in the sense that some single process merely increases its effect with time. Sometimes, different processes, such as inhibition and facilitation, for example, both occur as time or intensity is increased, either serially or with a temporal phase difference between them (Kolers and Rosner, 1960; Ikeda, 1965). Further evidence on the manner in which continuous stimuli are segregated temporally comes from the study of the interactions between successive presentations.[12]

*Serial perceptual events*

Early in this century Raymond Dodge (1907), knowing that the eyes do not move continuously when one is reading, inquired into the temporal limits over which two sequentially presented visual inputs can interfere with each other. He used the phrase "clearing-up time" to indicate the limit at which the input at time $t_0$ can no longer be interfered with by another at time $t_1$. In the past several years, clearing-up time, now called masking or metacontrast, has been subjected to considerable study (Alpern, 1953; Kolers and Rosner, 1960; Raab, 1963); for on the one hand the observed phenomena seem to defy reasonable explanation, and on the other, they demonstrate that temporal segregation of visual inputs cannot be accounted for in terms of a temporal "chopper."

The basis of some experiments on these phenomena is a spatial induction, the effect exerted by a contour on one region of the retina upon the contour on a neighboring region. When two retinal regions *b* and *c* are stimulated simultaneously for some interval — say a few seconds — a diminution in the apparent brightness of the target at *b* occurs when the intensity of illumination of $c/b \geqslant 1$ and the distances between the two are small (Leibowitz, Mote, and Thurlow, 1953). Alpern (1953) measured this induction as a function of the temporal separation between presentations to *b* and *c*.

The inset of Fig. 1.11 diagrams an experiment in which *a* (a standard) and *b* (a target) are made always to appear together. The subject's task is to say when *b* appears to be as bright as *a*. This brightness match is made as a function of the intensity of *c,c′* (the inducing stimuli) and of the temporal separation between *a*, *b* and *c,c′*. In some presentations *c,c′* would precede, and in others follow, *a,b*. All flashes are 5 msec in duration. To lessen the interaction between *a* and *b*, *a* is presented to one eye while *b* and *c,c′* are presented to the other, the observer fixating a single point (*z′*) with both eyes. The results are also shown in Fig. 1.11. The abscissa represents the time interval between *a,b* and *c,c′*, while the ordinate shows the intensity required for *b* to appear as bright

[12] Although time is often an important variable in psychophysical experiments, it has a different status from such variables as intensity, speed, and wave length. The difference lies in the fact that there is no evidence for the existence of "time detectors" in the visual system, analogous to detectors for color, movement, and the like. Time is an experimenter's variable, not a subject's variable. The fact that different perceptual processes vary with time merely indicates that they take different amounts of time to run off, not that time itself is experienced as part of the input. In fact the judged duration of an event is often related to the complexity of its processing, and not to its temporal duration.

as *a* when the latter was set at 10.6 ft-lamberts. The curve of Fig. 1.11 shows that when the two flashes, *b* and *c,c′*, are simultaneous (abscissa value of 0), *b* matches *a* at approximately equal physical intensities. As a temporal separation between *b* and *c,c′* is introduced, *b* must be made more intense in order to match *a*, about 10 times more intense when *b* *precedes* *c,c′* by 100 msec. Thus the induction effect of *c* on *b* takes time to occur and is greater when the target precedes the inducing flash

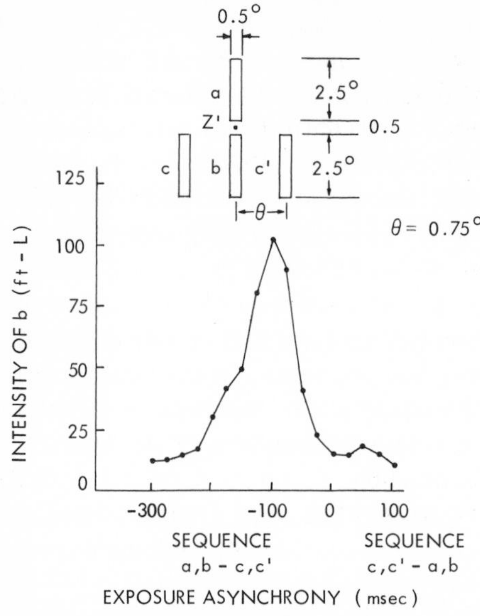


**Fig. 1.11** A flash of light *b* preceded or followed by two flanking flashes *c,c′* varies in apparent brightness with the time between the flashes. The maximum inhibition of *b* occurs when *b* precedes *c,c′*. The insert illustrates the geometrical arrangement of the flashing lights. (From Alpern, 1953.)

(sequence *a,b–c,c′*) than when it follows (sequence *c,c′–a,b*). It is obvious that some attribute of *b* is interfered with selectively when the presentations are sequential, an interference that does not occur when they are simultaneous.

A related phenomenon has also been studied (Kolers and Rosner, 1960): a black disk, normally visible, was preceded or followed by a black ring concentric with the disk. The probability of seeing the disk was found to be high when the ring was temporally near, decreased, and then recovered as the temporal separation was increased in either direction. In another study the magnitude of the inhibition in perceiving the disk was found to vary with the spatial separation, relative intensities of the two forms, contrast ratios, and similar variables (Kolers, 1962); it varies also as a function of the relative orientation of the masking and target forms (Sekuler, 1965), with the age of the subject (Pollack, 1965), whether the presentations are flashes of light or patterns (Schiller, 1965), and many other conditions. It also occurs in cascade, so that a second presentation can inhibit a first, and be inhibited in turn by a third (Piéron, 1935). I have shown (Kolers, 1962), however, that data such as those of Fig. 1.11, when taken for a range of values of *a* and *c*, may be represented as constant ratios between the intensities of standard, target, and inducing flash. In my report I suggested that under certain conditions the border or contour of a figure is processed as a separate perceptual event different from the interior; that is to say, a simple figure such as a black disk is actually constructed in the nervous system as two events — border and interior. I believe that the variations in perception that occur with time result from selective interference with the two constructions.

The import of this phenomenon of backward masking lies in the demonstration that the contour of a figure plays an important role in its being perceived, the contour of one figure can be interfered with by presenting a neighboring figure in close temporal proximity, the induction effect mediating the interference takes time to develop, and, most intriguingly, the magnitude of the induction is greater when it is on an earlier presentation than on a later one. These effects occur despite the fact that the conduction time of the neural impulses from retina to optic cortex is less than 30 msec. Clearly the visual system takes a significant amount of time to translate a physical presentation into a perceptual experience, otherwise a later presentation could not interfere with the perception of an earlier one. What is perceived is not the output of a straightforward transmission line from retina to brain; the visual system takes more than the 200 msec separating *a*, *b* and *c*,*c′* in Alpern's experiment to construct a visual impression — or there would be no interference. Further, the variety of stimulus conditions that modify this phenomenon preclude an explanation based on the simple integration of luminances of the serial presentations. Although the latter explanation has sometimes been suggested, it is usually rejected by those who consider the evidence fully.

Most explanations of visual masking have been made in terms of the interference the effects of one stimulus exert upon the effects of another; that is to say, the interference has been assumed to occur in the transmission channel itself. My own view is different, for I think the effects represent in part a distortion induced in a central processor that mediates perception, and are not only the effects of the stimuli upon each other. Consider the visual inputs as "data" and the visual system as possessed of various "subprograms." Too rapid presentation of data to a visual "program" loads the system down and interferes with its proper function. The question then is why the greater interference is exerted on the preceding rather than on subsequent presentations. The answer is implied by an analogy. A customer who enters a store is usually treated as fully as the attending clerk can treat him; a second customer then entering, the clerk tends to shorten the amount of time he spends with the first. In a store whose customers enter aperiodically, the amount of treatment given to any one depends upon whether a second enters; if he does, treatment of the first is usually shortened. In this analogy, the visual inputs are the "customers" and the central processor the "clerk." The interference that occurs so that the first customer is given short treatment is not due directly to the interference between the customers, but to their effect upon the clerk. I would say, therefore, that the loss of perceptibility of the first stimulus cannot be due to its "erasure" from the visual system, which is sometimes suggested as an explanation of masking; rather, the first stimulus is passed through the system hurriedly, so that some of the normal aspects of processing — its representation in consciousness, for example — are left undone or incomplete. Other effects of the masked stimulus may remain alive and active in the visual system despite the loss of perceptibility.

An interesting implication of this analogy is that the central processor apparently has to detect the incoming second presentation before actually beginning to operate on it. That is to say, the system may in fact keep track of the backlog of inputs it has to process at the same time that it is processing other data at rates appropriate to them.

This metaphor suggests the shape of an alternative explanation of masking phenomena. If the basic idea is correct, it stands as an interesting contrast between the functioning of most automatic pattern recognizers whose programs are usually unaffected by the data they are working on, and a psychological "program" which is itself subject to distortion when it is overloaded. The phenomenon of backward masking itself identifies a "formation time" and a perceptual "refractory period" in the nervous system governing the construction of a perceptual representation.[13]

Still another aspect of visual masking considers the apparent duration of the masked form. Kolers (1962) and Fehrer and Raab (1962) noted that the masked form seemed to last a shorter time than normal. I compared the duration of the masked form with that of a neighboring un-

[13] There are other examples of data-dependent processing in perception, notably the illusions of filled and unfilled space and filled and unfilled time. Filled time, when one is engaged in several activities, goes faster subjectively than unfilled time, when one is engaged in repetitious, monotonous tasks; but an event occurring in filled time seems more remote subjectively than an event occurring in unfilled time. Similarly, a visual extent filled with detail seems to be larger than the same extent empty, but any point in filled space seems farther away from another than when the same physical distances are judged in empty space. Compare footnote 12.

masked form presented at the same time and for a similar duration. The perceived duration of the masked form was much shorter, a finding consistent with the model just suggested.

One may note also that the phenomenon can occur dichoptically, that is, when the target is presented to one eye and the masking form to the other. Dichoptic presentation, however, introduces still other variables. For example, in another kind of masking experiment let two stimuli be separated in time and viewed with one eye. If the luminance threshold of a small target is found as a function of the intensity of a large surrounding disk on which it is superimposed, the threshold increases regu-

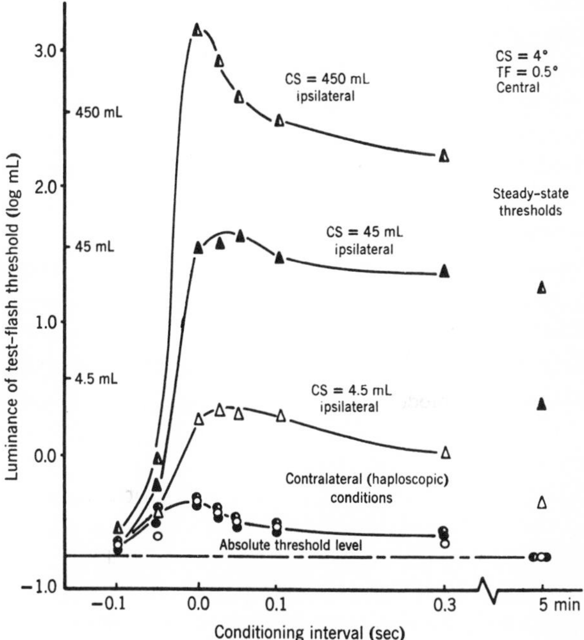


**Fig. 1.12** In another masking experiment, the target (*TF*) appears as if superimposed on the masking flash (*CS*).

Here too the apparent brightness of the target is lessened even though it is presented first; but now maximum inhibition occurs in the region of simultaneity (abscissa = 0). Note the inhibition of the target even when the target is more intense than the masking flash ($CS = 450$ mL, $TF = 1000$ mL). When the two flashes are presented to one eye, inhibition of TF varies with the intensity of CS; when TF goes to one eye and CS to the other ("Contralateral condition"), the inhibition of TF is not similarly graded. (From Boynton, 1961, p. 746.)

larly as the intensity of the disk is increased. But if the target is presented to one eye and the disk to the other, the threshold of the target is almost independent of the intensity of the disk (Fig. 1.12). In general, dichoptic presentation produces less inhibition than monoptic. Clearly, then, much of the processing of the inputs occurs in each eye before information is transmitted to higher visual centers. The fact that a presentation to one eye can be affected by a presentation to the other suggests that there is a duality of functional effects — in the retina and again in higher centers — a duality, but not a duplication. Each eye performs unique processing activities, and in addition contributes to a joint perceptual field where some of these same activities may recur (along with others unique to the joint field). The process may be schematized coarsely as in the flow chart of Fig. 1.13, whose outline is taken from Julesz (1960).

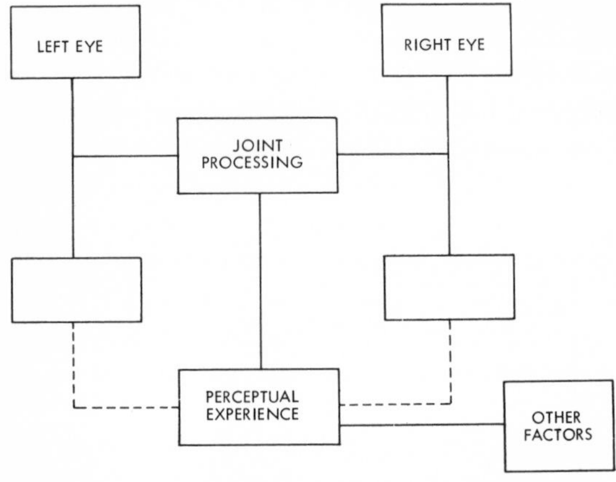


**Fig. 1.13** A schematic model of the perceptual processing of information presented to the two eyes separately.

It should not be assumed, however, that information in the visual channel goes only to the "perceptual experience," or that behavior based on visual inputs depends entirely upon the nature of the perceptual experience. An analytical experiment by Fehrer and Raab (1962) shows how perceptual and motor responses can be dissociated. In their study they measured motor reaction time to an inhibited visual target. Reaction time, as is well known, increases with a decrease in the luminance of the target. In one part of the experiment the reaction time was measured to the target alone, and in a second, to the same target followed by masking flashes, as in the *b–c,c′* arrangement of Fig. 1.11. When the target was followed by masking flashes after a delay of 75 msec, its apparent brightness was much less than when it was presented alone. Yet Fehrer and Raab found that reaction time was the same in the two conditions of the experiment, despite the great difference in appearance of the target. The reaction time was triggered by the physical onset of the target and was independent of its apparent brightness. Thus a signal in the visual system can activate a motor response independently of the way the signal is constructed into a perceptual representation. To put it another way, the motor response need not be based on a perception. Clearly there are many kinds of parallel processing in the visual system.

## *Perception of motion*

Certain phenomena of motion also depend upon timing. As one might expect, duration of exposure, luminance, and velocity of the target are closely related in the perception of motion (Graham, 1965): more intensely illuminated targets are seen in motion at shorter exposure durations than dimmer ones. More interesting is a phenomenon called streaming, which seems to be based at least in part on the angle subtended per unit time. Described by Gibson (1950) for the case of a pilot landing an airplane, the phenomenon can be observed from train windows or automobiles as well. The observation is that objects close to the observer and parallel to his path of motion appear blurred and seem to move in a direction opposite to his, while more distant ones are seen clearly and as stationary objects the observer is moving by. There are at least two components to this peculiar effect: one concerned with what is seen to be moving, the other with the relative distinctness of the stationary object. The former may find its explanation in terms of an "induced motion" effect analyzed by Duncker (1929; see also my quotation from Mach on p. 21) which shows that it is not the absolute physical displacements, but the relative displacement between reference frame and enclosed object that determines what will be perceived as moving. For nearby objects one's own motion is the reference frame, while for distant ones the environment is the frame. The explanation of streaming, however, cannot be so simple because, when one looks straight ahead in a moving car, the objects ahead appear stationary and the peripherally viewed ones appear to move, yet the reference frame is the same in both cases.

The relative distinctness of the objects is another matter. Note that nearer objects and objects seen peripherally while one is in motion subtend larger retinal angles per unit time than more distant or frontal ones. In light of the discussion of figure formation already described (pp. 37 ff.), it seems likely that the closer objects appear blurred because their images undergo too rapid a displacement on the retina for the input to be processed into a well-formed figure.

If this explanation is correct, it points again to the differences in perception that result from voluntary and involuntary action (Held and Freedman, 1963; Matin, et al., 1966): the environment does *not* appear to move when we voluntarily sweep our eyes across it rapidly, but it *does* appear to move if the eyeball is displaced mechanically, as by rapid tapping with a finger. The relation between figure-formation processes and motions of the eyes remains to be investigated; it is relevant for an understanding of perceiving, generally, and reading, specifically.

Aside from their role in establishing thresholds of velocity and of form, temporal relations play a significant part in another perception of motion, illusory motion. Under good laboratory conditions, two separated light sources, illuminated briefly in proper sequence, give the appearance of a single object moving smoothly and continuously across the space between them. Temporal variables are of great importance (Wertheimer, 1912; Kolers, 1964). Let the two lamps be illuminated each for 50 msec and the time between the offset of the first and the onset of the second be varied between 10 and 1000 msec. When the interval is 10 msec, the lamps appear to be on simultaneously; when the interval is more than 500 msec, they appear to follow in slow succession. As the interval is increased from 10 to 500 msec, most observers experience a regular sequence of perceptual events. First, simultaneity; next, partial movements, the first light appearing to move part of the way across the screen before disappearing, the second then appearing displaced and moving to its own true location; third, optimal motion, smooth continuous movement across the screen; fourth, objectless motion, a smear of light in movement, without an identifiable object (which may also occur at brief separations, between simultaneity and partial movement); and last, slow succession.

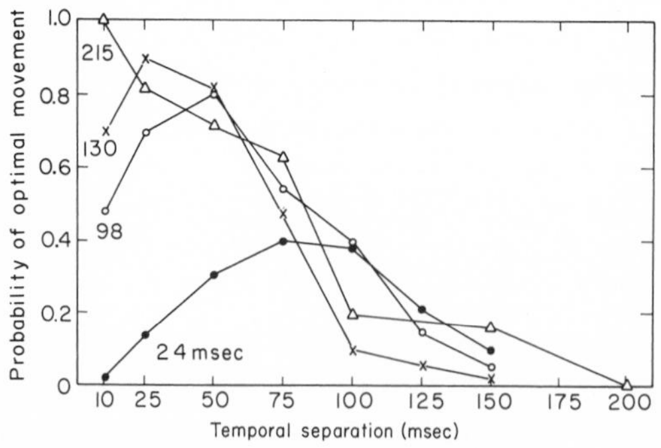


**Fig. 1.14** A psychophysical function for apparent motion.

The probability of seeing motion increases with an increase in the on-time of the lamps and varies regularly with the time interval between the flashes. (Modified from "The Illusion of Movement" by P. A. Kolers. Copyright © 1964 by Scientific American, Inc. All rights reserved.)

Optimal motion occurs as a regular psychophysical function extending over a broad range of temporal intervals, as shown in Fig. 1.14. This function varies with the duration of the first flash, but is virtually independent of the second: as long as the second flash is visible, movement is perceived. The second flash seems to serve only the function of giving the first flash "a place to go." [14]

Transformed to plot the frequency of seeing motion as a function of the sum of the duration of the first flash and the interval between flashes, the data yield a single growth function which rises to a plateau in the region of 300 msec, remains there, and then falls rapidly (Fig. 1.15).

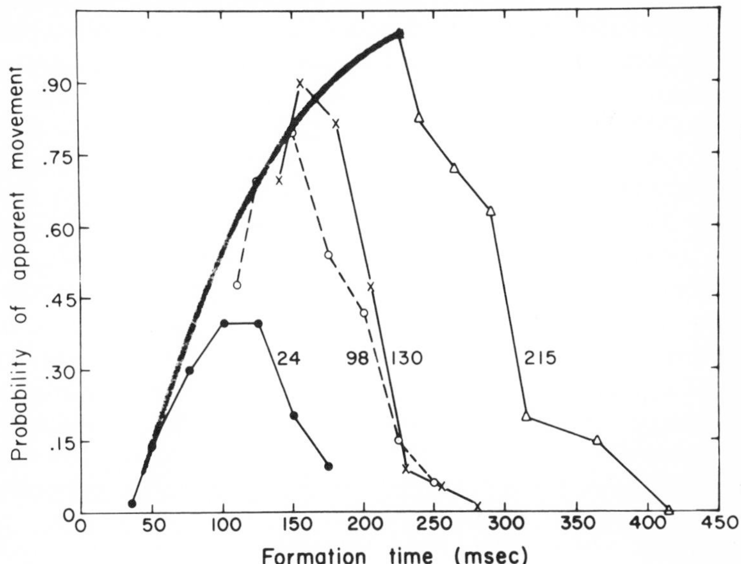


**Fig. 1.15** The data of Fig. 1.14 are redrawn to sum the duration of the first lamp and the interval between flashes, representing a theoretical formation time of visual presentations.

The heavy curve represents the hypothetical figure-forming process that is tapped by the individual curves. (Modified from "The Illusion of Movement" by P. A. Kolers. Copyright © 1964 by Scientific American, Inc. All rights reserved.)

The data were interpreted to show a basic distinction between the sense of motion derived from the properly sequenced presentation of two spatially separated configurations, and a time-bound, figure-forming mechanism in the visual nervous system from which it derives. That is to say, the figure-forming mechanism was related to that mentioned

[14] The second flash can be incorporated into the perception in other ways, however. If the configuration or color of the second is different from the first, the perceived object changes shape or color in midflight to accommodate the differences (Kolers, 1964; Orlansky, 1940; Van der Waals and Roelofs, 1930). In addition, the direction of motion depends upon the location of the second flash with respect to the first. Thus, while the second flash only creates a place to go, the visual system cannot know the direction or the form the moving object is to take until the second flash is presented.

earlier in the discussion of masking and metacontrast, while the experimental results imply that motion is a unique perceptual experience independent of the objects perceived to be moving.[15] (Compare the description of the Archimedes spiral, p. 27.)

The conditioning of motion per se can be seen in certain other illusions, for example, the aftereffect of looking at moving objects that subtend a relatively small visual angle. After looking for 30–40 sec at such an object, looking at another, entirely stationary scene gives the sense that objects in the latter are moving in the opposite direction, as in the waterfall illusion mentioned earlier. However, efforts to line up the apparently moving objects with parts of the visual scene that do not appear to be displaced show that the *objects* line up and it is only a *sense* of motion that is present (Papert, 1967). Normally, this sense of motion is interpreted in a way that yields a displacement of the apparent location of viewed objects, as in the autokinetic illusion discussed earlier, until reference marks are called into play. These various peculiarities that attend the perceiving of motion indicate clearly that motion can be *attributed* to stimuli under many conditions. They imply also that the perception of an object is constructed by means of a number of separate part-processes, or by the activity of different subsystems: motion, contour, color, and the like. It is not clear how the output of these subsystems is synthesized into a perceptual whole, however.

Another property of apparent motion that bears mention is the result obtained when the two flashes of light occur at unequal intervals. Let the two flashes be presented for 50 msec each with intervals between them of 125 msec. Most observers see good optimal motion: a single object oscillating in a plane. If one of the dark intervals is reduced — to 75 msec, for example — motion is still perceived, but partly in depth: the lights appear to move in the plane of the stimuli during the shorter interval and in depth (or bow movement) during the longer one (Kolers, 1963). This experiment shows that the temporal disparity that produces depth may occur in a single half of the visual system, which again sug-

[15] Several workers have been struck by the fact that in masking experiments, the temporal interval between target and masking figures can be manipulated to yield masking *or* apparent movement; a few have suggested that one is a form of the other. It may be the case that they are *both* derived from different stages of a complex figure-formation process (Kolers, 1964), but it is unlikely that they are both based on similar mechanisms. For example, apparent motion can occur even at the briefest temporal separations when the first stimulus is presented for a long enough duration (Fig. 1.14); but lengthening the first acts against its being masked in a masking experiment (Kolers and Rosner, 1960). Similarly, manipulating the second affects its ability to mask the first, but does not affect the likelihood of perceiving movement as long as the second is visible. These two differences alone make it seem unlikely that masking and apparent motion can be alternate forms of the same phenomenon; but each may represent mechanisms active at different stages in the figure-forming process.

gests that a trade-off can take place between space and time in many visual functions. This phenomenon occurring in one eye may be related to a discovery made by Pulfrich with two eyes (1922). Let a luminous pendulum swing in a dark room and let one of the observer's eyes be covered with a light-attenuating filter. The pendulum oscillating in the plane is seen to form ellipses. Presumably the nerve impulses from the covered eye have a longer latency than the others, producing a temporal disparity at some integrating center of the visual system. The perception of depth resolves the disparity in their time of arrival in the central nervous system, indicating the trade-off between spatial and temporal disparity in another way. What remains a puzzle, however, is the means by which the impulses from the two eyes are attributed to a single perceptual figure; but the phenomenon further implies the existence of a space-time equivalence for some aspects of human perception.

### *Internal scanning*

It is a commonplace of experience that, having seen something we subsequently describe, we know that we saw more than we can say. What we can subsequently describe depends on a great many things: what we were looking for, our familiarity with the materials, the time elapsed since looking, the duration of the glance, and so on. It has been known for some time that a perception is not a full representation of a scene the way a photograph can be. In one experiment concerned with the storage and accessibility of briefly viewed scenes, Sperling (1960) presented subjects with an array of nine to twelve letters arranged in three rows, and instructed the subjects that after the array was turned off a tone would sound indicating a row they were to report. The tone was high-pitched, medium, or low, indicating that they were to report the top, middle, or bottom row of the array. In the absence of a tone the subjects were able to report about five items correctly, sampled from different parts of the array. When the tone was presented, the subjects were able to select the items of the row indicated, their ability to do so falling off with an increase in the delay of the tone. That is to say, the subjects were able to scan an internal representation of a briefly presented scene no longer present to view. Sperling argued that the array, after being seen briefly, was placed in short-term storage and that the subject could sample this store as it faded during the one-third to one-half second after presentation of the array. These results, considered in the light of the earlier discussion of figure-formation time, may also indicate that the subject is able to read out from a representation of an array at the same time that it is undergoing construction into a well-formed percept. That is, Sperling argues that a completed representation is placed in temporary storage from which it can be read out; the alternative I suggest is that the read-out can occur during the actual construction of the representation. The difference is between serial and parallel processing. Note, however, that in any case the active read-out occurs at some time well after the tone is presented, since the reaction-time to the tone itself occupies several hundred milliseconds.

Sperling (1963) has interpreted these and other data to mean that visual inputs normally are recoded into auditory ones (names), and that the names are the items stored in long-term memory. Although this hypothesis may be true for some conditions, it is necessarily faulty for many. Since the items presented were all distinctly namable (letters, numbers, and so on), it was likely that some form of linguistic encoding would occur. A better test would have been to use items that were strange designs, hieroglyphs, or other unfamiliar complex shapes (for example, Chinese ideograms for nonreaders of Chinese) to test the possibility that storage may occur in purely visual terms independently of names.[16] Second, while names actually facilitate recall (for example, Glanzer and Clark, 1963), they may not be essential to it. Visual experiences can be more subtle and complex than our linguistic skills can describe: The scene was beautiful beyond words, I can not describe what then I saw, Words fail me — these are clichés that describe the fact that some perceptual attributes and the existential states they generate lack a full mapping into linguistic form. Indeed, some perceptions, for example landscapes, lack a "true" mapping even in pictorial form (Gombrich, 1961); yet recall or recognition of the scene or event can occur (Shepard, 1967).

It is still an open question whether names as such are what is stored. Animals such as rats, dogs, and horses easily identify visual objects and learn to make visual distinctions even in the absence of language, as that term is usually understood. Indeed, there is some suggestion that the relative difficulty of perceptual problems involving brightness and form is roughly similar across different species of animals (Lashley, 1949; Zimmerman, 1961; Nash and Michels, 1966). A formal correspondence in the order of difficulty of classes of problems across species

[16] People differ markedly in their ability to visualize and manipulate geometric shapes. Some geometers report that they can move imagined three-dimensional shapes at will and see the relations between sections. Many other people report little success with this kind of imaging of structures. Since the names of the shapes are identical for both groups of people, the names themselves cannot be the variable of principal effect. Thus the name by itself tells little about the psychological representation of the object named.

would implicate forms of visual encoding necessarily independent of language. But these remarks in no way detract from Sperling's demonstration that more is reportable than is reported in a scene, and that the perceptual representation of what is reportable has its own half-life.

Still another kind of scanning of internally represented information has been demonstrated by Neisser (1963). His basic experiment requires a subject to find a target letter or target sequence embedded in a long list. The position of the target is varied from list to list and the time taken to find it is measured. A plot of time taken to find the target (ordinate) against position of the target in the list (abscissa) produces a curve whose slope may be taken as the scanning time per item. With well-practiced subjects and sufficiently large numbers of lists, the resulting slope is found to be about 200 msec per line. Depending on the number of letters in a line, this means as little as 10 msec per letter, if every letter were scanned serially; but, of course, they are probably not scanned individually. More interesting, Neisser, Novick, and Lazar (1963) found that well-practiced subjects can search lists for as many as ten targets simultaneously at a rate no different from that for searching for one. This startling result they interpret as evidence for parallel processing. They assume the scanning may be divided into two stages: feature extraction and identification. To identify a *k*, a first step of extracting distinctive features occurs, which is then supplemented by an additional process of identification (implicit naming). The *k* "pops out" of the list one is scanning because it meets the internally generated set of feature categories for *k*. In subsequent experiments Neisser and Beller (1965) showed that when subjects are looking for classes of objects (for example, men's names, animals, names of states), scanning time per item is longer. The subjects must search memory as well as the lists, for then the pool of names exists only in the subject's mind.

On the basis of experiments of this kind, Neisser postulates a hierarchical arrangement to the search process, different functions of the pattern-recognizing machinery being run off at different levels of depth in the hierarchy. Not enough additional experimental data are available to evaluate this hypothesis correctly; yet we may note in passing that should it be substantiated, it would be the first significant evidence that demonstrates parallel processing within a single modality. While intuitively obvious for macro behavior — for example, we walk to the store while thinking about something else, have ideas and notions while driving to work — parallel processing has not been unequivocally demonstrated at the level of analysis of stimuli except in Neisser's experiments, if in fact they do so demonstrate it.

A word is in order about the concept of distinctive features in pattern perception, which has come into vogue in the past few years following the analysis by Jakobson and Halle (1956) for the perception of speech. While easily defined and of great use there, the concept imported into the study of visual pattern recognition has not met with much success. As used in phonetics, the concept of distinctive features notes that the sounds of a language can be represented as sets of binary variables (see the following chapter by Keyser and Halle for examples). Their role in the actual recognition of words, however, is not yet well understood. The words of a language can be recognized by someone who knows them through different accents, when sounds have been clipped, and through many other distortions. The concept applied to visual perception is used to try to identify specific geometrical attributes of a stimulus and to suggest that recognition occurs by the person's discriminating and integrating these particular attributes. But written words, for example, can be recognized through many distortions of type face, through many changes in font, and even when some of their parts are missing (Huey, 1908). Because the range of perceptible objects is infinite, one problem is to establish the characteristics of an object that are used in constructing its perceptual representation. The concept of distinctive features seems to be used in this way; but from all that has been said already, it should be clear that perception does not usually go forward by the piecemeal discrimination and subsequent integration of individual features. Whether more abstract feature analyzers are active in human perception remains to be worked out.[17] The problem in Neisser's analysis concerns the unit on which the categorizing is based. His assumption is that the unit has to do with geometrical properties of the target; an alternative is that the unit is far more complex, and is based on semantic properties attributed to a stimulus. While individual targets do, in fact, have distinctive features that may be named (for example, HAS has features that distinguish it from WERE), a fantastically vast amount of material would have to be continuously retrieved from memory to make successful identification of these targets hang on the detection of such features.

To return now to perception, one example that identifies a still more complex kind of recognition is taken from an experiment by Parks (1965). He presented an outline figure on a strip of paper which was passed behind a narrow slit that permitted only a small vertical slice of the drawing to be seen at any one time. Nevertheless, subjects saw the whole figure. The rate of movement of the drawing and the width

[17] Such abstract-feature analyzers in visual perception would answer questions about a target relative, for example, to size, movement, general configuration, and the like. See Lettvin, et al. (1959) for some preliminary attempts to identify evolutionarily useful perceptual categories in the frog.

of the slit were crucial variables to this achievement, the probability of its occurrence varying with speed and slit width. Parks found that the effect was optimal when the total traverse time of the drawing across the slit was in the region of ¼–½ sec — similar to the values for figure-formation time already described — and that the effect occurred with slits as small as 1/64 inch. The effect is schematized in Fig. 1.16. The

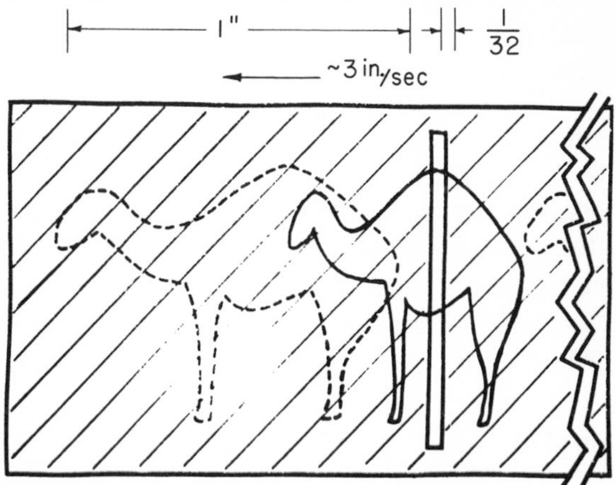


**Fig. 1.16** Passing a camel through the eye of a needle.

A simple outline figure (dashed line) is passed behind a slit in an opaque screen. If it passes in approximately ½ sec, it will be seen briefly in the region of the slit, to move slightly, and to be foreshortened (solid line). The foreshortening increases with the speed of its passage until only a blur is seen. At slow speeds, the figure may be identified but will not be seen as a whole. (From Parks, 1965.)

dependence upon speed argues that the process is not merely judgmental, but is closely tied to the intrinsic rate for forming visual figures.[18]

In discussing the role of time in human pattern recognition, I have

[18] Additional observations on this phenomenon made by Phillip Liss (unpublished) relate it in an interesting way to backward masking. If the small slit is oscillated rapidly in front of a page of print which itself remains stationary, the observer clearly sees a whole word or a whole phrase, depending on the range of the oscillation. On the other hand, if the page is moved at the same rate while the slit is now kept stationary, perceptibility of the word or phrase is severely reduced. In the first case the retina is stimulated at different places because the eye does not track the oscillating slit faithfully, while in the second case a fixed region of the retina is stimulated by the different inputs as in backward masking. Liss also noted that eye movements are themselves involved in the phenomenon: slow movements of the target *or* the slit with the eye fixated on the slit (that is, either visually tracking the slit or fixating upon it) produces apparent motion of the words and a decrease in the ability to read them. Similar relative motion of the page and the slit, however, sometimes results in easy recognition of the words and no apparent motion; observation shows that the eyes are rapidly flicking back and forth saccadically when this clear perception occurs.

shown two kinds of processes at work. First, that the human visual system takes measurable amounts of time to construct representations of visual arrays, the amount varying with the nature of the task and the complexity of the array. Second, that perception is not an immediate and direct consequence of stimulation; a number of different kinds of processes appear to be involved in the construction the subject makes, the representation he creates for himself, of the array being observed. Different kinds of internal actions can be taken with respect to a single array. The subject may read out from an image or from memory, supply himself with information not in the array, scan at high rates, act to establish a whole figure when only parts are presented over time, and so on. Much ingenuity has gone into the isolation of these processes, much more than is required by the ordinary psychophysical experiment that studies the effect of energy or time on perception. But still more formidable are the problems that remain, concerning the interplay between perceptual recognition, thought, and action, and between linguistic and perceptual encoding.

## Pattern Conception

Miller and Chomsky (1958) have illustrated an important distinction between pattern detection or pattern recognition and higher level processes. Typically, an analysis of pattern perception focuses on the temporal or geometric properties of the arrays or individual differences in the perceivers. Another activity, which they call pattern conception, involves higher level abstracting and concept-forming behavior, and is based on the identification of relational invariants abstracted from complex disguises. To make the abstraction, the subject must find the rules of relation or algorithms that generate a diverse array of objects from a few parental instances. The concept of finite state language is useful to illustrate the point (Chomsky and Miller, 1958). One such language taken from a study by Shipstone (1960) is shown in Fig. 1.17; the graph represents a pattern as "states" and the rules for moving between them. Thus, ZNZP, ZPPNZP, and ZNZNNNNP are variations of the same basic string, having common formation rules. While few people would be likely to identify the nature of the generator from these three instances, adding instances permits the college student subject to recognize the invariance behind them, to conceptualize the pattern underlying the strings. He may never see two identical instances, or similar patterns of identical number, which are the usual ways of presenting patterns for recognition or studying concept formation; yet he is able to adduce the rule of string formation without too much difficulty. In doing so, he demonstrates a capacity for forming categories out of apparently dissimilar objects and for conceptualizing (and subsequently inventing) rules for establishing category membership; that is, he is engaged in "pattern conception."

The advantage to human memory of the ability to recode by categories rather than retain the billions of instances of events one encounters is obvious. In fact the whole range of intellectual activities that face the

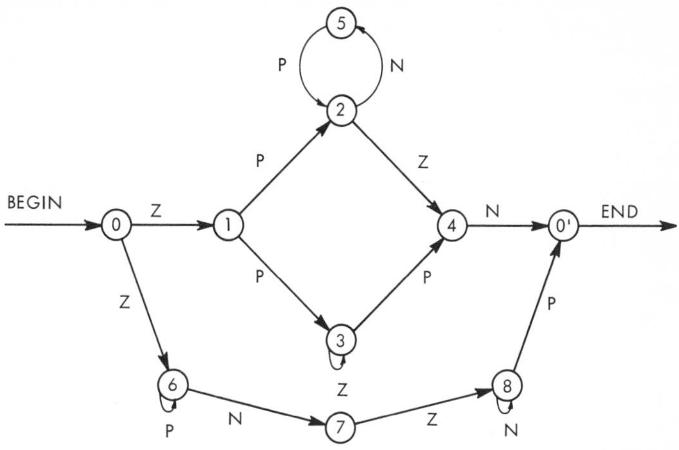


| RULES OF TRANSITION | | BASIC STRINGS | CANONICAL |
|---|---|---|---|
| 0, Z, 1 | 1, P, 3 | ZPZN | ZP (NP) ZN |
| 0, Z, 6 | 2, N, 5 | ZPPN | ZP (Z) PN |
| 1, P, 2 | etc. | ZNZP | Z (P) NZ (N) P |

**Fig. 1.17** A finite-state generator used to create patterns whose category membership is detected in studies of pattern conception. (After Shipstone, 1960).

practicing engineer or scientist involves the adducing of rules and the finding of invariances, often called concepts, that underlie experimental data. One important characteristic that can, but need not, distinguish perception from conception is the degree to which events are spread out in time: events whose rules of relation are being sought are usually spread out more thinly in time than entities or patterns being recognized. In contrast with pattern perception, the *variety* of different but related instances plays a greater role in pattern conception than the repetition of identical instances does. This work on pattern conception and the conceptually simpler work on concept formation that it illuminates (for example, Bruner, Goodnow, and Austin, 1956) define a level of pattern recognition that is only now coming to be studied. This kind of information-processing is of course altogether inconsistent with any notions of template-matching; rather, it emphasizes the constructional, symbolic, and rational activities of mind engaged in action rather than mere passive detection.

Humans categorize because the limitations of channel capacity of the various sensory modalities, and the profound limitations on retrieval from memory, make it impossible to treat of individual instances all the time. By channel capacity in this sense is meant the number of items that can be processed per unit time within a single sensory domain. Miller (1956) summarized a considerable amount of data to indicate that both short-term memory and channel capacity have very narrow limits, and that both perceiving and remembering seem to be limited to a small number of items in the general region of 5–9. The items, however, appear to be indifferent to the nature of the unit they represent: one may be able to recall about seven digits and seven triplets equally well. By suitable recoding, a mass of individual items may be transformed into appropriate category members or instances of a rule, converting hosts of *facts* into a manageable number of categories and their rules of relation. Recoding, however, too often depends upon the existence of preformed categories and too rarely upon a perceiver's inventiveness in establishing new ones. We may note that in practice, particularly in scientific practice, breakthroughs usually follow on a conceptual simplifying of a mass of data: the law of gravitational attraction categorizes into a new pattern an enormous number of instances regarding the fall of many different objects and the trajectories of missiles. The conceiving of this pattern — $S = \frac{1}{2}gt^2$ — is the process that goes beyond the recognition of *a, b, d* . . . as falling objects.

While it is the case that humans very often recode multiple instances into conceptually simpler formulas, coding or codability is itself limited. Not everything that has a perceptual representation has a name: there is always more to be represented, more that can be perceived, than is perceived at any time. The stock in trade of experimental science is the establishing and naming of patterns of events, and relations among objects and concepts — patterns and relations that had gone undetected or "unperceived" until brought into focus by an experimenter or theoretician. The establishment of disease syndromes is one such example. The details were always there to be seen, and most usually were. It is their relation or pattern that had not been perceived until they were brought together and named. Having been named, they became more visible. Yet while pattern recognition is greatly facilitated by the availability of coding categories and names of the objects to be coded, naming may not be a necessary condition for the process. Certain perceptual events or relations can be encoded in a manner not yet known. Consider, for example, whether words in a long list have "names." Subjects can scan long lists of words looking for a target item and find that item in short order with virtually no recall of other items in the list (Neisser and Beller, 1965); on the other hand, subjects presented with a long list, in this case 612 words or pictures, can, on tests made two to three hours later, identify with better than 90 per cent accuracy which items were on the original list (Shepard, 1967). While it is not known how this comes about, probably the subject does not name each word or each picture he sees; rather, he may form some other internal representation, with respect to which the item is encoded.

In certain cases it seems clear that the recoding of verbal material, and perhaps of other kinds as well, is into some form of conceptual or symbolic state. An experiment carried out with French-English bilinguals makes this point (Kolers, 1966a). The basis of the experiment is the finding that subjects who are presented with a long list of words one at a time recall items from it in proportion to their frequency of occurrence within the list. Thus a word that appears four times in a list is twice as likely to be recalled as a word appearing only twice (Waugh, 1963, 1967). I constructed lists in which some words appeared only in English, others only in French, and still others in both languages — that is to say, a word and its translation appeared in the same list. Most of these translations were visually and phonetically distinct — for example, wheat-blé, rug-tapis. The finding was that the recall of a word in English (or in French) was proportional to the frequency of occurrence of the concept, irrespective of its linguistic form, and not to the frequency of occurrence of a word in a language. Thus, two occurrences of a word in English and two occurrences of its translation in French yielded a probability of recall (in English *or* in French) equal to four occurrences of another word in one language only. Control tests made it unlikely that the subjects were merely translating the words of one language into the other, and so the experiment may be taken as evidence that the storage is in terms of concepts rather than of items (templates).

In other experiments we find that bilingual subjects who are reading aloud as rapidly as they can passages which contain a mixture of two languages (for example, "His horse, followed de deux bassets, faisait la terre résonner under its even tread") will often substitute a word in Language 2 for one printed in Language 1 — will say, for example, "faisait the earth" in place of "faisait la terre" — often without recognizing that the substitution was made (Kolers, 1966c). This again may be taken as evidence for the conceptual equivalence of the words in the two languages, making altogether untenable any argument that one reads by recognizing templates or words as such. The words appear to be recognized by virtue of their relation to concepts, to a schema or set of relations that the reader himself generates. Pattern recognizing in these cases is an everyday occurrence for humans; it appears to be based on a process in which the words are merely cues for constructing a representation of the message generated by syntactic and semantic variables, but are not the things that are themselves perceived and stored. Skilled readers typically do not recognize words as such, but the sets of relations they have with other words of the material being read; it is these relations or concepts which appear to be stored and not, usually, the items themselves.

While recognizing the semantic content and inferring the concepts represented by words are fairly literal processes in the cases cited, in the sense that the message stands in moderately good agreement with the usual meaning of the words used to generate it, other kinds of language use are more abstract. Ancona (1965), for example, has pointed to a counterfactual use of language: the speaker says something he does *not* mean in order to learn whether he will be disagreed with. Language used in this way is a testing or sensing tool, a kind of ranging instrument in which information is inferred from properties other than the literal meaning of the return. Sometimes used as byplay, sometimes as a search for reassurance, language used in this way requires a subtle pattern recognizer for its "real" meaning to be detected, and its point is missed when it is taken literally (Fig. 1.18).

The relation of language to behavior and pattern recognizing generally is almost entirely obscure at this time. The information people pick up from the environment seems to be recoded into various information systems, so that things learned or known in one context are often not available for use in another. Further, the ability of such systems to interact and influence each other within a single individual has not been well explored, particularly the ability of language to influence perception and perception language. Our intuitive evidence is that we often do not know what we are seeing until we know what we are looking at — that is to say, identification precedes recognition — especially when there are several equally good signals in the array, as with a microscope slide, disease syndrome, or set of data. The history of experimental science, of culture at large, is full of such cases. Later investigators add to the richness and complexity of description of a phenomenon, a richness and complexity simply not seen by earlier investigators who looked at the "same" thing.

The development of such "conceptual perceptions" does not always require a modification of apparatus external to the observer: many an experimenter has looked repeatedly at a phenomenon and simply not seen some aspect of it that appeared at once to a colleague who happened by. The modification required is of the first observer's internal apparatus, his way of seeing and his notions of what he is looking at.

Names clearly affect our ability to see things — aspects of a perceptual complex that have been artificially segmented by being given a name; and in some ways our perceiving must influence our ability to name, else nothing new would ever be named. Similarly, "knowing" what one

*"Confound it, I'm not just saying it! When I say you're the cutest girl I've ever met, then I mean you're the cutest girl I've ever met, and let that be an end to it."*

Drawing by Stan Hunt


**Fig. 1.18** Illustrating a failure to detect the "true meaning" of a linguistic pattern.

is looking at affects what one sees, but also can blind one to "seeing" details inconsistent with the knowledge that is rigidly held. But how these kinds of complexities of pattern recognizing come about and are modified has been little studied to date.

Despite these holes in our understanding, it is clear that there are no inadequate "programs" in human information-processing. Once his input threshold is reached, the human will make something of the information. Unlike the computer, the human program rarely fails to run. Although he may not be efficient, the human will do the best he can with what is presented to him, within the limits defined by the input and his modes of categorizing. Scotomatous patients see complete forms, the problem-solver invents explanations of events, the handicapped ambulate. We can understand observed outputs only when we understand what the subject is trying to do and how he operates. The life sciences deal with living organisms filled with needs, plans, goals, and the ability to perceive relations, and not with the involuntary objects of the natural sciences. We cannot fully understand living systems if we treat them as black boxes, correlating outputs with inputs only. We must "get inside" a living system, understand its purpose, in order to understand *it;* for living systems have options in their performance and can function at different levels of complexity as a task demands and as they are inclined.

The question the human visual system tries to answer is "What might it be?" or "What is it doing?" and not "What is it composed of?" The human visual system categorizes; it does not analyze. It forms hypotheses and makes decisions, usually on the basis of sparse evidence; it does not typically decompose the world into its elements. It is a system designed to facilitate orientation and survival, not a system to represent the world "as it really is." The analysis of the world that we do perform — as scientists, engineers, scholars, or simple human beings — comes later. These propensities and biases should be borne in mind by anyone who seeks to make a machine that emulates the human visual system, or who tries to use his own sophistication to model another human being.

## Acknowledgment

I thank my friends Lila Ghent Braine, Nelson Goodman, Phillip Liss, Ulric Neisser, and Joel Norman for their helpful comments on this review. Its preparation was supported principally by the National Institutes of Health (Grant 1 PO1 GM-14940-01) and in part by the Joint Services Electronics Program (Contract DA-28-043-AMC-02536(E)).

## References

Alpern, M. Metacontrast. *J. opt. Soc. Amer.,* 1953, *43,* 648–657.

Ancona, L. Discussion. In F. A. Geldard (Editor), *Communication Processes.* Oxford: Pergamon Press, 1965. Pp. 129–133.

Attneave, F. Informational aspects of visual perception. *Psychol. Rev.,* 1954, *61,* 183–193.

Bartlett, F. C. *Remembering.* London: Cambridge University Press, 1932.

Basmajian, J. V. Control and training of individual motor units. *Science,* 1963, *141,* 440–441.

Blake, R. R., and G. V. Ramsey. *Perception, an Approach to Personality.* New York: Ronald Press, 1951.

Boynton, R. M. Some temporal factors in vision. In W. A. Rosenblith (Editor), *Sensory Communication.* New York: M.I.T. Press and Wiley, 1961. Pp. 739–756. Third printing, Cambridge, Mass.: M.I.T. Press, 1964.

Boynton, R. M., and W. R. Bush. Recognition of forms against a complex background. *J. opt. Soc. Amer.*, 1956, *46,* 758–764.

Broadbent, D. E. *Perception and Communication.* New York: Pergamon Press, 1958.

Brown, J. L., and C. G. Mueller. Brightness discrimination and brightness contrast. In C. H. Graham (Editor), *Vision and Visual Perception.* New York: Wiley, 1965. Pp. 208–250.

Brown, K. T. Factors affecting differences in apparent size between opposite halves of a visual meridian. *J. opt. Soc. Amer.*, 1953, *43,* 464–472.

Bruner, J. S., J. J. Goodnow, and G. A. Austin. *A Study of Thinking.* New York: Wiley, 1956.

Bruner, J. S., and D. Krech. *Perception and Personality, a Symposium.* Durham: Duke University Press, 1950.

Chomsky, N., and G. A. Miller. Finite state languages. *Information and Control,* 1958, *1,* 91–112.

Cornsweet, T. N. Determination of the stimuli for involuntary drifts and saccadic eye movements. *J. opt. Soc. Amer.*, 1956, *46,* 987–993.

Ditchburn, R. W., and B. L. Ginsborg. Vision with a stabilized retinal image. *Nature, Lond.*, 1952, *170,* 36–37.

Dodge, R. An experimental study of visual fixation. *Psychol. Rev. Monogr. Suppl.*, 1907, *8,* No. 35.

Duncker, K. Ueber induzierte Bewegung, *Psychol. Forsch.*, 1929, *12,* 180–259.

Eden, M. A three-dimensional optical illusion. Quart. Prog. Rep. No. 64, Res. Lab. Electronics, M.I.T., Jan. 15, 1962, pp. 267–274.

Evans, C. R. Some studies of pattern perception using a stabilized retinal image. *Brit. J. Psychol.*, 1965, *56,* 121–133.

Fehrer, E., and D. Raab. Reaction time to stimuli masked by metacontrast. *J. exp. Psychol.*, 1962, *63,* 143–147.

Fiske, D. W., and S. R. Maddi. *Functions of Varied Experience.* Homewood, Ill.: Dorsey Press, 1961.

Fry, G. A. *Blur of the Retinal Image.* Columbus: Ohio State University Press, 1955.

Ghent, L. Perception of overlapping and embedded figures by children of different ages. *Amer. J. Psychol.*, 1956, *69,* 575–587.

Gibson, J. J. *The Perception of the Visual World.* Boston: Houghton Mifflin, 1950.

Glanzer, M., and W. H. Clark. The verbal loop hypothesis: binary numbers. *J. Verbal Learning and Verbal Behav.*, 1963, *2,* 301–309.

Gombrich, E. H. *Art and Illusion.* Second Edition, New York: Pantheon, 1961.

Gottschaldt, K. Ueber den Einfluss der Erfahrung auf die Wahrnehmung von Figuren. *Psychol. Forsch.*, 1926, *8,* 261–317.

Graham, C. H. (Editor). *Vision and Visual Perception.* New York: Wiley, 1965.

Graham, C. H., and E. H. Kemp. Brightness discrimination as a function of the duration of the increment in intensity. *J. gen. Physiol.*, 1938, *21,* 635–650.

Green, R. T., and M. C. Courtis. Information theory and figure perception. *Acta psychol.*, 1966, *25,* 12–35.

Gregory, R. L. *Eye and Brain.* New York: McGraw-Hill, 1966.

Harris, C. S. Perceptual adaptation to inverted, reversed and displaced vision. *Psychol. Rev.*, 1965, *72,* 419–444.

Held, R., and S. J. Freedman. Plasticity in human sensorimotor control. *Science,* 1963, *142,* 455–462.

Hirsch, I. J., and C. E. Sherrick. Perceived order in different sense modalities. *J. exp. Psychol.,* 1961, *62,* 423–432.

Hochberg, J. E., and E. McAlister. A quantitative approach to figural "goodness." *J. exp. Psychol.,* 1953, *46,* 361–364.

Howard, I. P., and W. B. Templeton. *Human Spatial Orientation.* New York: Wiley, 1966.

Hubel, D. H., and T. N. Wiesel. Receptive fields, binocular interaction and functional architecture in the cat's visual cortex. *J. Physiol.,* 1962, *160,* 106–154.

Hubel, D. H., and T. N. Wiesel. Receptive fields and functional architecture in two nonstriate visual areas (18 and 19) of the cat. *J. Neurophysiol.,* 1965, *28,* 229–289.

Huey, E. B. *The Psychology and Pedagogy of Reading.* New York: Macmillan, 1908. Paperback edition, Cambridge, Mass.: M.I.T. Press, 1968.

Hunter, W. S., and M. Sigler. The span of visual discrimination as a function of time and intensity of stimulation. *J. exp. Psychol.,* 1940, *26,* 160–179.

Ikeda, M. Temporal summation of positive and negative flashes in the visual system. *J. opt. Soc. Amer.,* 1965, *55,* 1527–1534.

Jakobson, R., and M. Halle. *Fundamentals of Language.* The Hague: Mouton, 1956.

Jammer, M. *Concepts of Space.* New York: Harper Torchbooks, 1960.

Julesz, B. Binocular depth perception of computer-generated patterns. *Bell Syst. Tech. J.,* 1960, *39,* 1125–1161.

Julesz, B. Binocular depth perception without familiarity cues. *Science,* 1964, *145,* 356–362.

Kahneman, D., and J. Norman. The time-intensity relation in visual perception as a function of the observer's task. *J. exp. Psychol.,* 1964, *68,* 215–220.

Kaufman, L. Some new stereoscopic phenomena and their implications for the theory of stereopsis. *Amer. J. Psychol.,* 1965, *78,* 1–20.

Kaufman, L. and C. Pitblado. Further observations on the nature of effective binocular disparities. *Amer. J. Psychol.,* 1965, *78,* 379–391.

Koffka, K. *Principles of Gestalt Psychology.* New York: Harcourt, Brace, 1935.

Köhler, W., and H. Wallach. Figural after-effects. *Proc. Amer. phil. Soc.,* 1944, *88,* 269–357.

Kolers, P. A. Intensity and contour effects in visual masking. *Vision Res.,* 1962, *2,* 277–294.

Kolers, P. A. Some differences between real and apparent visual movement. *Vision Res.,* 1963, *3,* 191–206.

Kolers, P. A. The illusion of movement. *Scient. Amer.,* 1964, *211* (4), 98–106.

Kolers, P. A. Interlingual facilitation of short-term memory. *J. Verbal Learning and Verbal Behav.,* 1966a, *5,* 314–319.

Kolers, P. A. An illusion that dissociates motion, object, and meaning. Quart. Prog. Rep. No. 82, Res. Lab. Electronics, M.I.T., July 15, 1966b, pp. 221–223.

Kolers, P. A. Reading and talking bilingually. *Amer. J. Psychol.*, 1966c, *79*, 357–376.

Kolers, P. A., M. Eden, and A. C. Boyer. Reading as a perceptual skill. Quart. Prog. Rep. No. 74, Res. Lab. Electronics, M.I.T., July 15, 1964, pp. 214–217.

Kolers, P. A., and B. S. Rosner. On visual masking (metacontrast): dichoptic observation. *Amer. J. Psychol.*, 1960, *73*, 2–21.

Krauskopf, J. Effect of retinal image stabilization on the appearance of heterochromatic targets. *J. opt. Soc. Amer.*, 1963, *53*, 741–744.

Krauskopf, J., V. Graf, and K. Gaarder. Lack of inhibition during involuntary saccades. *Amer. J. Psychol.*, 1966, *79*, 73–81.

Külpe, O. *Outlines of Psychology*. . . . Translated by E. B. Titchener. New York: Macmillan, 1895.

Land, E. The retinex. *Amer. Scientist*, 1964, *52*, 247–264.

Lashley, K. S. Persistent problems in the evolution of mind. *Quart. Rev. Biol.*, 1949, *24*, 28–42. Reprinted in F. A. Beach et al. (Editors), *The Neuropsychology of Lashley*. New York: McGraw-Hill, 1960.

Leibowitz, H., F. A. Mote, and W. R. Thurlow. Simultaneous contrast as a function of separation between test and inducing fields. *J. exp. Psychol.*, 1953, *46*, 453–456.

Lettvin, J. Y., H. R. Maturana, W. S. McCulloch, and W. H. Pitts. What the frog's eye tells the frog's brain. *Proc. Inst. Radio Engr.*, 1959, *47*, 1940–1951.

Lindsley, D. B. Psychological phenomena and the electroencephalogram. *EEG clin. Neurophysiol.*, 1952, *4*, 443–454.

Lynch, K. *The Image of the City*. Cambridge, Mass.: The Technology Press & Harvard University Press, 1960. Paperback edition, Cambridge, Mass.: M.I.T. Press, 1964.

Mach, E. *The Analysis of Sensations*. New York: Dover Publications, 1959.

Maier, N. R. F., and T. C. Schneirla. *Principles of Animal Psychology*. New York: McGraw-Hill, 1935.

Marshall, J. E. Eye movements and the visual autokinetic phenomenon. *Perceptual and Motor Skills*, 1966, *22*, 319–326.

Matin, L., and G. E. MacKinnon. Autokinetic movement: selective manipulation of directional components by image stabilization. *Science*, 1964, *143*, 147–148.

Matin, L., D. Pearce, E. Matin, and G. Kibler. Visual perception of direction in the dark: roles of local sign, eye movements, and ocular proprioception. *Vision Res.* 1966, *6*, 453–469.

Miller, G. A. The magical number seven, plus or minus two: some limits on our capacity for processing information. *Psychol. Rev.*, 1956, *63*, 81–97.

Miller, G. A., and N. Chomsky. Pattern conception. *Proc. Univ. Michigan Symp. on Pattern Recognition*, 1958. Mimeographed.

Miller, G. A., E. Galanter, and K. H. Pribram. *Plans and the Structure of Behavior*. New York: Holt, 1960.

Miller, J. W., and E. Ludvigh. Visual detection in a uniformly luminous field. *J. Aviation Med.*, 1958, *29*, 603–608.

Nash, A. J., and K. M. Michels. Squirrel monkeys and discrimination learning: figural interactions, redundancies, and random shapes, *J. exp. Psychol.*, 1966, *72*, 132–137.

Necker, L. A. Observations on some remarkable phenomena seen in Switzerland. . . . *Phil. Mag.*, 1832, *3*, 329–337.

Neisser, U. Decision time without reaction time: experiments in visual scanning, *Amer. J. Psychol.*, 1963, *76*, 376–385.

Neisser, U., and H. K. Beller. Searching through word lists. *Brit. J. Psychol.*, 1965, *56*, 349–358.

Neisser, U., R. Novick, and R. Lazar. Searching for ten targets simultaneously. *Perceptual and Motor Skills*, 1963, *17*, 955–961.

Orlansky, J. The effect of similarity and difference in form on apparent visual movement. *Arch. Psych.*, 1940, *35*, 246.

Papert, S. Paradoxical perception. *A. I. Memo 124*, Project *MAC*, Massachusetts Institute of Technology, 1967.

Parks, T. E. Post-retinal visual storage. *Amer. J. Psychol.*, 1965, *78*, 145–147.

Piéron, H. Le processus du métacontraste. *J. Psychol. norm. path.*, 1935, *32*, 5–24.

Pollack, R. H. Backward figural masking as a function of chronological age and intelligence. *Psychonomic Science*, 1965, *3*, 65–66.

Polyak, S. L. *The Vertebrate Visual System*. Chicago: University of Chicago Press, 1957.

Pritchard, R. M. Visual illusions viewed as stabilized retinal images. *Quart. J. exp. Psychol.*, 1958, *10*, 77–81.

Pritchard, R. M., W. Heron, and D. O. Hebb. Visual perception approached through the method of stabilized images. *Canad. J. Psychol.*, 1960, *14*, 67–77.

Pulfrich, C. Die Stereoskopie im Dienste der isochromen und heterochromen Photometrie. *Naturwiss.*, 1922, *10*, 553–564, 569–574, 714–722, 735–743, 751–761.

Raab, D. H. Backward masking. *Psychol. Bull.*, 1963, *60*, 118–129.

Ratliff, F. The role of physiological nystagmus in monocular acuity. *J. exp. Psychol.*, 1952, *43*, 163–172.

Ratliff, F. *Mach Bands*. San Francisco: Holden-Day, 1965.

Riggs, L. A. Visual acuity. In C. H. Graham (Editor), *Vision and Visual Perception*. New York: Wiley, 1965. Pp. 321–349.

Riggs, L. A., F. Ratliff, J. C. Cornsweet, and T. N. Cornsweet. The disappearance of steadily fixated visual test objects. *J. opt. Soc. Amer.*, 1953, *43*, 495–501.

Rubin, E. *Visuell Wahrgenommene Figuren*. Copenhagen: Gyldendalska Boghandel, 1921.

Ryan, T. A., and C. B. Schwartz. Speed of perception as a function of mode of representation. *Amer. J. Psychol.*, 1956, *69*, 60–69.

Schiller, P. H. Monoptic and dichoptic visual masking by patterns and flashes. *J. exp. Psychol.*, 1965, *69*, 193–199.

Sekuler, R. W. Spatial and temporal determinants of visual backward masking. *J. exp. Psychol.*, 1965, *70*, 401–406.

Semmes, J., S. Weinstein, L. Ghent, and H.-L. Teuber. Spatial orientation in man after cerebral injury. *J. Psychol.*, 1955, *39*, 227–244.

Shepard, R. N. Recognition memory for words, sentences, and pictures. *J. Verbal Learning and Verbal Behav.*, 1967, *6*, 156–163.

Shipstone, E. I. Some variables affecting pattern conception. *Psychol. Monogr.*, 1960, *74*, 17 (Whole No. 504).

Sperling, G. The information available in brief visual presentations. *Psychol. Monogr.*, 1960, *74*, 11 (Whole No. 498).

Sperling, G. A model for visual memory tasks. *Human Factors*, 1963, 5, 19–31.

Sperry, R. W. Mechanisms of neural maturation. In S. S. Stevens (Editor), *Handbook of Experimental Psychology*. New York: Wiley, 1951. Pp. 236–280.

Stratton, G. M. Vision without inversion of the retinal image. *Psychol. Rev.*, 1897, *4*, 341–360, 463–481.

Stroud, J. M. The fine structure of psychological time. In H. Quastler (Editor), *Information Theory in Psychology*. Glencoe, Ill.: Free Press, 1956. Pp. 174–207.

Sutherland, N. S. Shape discrimination by animals. *Exp. Psychol. Soc. Monogr.* No. 1, n.d.

Teuber, H.-L., W. S. Battersby, and M. B. Bender. *Visual Field Defects after Penetrating Missile Wounds of the Brain*. Cambridge: Harvard University Press, 1960.

Teuber, H.-L., and S. Weinstein. Ability to discover hidden figures after cerebral lesions. *Arch. Neurol. Psychiat.*, 1956, *76*, 369–379.

Titchener, E. B. *Lectures on the Experimental Psychology of the Thought Processes*. New York: Macmillan, 1909.

Van der Waals, H. G., and C. O. Roelofs. Optische Scheinbewegung. *Z. Psychol. Physiol. Zinnesorgane*, 1930, *114*, 241–288; 1931, *115*, 91–190.

Volkmann, F. Vision during voluntary saccadic eye movements. *J. opt. Soc. Amer.*, 1962, *52*, 571–578.

Wallach, H., and D. N. O'Connell. The kinetic depth effect. *J. exp. Psychol.*, 1953, *45*, 205–217.

Wallach, M. A. The influence of classification requirements on gradients of response. *Psychol. Monogr.*, 1959, *73*, 8 (Whole No. 478).

Walls, G. L. The problem of visual direction. *Amer. J. Optom.*, 1951, *28*, 55–83; 115–146; 173–212.

Wapner, S., H. Werner, and K. A. Chandler. Experiments on sensory-tonic field theory of perception: I. Effect of extraneous stimulation on the visual perception of verticality. *J. exp. Psychol.*, 1951, *42*, 341–345.

Wapner, S., and H. Werner. *Perceptual Development*. Worcester: Clark University Press, 1957.

Waugh, N. C. Immediate memory as a function of repetition. *J. Verbal Learning and Verbal Behav.* 1963, *2*, 107–112.

Waugh, N. C. Presentation time and free recall. *J. exp. Psychol.*, 1967, *73*, 39–44.

Wertheimer, M. Experimentelle Studien über das Sehen von Bewegung. *Z. Psychol.*, 1912, *61*, 161–265.

Wertheimer, M. Untersuchungen zur Lehre von der Gestalt. *Psychol. Forsch.*, 1923, *4*, 301–350.

White, C. T. Temporal numerosity and the psychological unit of duration. *Psychol. Monogr.*, 1963, *77*, 12 (Whole No. 575).

Zimmermann, R. R. Analysis of discrimination learning capacities in the infant Rhesus monkey. *J. comp. physiol. Psychol.*, 1961, *54*, 1–10.

Zuber, B. L., and L. Stark. Saccadic suppression: elevation of visual threshold associated with saccadic eye movements. *Exp. Neurol.*, 1966, *16*, 65–79.

*The perception of spoken language clearly involves pattern recognition, as we have defined the term. The flow of speech is physically continuous, but its perception is of separate words. The perception of distinct words in the spoken flow is a psychological imposition the listener makes. That this is true is easy to demonstrate. Listen to speech in a language unknown to you and you will find that you usually cannot identify word boundaries correctly.*

*Linguists divide language into three great areas: phonology, syntax, and semantics. Phonology is concerned with sounds and sound sequences; syntax with the grammatical aspects of words and their order; and semantics with meaning. Enormous advances have been made in the past decade in the study of phonology and syntax, largely motivated by the group of workers known as transformational or generative grammarians. The key concept of their work is that language can be represented as a set of structures on which transformations operate to convert an abstract base into a perceptible surface. The principal thrust of their discoveries is that these transformations can be represented as sets of rules, some obligatory and others optional, and that using rules to create novel utterances is a specific characteristic of Man. A few instances of rule following and rule manipulation are discussed in the following paper as they are seen in examples taken from phonology and syntax.*

*Samuel Jay Keyser and Morris Halle are both linguists interested principally in phonological aspects of language. Keyser is an assistant professor in the Department of English at Brandeis University. Halle is a professor in the Department of Modern Languages and Linguistics and conducts his research at the Research Laboratory of Electronics at M.I.T.*

# 2. What We Do When We Speak

*Samuel Jay Keyser and Morris Halle*

There are many facts of language to engage our attention, but none is more important than the fact that the ability to speak a language entails the ability to utter any of an infinite number of sentences. For example, a speaker of English may say, "John forced Mary to tell Bill." But he may also say, "John forced Mary to tell Bill to force Jim to tell George to force Frank to tell Sidney." In fact, it is possible, in English, to go on adding to this sentence indefinitely. It is true that such sentences are difficult to understand as they grow in length. It is also true that such sentences may never be uttered by a speaker of English during his lifetime. But it is equally true that such sentences are perfectly possible sentences in English and must be accounted for by any serious explanation of language. Indeed, it is not necessary to limit ourselves to such bizarre examples. Thus, a speaker of English may say, "John is very nice." But he may also say, "John is very, very nice," and "John is very, very, very . . . nice." Or again he may say, "The rat ate the cheese," or "The cat killed the rat that ate the cheese," or "The dog chased the cat that killed the rat that ate the cheese," or "The boy loved the dog that chased the cat that killed the rat that ate the cheese," or ". . . the boy that loved the dog that chased the cat that killed the rat that ate the cheese." In all of these sentences there is no upper bound on the length of each sentence type and there is no good grammatical reason for imposing one.

It is true that if one were to study the actual performance of speakers, then one would probably never observe in a given sentence more than, say, two *force-tell* constructions or five *that* clauses or even three *very*s, even after a lifetime of observation. And these facts would be extremely relevant to a study of the performance of speakers. Indeed, a student of speaker performance would be interested in other facts as well. For example, people make mistakes when they speak and even though they often know perfectly well the difference between a correct and incorrect construction, still the errors occur. People often hesitate when they speak, and when they do they commonly inject little noises like *uh* or *ah*. Why they do this and whether one can predict where in sentences these so-called hesitation noises will appear is also a matter of interest to students of speaker performance. Furthermore, as we have already seen, as certain sentences become longer they become more difficult to understand. At first glance, one might think this increase in difficulty is simply a function of length. But that cannot be true, for it is much easier to understand a sentence like, "The dog chased the cat that killed the rat that ate the cheese," than a sentence like, "The rat the cat the dog chased killed ate the cheese," even though the second sentence is shorter than the first and even though both sentences are perfectly grammatical. Why one should be more easily understood than the other is a still unanswered question of performance.

In the discussion to follow, however, we shall be concerned with a somewhat different problem. We shall not attempt to account for the actual performance of speakers, but rather we shall attempt to characterize what it is a speaker must know in order to be able to speak a language. In other words, we shall take up the matter of competence. Thus, while no speaker will ever be observed uttering a sentence such as "The rat the cat the dog chased killed ate the cheese," or one with twenty *force-tell* constructions in it, it is nonetheless within his competence to do so. In fact, as we have said, it is within his competence to utter an infinite number of such sentences.

A second fact about language which demonstrates another aspect of a speaker's competence is that speakers possess the ability to understand any of an infinite number of sentences. For example, every reader will have no trouble understanding, "Mr. Campbell spent the summer on the beach at Brighton pondering the Anglo-Saxon corpus," even though he almost certainly has never encountered it before. Indeed, almost every sentence one hears in a day is a novel sentence never encountered before, and yet our ability to speak a language enables us to deal with such sentences as if we had heard and understood them many times over.

A third fact about linguistic competence is that mastery of a language not only entails the ability to utter and to understand any of an infinite number of sentences, but it also entails the ability to determine, given an arbitrary string of words, whether that string is a sentence in a language. For example, every speaker of English knows that the string of words, "George Washington is the father of our country," is a sentence, while the same string backwards is not. Indeed, masters of a language are able to make even finer distinctions. Thus, while some sentences are perfectly acceptable and others perfectly unacceptable, there is between these poles a whole range of deviant sentences. Speakers are capable of telling when sentences are deviant and, in certain instances at least, in understanding them in spite of their deviancy. For example, speakers of English quite easily understand, "Up

I you pick at eight o'clock will," as meaning, "I will pick you up at eight o'clock," even though certain principles of word order have been distorted. But notice that if these principles are too severely distorted, then the sentence becomes thoroughly unintelligible, thus: "Eight will up at I pick o'clock you." (Why some distorted sentences are more easily understood than others is another question of performance, while the essential difference between a distorted and an undistorted sentence is a question of competence.)

Another example of a deviant sentence is, "The ugly girl frightened the chair." Since we normally regard only animate things as capable of fright, we perceive this sentence as deviant precisely because it runs counter to our association of fright with animacy. If we are willing to suspend this association — perhaps by temporarily entertaining the fiction that the chairs can feel — then we can make sense of, "The ugly girl frightened the chair." Notice, however, that no such effort is required to make sense of the sentence, "The ugly chair frightened the girl," since no association is violated.

In what follows we shall assume that the essence of the ability which gives rise to all of the facts of competence described above is the capacity which human beings possess to manipulate symbols.

There is a game any father can play with his child which will serve to illustrate what is meant by this. The game is called the plural game and is played quite successfully with three-year-olds. The father says "one chair" and the child answers "two chairs," or "one hedge," "two hedges," "one cup," "two cups," and so on. The interesting thing is that the plural in English is actually pronounced three different ways, namely *iz* as in *hedges, s* as in *cups,* and *z* as in *chairs.*

**Table 2.1** Words Classified According to Their Plurals

| *iz* | *s* | *z* |
|---|---|---|
| hedge → hedges | cup → cups | chair → chairs |
| church → churches | cat → cats | ring → rings |
| bus → busses | cake → cakes | cab → cabs |
| fuse → fuses | fourth → fourths | cog → cogs |
| bush → bushes | cuff → cuffs | lathe → lathes |
| garage → garages | | key → keys |
| | | clue → clues |
| | | hoe → hoes, |
| | | and so on |

That even a 3-year-old child can sort out which plural ending goes with which word is apparent, even when the father tries to trick him. To make sure the child is actually manipulating symbols and not simply repeating, parrot fashion, plurals already learned elsewhere, the father might make up words which the child could never have heard before the game, words like *gib, bik,* and *glice.* The child will sort out the three plurals and assign them correctly. Even more telling are the mistakes children are bound to make, saying things like "two childs," "two oxes," or "two foots." Children could not possibly have heard and therefore remembered replies like "two childs." These replies are simply not English. But where, then, did they come from? The only possible explanation is that children make them up according to a rule. Using this rule they create them spontaneously, as it were, and memory has precious little to do with it in any direct sense.

Though every speaker of English knows the rule (otherwise he would not be a speaker of English), he may well find it difficult to state the rule explicitly.

Words whose plural is pronounced *iz,* such as *hedge, church,* and *bus* (see Table 2.1), are words which end in similar sounds, sounds which share the so-called "hissing and hushing" quality. Words whose plural is pronounced *s,* such as *cup, cat,* and *cake,* are also words which end in similar sounds, the so-called "nonvoiced" sounds, sounds made without use of the vocal cords. Finally, the words whose plural is pronounced *z* are all other words in the English language, that is words whose final sounds are neither of the "hissing and hushing" nor of the "nonvoiced" sort. (See also discussion on pp. 70 ff. and Table 2.2.)

The rule, therefore, which children (and adults as well) know to make the regular plural of these and of all other words in English is this:

**Rule 1** The Plural Rule in English

<table>
<tr><td rowspan="3">Plural →</td><td>iz</td><td>when the last sound of the word is "hissing and hushing."</td></tr>
<tr><td>s</td><td>when the last sound of the word is "nonvoiced"</td></tr>
<tr><td>z</td><td>when the last sound of the word is neither of the above.</td></tr>
</table>

The ability to apply rules like the plural rule presupposes the ability to perform analyses such as dividing words into a final sound and the rest, and classifying the former into three distinct classes. The astounding thing, of course, is that 3-year-olds perform all these acts naturally. They do not have to be taught the plural rule. They can learn it for themselves easily, simply, quickly, unconsciously. This is what is meant by saying that language is a special manifestation of man's innate ability to manipulate symbols.

A rather interesting example of the linguistic ability of children came to light recently in the city of Boston, when a mother consulted a psychiatric social worker about a domestic situation which had become, if not intolerable, at least difficult.[1] Her youngest children, aged 4 and 5, spoke a strange, incomprehensible language which neither she nor her husband could decode. They were forced to resort to the services of their eldest boy, 8½ years, who acted as translator, apparently a very good one, for while both parents waited patiently at the dinner table, he would listen intently to the jabberings of the younger members of the family and then proceed to translate them into perfectly good English for his parents. The social worker, with suitable reference to secret languages and childhood phases, rendered necessary consolation and there the matter ended. But the secret language of the 4- and 5-year-olds ultimately turned out to be just another example of the natural inventiveness of young minds in making up language rules and using them; that is, in manipulating symbols. The 8½-year-old brother understood the children because he, too, was adept, while the parents were completely at a loss.

As it turned out, the rules the children used in their secret language were very much like the rules for speaking Pig Latin. In that language the rule used to manipulate English is the following:

**Rule 2** Pig Latin Rule

Shift the initial consonant (s) to end of word and add *ay*.

Example: Pig Latin → igpay atinlay

The youngsters were manipulating English in a similar, though more complex, fashion. In order to understand precisely what they were doing, however, it is necessary to understand a little more about the sounds of a language. The plural rule illustrated that sounds are really bundles composed of certain features. The rule made use, for example, of the "hissing-hushing" feature which is a component of sounds like *s* (as in *seal*), *z* (as in *zeal*), *sh* (as in *ship*), *zh* (as in *rouge*), *tsh* (as in *choice*), and *dzh* (as in *John*).

But if the "hissing-hushing" feature is only one component of certain sounds, then there are other sounds which lack this feature, namely the "non-hissing-hushing" sounds. Among them are all English consonants other than those just enumerated; namely, *p* (as in *pig*), *b* (as in *big*), *m* (as in *mother*), *k* (as in *cot*), *g* (as in *got*), *t* (as in *tip*), *d* (as in *dip*), *TH* (as in *thin*), *th* (as in *though*), and *n* (as in *never*).

[1] J. R. Applegate. Phonological rules of a subdialect of English. *Word,* 1961, *17,* 186–193.

There are two more "hissing-hushing" sounds, *f* (as in *fat*) and *v* (as in *vat*). These, however, share yet another feature which separates them from the "hissing-hushing" sounds listed. This feature is a function of where sounds are produced. It distinguishes sounds that are made at the periphery of the mouth — either at the very front like *f, v, p, b,* and *m,* or at the very back, like *k* and *g* — from nonperipheral sounds that are made in the middle of the mouth such as *t, d, TH, th, n, sh, zh tsh, dzh.*

Thus while *f* and *v* are both "hissing-hushing" and "peripheral," *s, z, tsh, dzh, sh,* and *zh* are "hissing-hushing," but "nonperipheral."

Terms like "peripheral" describe the place where the mouth is maximally constricted. A different feature locates this point of constriction more precisely. The tongue placed against the upper palate can impede the flow of air toward the back of the mouth, or else toward the front. The "back" sounds are *k, g, tsh, dzh, sh,* and *zh.* All those made with constriction at a point in the mouth in front of the "back" sounds are "nonback."

Thus *k* and *g* are sounds which are both "peripheral" and "back," and are distinguished from *f* and *v* which are "peripheral" but "nonback."

If sounds can be described by where they impede the air flow, they can also be described by how much they impede the air flow. Sounds which slow the flow of air but do not shut it off completely possess the "continuing" feature. These are *f, v, TH, th, s, z, sh,* and *zh.* The remaining "noncontinuing" sounds are made by shutting off the flow of air completely for a short time and then suddenly releasing it again. The "noncontinuing" sounds are *p, b, m, k, g, t, d, n, tsh, dzh.*

The feature which distinguishes the sounds *m* (as in *mother*), *n* (as in *never*), and *ng* (as in *hang*) from all other English sounds is the "nasal" feature, the feature whose presence gives the impression that these three sounds are spoken through the nose, as it were. All the other sounds are "nonnasal."

There are several other features that sounds possess. But to understand what the youngsters were doing, only one more need be discussed. In the plural rule use was also made of a "silent" or "nonvoiced" feature which sounds like *p, t, k, f, TH, s, sh,* and *tsh* possess. The remaining "voiced" sounds are *b, m, v, g, d, th, n, z, dzh* and *zh.* (An easy way to tell whether a sound is "voiced" or "nonvoiced" is to place the thumb and forefinger gently against the Adam's apple while pronouncing the sound. "Voiced" sounds will produce a very noticeable vibration; "nonvoiced" sounds will not.)

In sum, the English sounds, which are generally indicated by letters such as *p, b, m, f,* and *v,* are not indivisible entities but rather bundles of distinctive features, and the letters are nothing but abbreviations for certain separate (and distinct) bundles.

**Table 2.2** Distinctive Features of English Sounds

| | *p* | *b* | *m* | *f* | *v* | *k* | *g* | *t* | *d* | *TH* | *th* | *n* | *s* | *z* | *tsh* | *dzh* | *sh* | *zh* |
|---|---|---|---|---|---|---|---|---|---|---|---|---|---|---|---|---|---|---|
| peripheral | + | + | + | + | + | + | + | – | – | – | – | – | – | – | – | – | – | – |
| back | – | – | – | – | – | + | + | – | – | – | – | – | – | – | + | + | + | + |
| hissing-hushing | – | – | – | + | + | – | – | – | – | – | – | – | + | + | + | + | + | + |
| nasal | – | – | + | – | – | – | – | – | – | – | – | + | – | – | – | – | – | – |
| continuing | – | – | – | + | + | – | – | – | – | + | + | – | + | + | – | – | + | + |
| voiced | – | + | + | – | + | – | + | – | + | – | + | + | – | + | – | + | – | + |

(The symbol + means having the relevant feature; – that it is lacking.)

Thus the letter *p* stands for the feature bundle:

$$\begin{bmatrix} + & \text{peripheral} \\ - & \text{back} \\ - & \text{hissing-hushing} \\ - & \text{nasal} \\ - & \text{continuing} \\ - & \text{voiced} \end{bmatrix}$$

while the letter *b* stands for the feature bundle:

$$\begin{bmatrix} + & \text{peripheral} \\ - & \text{back} \\ - & \text{hissing-hushing} \\ - & \text{nasal} \\ - & \text{continuing} \\ + & \text{voiced} \end{bmatrix}$$

The only difference between these two bundles is that the *p* bundle contains the feature [– voiced] while the *b* bundle contains the feature [+ voiced]. If one wanted to change a *p* into a *b,* one would merely have to shift this single feature. All the others would remain unchanged.

The English letter *m* stands for the feature bundle:

$$\begin{bmatrix} + & \text{peripheral} \\ - & \text{back} \\ - & \text{hissing-hushing} \\ + & \text{nasal} \\ - & \text{continuing} \\ + & \text{voiced} \end{bmatrix}$$

The only difference between the *m* bundle and the *b* bundle is that the *m* bundle contains the feature [+ nasal] while the *b* bundle contains the feature [– nasal]. If one wanted to change a *b* into an *m,* one would merely have to shift this single feature. All the others would remain unchanged.

**Rule 3** Rule to Change *p* into *b*

[– voiced] → [+ voiced] in the bundle which also contains

$$\begin{bmatrix} + & \text{peripheral} \\ - & \text{back} \\ - & \text{hissing-hushing} \\ - & \text{nasal} \\ - & \text{continuing} \end{bmatrix}$$

**Rule 4** Rule to Change *b* into *m*

[– nasal] → [+ nasal] in the bundle which also contains

$$\begin{bmatrix} + & \text{peripheral} \\ - & \text{back} \\ - & \text{hissing-hushing} \\ - & \text{continuing} \\ + & \text{voiced} \end{bmatrix}$$

That it is not sounds as indivisible entities which English speakers are manipulating when they speak, but rather features of sounds, has already been illustrated by the plural rule. The first part of that rule said that when a noun ends in a bundle of features, one of which is "hissing-hushing," then choose the *iz* plural, though it is now clear that this formulation was not quite correct. Rather it should have been: choose *iz* when the noun ends in a bundle containing both the features "hissing-hushing" and "nonperipheral." (The inclusion of the "non-peripheral" feature in the first part of the plural rule is necessary to eliminate *f* and *v* since words like *cuff* and *cave* do not take an *iz* plural.)

The second part of the plural rule said that if the noun to be pluralized ends in a bundle of features, one of which is "nonvoiced," then choose the plural *s*. The third part of the rule stated that, once the first and second parts of the rule have been satisfied, it makes no difference what features the noun's final bundle may contain. The plural will always be *z*.

**Rule 5** The Plural Rule in English Stated in Features

$$Plural \rightarrow \left\{ \begin{array}{ll} iz & \text{when final bundle contains} \begin{bmatrix} + \text{ hissing-hushing} \\ - \text{ peripheral} \end{bmatrix} \\ s & \text{when final bundle contains } [- \text{ voiced}] \\ z & \end{array} \right\}$$

The youngsters were performing manipulations of precisely these kinds. The "secret" dialect which they spoke and which their older brother could understand but their parents could not is represented by the following words:

**Table 2.3** Youngsters' "Secret" Dialect of English

| 1 | | 2 | | 3 | |
|---|---|---|---|---|---|
| cuff, cup | → *kup* | puff | → *pup* | pup | → *pu ?* |
| gave, Gabe | → *gayb* | brave | → *brayb* | babe | → *bay ?* |
| thought, sauce, sought | → *tawt* | mouse, mouth | → *mout* | taught | → *taw ?* |
| lies, lied | → *lide* | dies | → *dide* | died | → *di ?e* |

(Unitalicized words represent normal English, the corresponding italicized words represent the children's distortions of them, and the symbol *?* represents the "glottal stop," the sound common to certain New York dialects in words like *kettle* (ke ?l) and *bottle* (bo ?l), which is made by catching the air in the bottom of the throat at the vocal cords.)

The most obvious difference between the sounds of standard English (the unitalicized words) and the sounds of the children's dialect (the italicized words) is the absence in the children's dialect of any feature bundle containing [ + continuing]. In other words, the children devised a rule which required them to take every bundle containing the [ + continuing] feature and replace it by a

$$\begin{bmatrix} - & \text{back} \\ - & \text{continuing} \\ - & \text{hissing-hushing} \end{bmatrix}$$

complex, but without altering any of the other features in the bundle. In terms of the letters, the abbreviations for feature bundles, the children have distorted standard English in the following fashion:

**Table 2.4** The Children's Distortions of Standard English

| *English sounds* | *Children's distortion* |
|---|---|
| f | → p |
| v | → b |
| s | → t |
| TH | → t |
| z | → d |
| th | → d |
| sh | → t |
| zh | → d |

In terms of the features which the children were manipulating, the rule they devised was simply this:

**Rule 6** The Children's First Rule

$$[+\text{ continuing}] \rightarrow \begin{bmatrix} -\text{ back} \\ -\text{ continuing} \\ -\text{ hissing-hushing} \end{bmatrix}$$ in every bundle no matter what other features it may contain

This rule will account for all the changes listed in the preceding letter chart. As one example, consider the *f* bundle:

$$\begin{bmatrix} + & \text{peripheral} \\ - & \text{back} \\ + & \text{hissing-hushing} \\ - & \text{nasal} \\ + & \text{continuing} \\ - & \text{voiced} \end{bmatrix}$$

The rule requires that this bundle, which contains a [ + continuing] feature, be replaced by a

$$\begin{bmatrix} - & \text{back} \\ - & \text{continuing} \\ - & \text{hissing-hushing} \end{bmatrix}$$

complex. This produces a new feature bundle:

$$\begin{bmatrix} + & \text{peripheral} \\ - & \text{back} \\ - & \text{hissing-hushing} \\ - & \text{nasal} \\ - & \text{continuing} \\ - & \text{voiced} \end{bmatrix}$$

and a glance at Table 2.2 shows that this new bundle is now the one abbreviated by the letter *p*. It is this manipulation of features which accounts for the children's pronouncing standard English *cuff* as *cup,* and, in fact, for all the distortions listed in columns 1 and 2 of Table 2.3.

Column 3 of Table 2.3, however, indicates that they devised yet another rule. In column 3 the standard English words which were distorted all share a common characteristic, namely: they all have two identical consonants which, moreover, share the feature [ − continuing]. In the children's dialect, however, the second of the identical non-continuing consonants has been changed into a "glottal stop."

**Rule 7** The Children's Second Rule

[− continuing] → *glottal stop* when it follows an identical
[− continuing] bundle in the same word

This manipulation of features accounts for the children's pronouncing standard English *pup* as *pu?, babe* as *ba?e, taught* as *tau?,* and *died* as *di?e.*

These two rules, devised by the children, completely account for their peculiar dialect of English. It was these two rules whose secret their parents could not penetrate, which their 8½-year-old brother learned quickly and easily.

It was not at all obvious that essentially the same kind of symbol manipulation could be used to describe not only the secret language of the Boston children and of Pig Latin, which most children learn to speak at one time or another, but also the way in which every speaker of English, child or adult, forms regular plurals in his language. It is all the more significant, then, that on the higher levels of language, the levels where whole sentences are involved (and not just the sounds of certain words), essentially the same kind of activity seems to be involved, namely the manipulation in highly regular fashion of certain symbols. The difference lies in the nature of the symbols that are manipulated and in the complexity of the manipulations, for, as one might well expect, the rules which govern the syntax of a language are far more complicated than the rules which govern the sounds of a language.

An example of syntactical manipulations of symbols in English is the way in which English speakers make reflexive pronouns. As with the formation of the plural, speakers must know a rule. This rule will tell them when to say *me* and when to say *myself;* when to say *you* and when to say *yourself;* when to say *him* and when to say *himself.*

There is such a rule, one which a child could not even begin to explain (nor many adults for that matter), though every English speaker knows it implicitly (otherwise he would not be a speaker of English).

One can discover the rule by starting out with a list of sentences, some of which are correct, some of which are not:

| | |
|---|---|
| 1a. *I help me.* | 1b. I help myself. |
| 2a. I help you. | 2b. *I help yourself.* |
| 3a. I help him. | 3b. *I help himself.* |
| 4a. You help me. | 4b. *You help myself.* |
| 5a. *You help you.* | 5b. You help yourself. |
| 6a. You help him. | 6b. *You help himself.* |

Any speaker of English will recognize that the italicized sentences are not correct. But notice that sentences on the left which are incorrect (italicized) are complemented by correct sentences on the right and vice versa. Thus if 1a is wrong, then 1b is right. And if 2b is wrong, then 2a is right. Similarly 3b, 4b, 5a, and 6b are wrong, while 3a, 4a, 5b, and 6a are right. This suggests strongly that a systematic rule is operating. The problem is to find the rule. One need not look far. The rule which every speaker of English employs to form reflexive pronouns is the following: Whenever the subject of a sentence is a pronoun and the object of the same sentence is a pronoun and both pronouns refer to the same person, the object must add the word "self."

**Rule 8** The Reflexive Rule in English

$\text{Pronoun}_1 + \text{Verb} + \text{Pronoun}_2 \rightarrow \text{Pronoun}_1 + \text{Verb} + \text{Pronoun}_2 + \text{self.}$
Condition: $\text{Pronoun}_1$ & $\text{Pronoun}_2$ refer to same person.

By this rule the sentence "I help me" (1a) becomes "I help myself" (1b) because "I" and "me" refer to the same person. Similarly "You help you" (5a) becomes "You help yourself" (5b) because "You" and "you" refer to the same person. This rule was not simply invented. There is very good reason to suppose that speakers of English are using precisely this rule whenever they use reflexive pronouns. The rule explains the way speakers feel about certain sentences in their language. To illustrate this point we may consider the following set of sentences, only some of which are correct:

| | |
|---|---|
| 7a. He helps me. | 7b. *He helps myself.* |
| 8a. He helps you. | 8b. *He helps yourself.* |
| 9a. *He helps him.* | 9b. He helps himself. |

Sentences 7a and 8a are correct because their subjects and objects do not refer to the same person. Their complements, sentences 7b and 8b, are incorrect. But what about 9a? "He helps him." This sentence is further proof that the reflexive rule is correct as stated because English speakers feel that "he helps him" is correct only if "he" and "him" do not refer to the same person. Otherwise one must apply the reflexive rule and change it to "he helps himself."

Every English speaker, 3-year-olds on up, feels that imperatives like "Help me!", "Help him!" and "Help yourself!" are really formed from simple sentences with the "you" left out. But why should English speakers feel that the omitted subject is "you"? Why not "I," for example? The answer is hidden in the sentences produced by the reflexive rule, in particular those with the pronoun "you" as subject:

| | |
|---|---|
| 4a. You help me. | 4b. *You help myself.* |
| 5a. *You help you.* | 5b. You help yourself. |
| 6a. You help him. | 6b. *You help himself.* |

It can be no coincidence that the correct sentences in this group (the unitalicized sentences) bear a strong resemblance to the correct imperative sentences corresponding to them:

| *Correct Reflexive Sentence* | *Corresponding Correct Imperative* |
|---|---|
| 4a. You help me. | Help me! |
| 5b. You help yourself. | Help yourself! |
| 6a. You help him. | Help him! |

By simply leaving out the "you" subject in the sentence on the left, one produces the correct imperative on the right. This "leaving out of the 'you' " corresponds exactly to the way English speakers feel about imperatives. To assume that it is indeed the subject 'you' which has been omitted from a sentence fits in nicely with the way speakers feel, and also offers a ready explanation for the fact that "yourself" is the only reflexive pronoun appearing after an imperative. The word "yourself" could only appear in a sentence which had had, at some stage at least, a "you" subject.

**Rule 9** The English Imperative Rule

$$\text{You} + \text{Verb} + X \rightarrow \text{Verb} + X$$

(Here $X$ can be an object such as "me" in "Help me!" or $X$ can be blank as in "Help!")

It is often a useful heuristic, when dealing with phenomena as complicated as language, to try to construct a mechanical model, such as a computer or some other device, which is capable of emulating the phenomena under study.

If one were to build a model embodying the linguistic ability that human beings possess, that model would have to take sentences which are composed of words like "you" and "help" and "yourself," and symbols like "plural" and "subject" and "pronoun," and relationships like "refer to the same person" and "the same kind of sound," and manipulate them in an orderly fashion.

But there is something more which rules like the imperative and reflexive rules tell us about the things the model must be able to do — something quite unexpected.

Anyone, child or adult, who knows how to make correct reflexive sentences and correct imperative sentences in English has unconsciously grasped a definite relationship between these two rules.

In the same way that a person who prepares to drive a car must perform certain operations in a certain prescribed order (first turn on the ignition, then press the starter, then release the brake, then check traffic, and so on), so any speaker of English who wants to give a command like "Help yourself!" must apply the rules of his language in a certain prescribed order. He must apply the reflexive rule first, and then he must apply the imperative rule. Starting with the basic sentence "You help you," for example, the reflexive rule applied first, changes it to the proper "You help yourself." Then the imperative rule omits the "you" subject, and the speaker ends up with "Help yourself!"

What would happen if the order of the two rules were reversed? Starting with the basic sentence "You help you," the imperative rule would omit the subject, changing it to "Help you!" But now the reflexive rule could not possibly change "Help you!" to the correct "Help yourself!" because the reflexive rule requires that a comparison be made between subject and object pronouns to determine whether they refer to the same person. The consequence of applying the imperative rule first was to omit the subject, preventing the necessary comparison, and thereby preventing the application of the reflexive rule.

**Application of English Grammar Rules in Their Proper Order**

Beginning with the basic sentence →

You + help + You

*First:* apply the reflexive rule to yield →

You + help + yourself

*Second:* apply the imperative rule to yield →

Help + yourself!

This relationship of ordering is not unique to the syntactical level. In fact, tacit use was already made of rule ordering in the discussion of the plural rule and in the two rules devised by the 4- and 5-year olds in their "secret" language.

In the plural, ordering was used because, without it, the rule would have required a much more complicated statement.

**Rule 10** Unordered Plural Rule

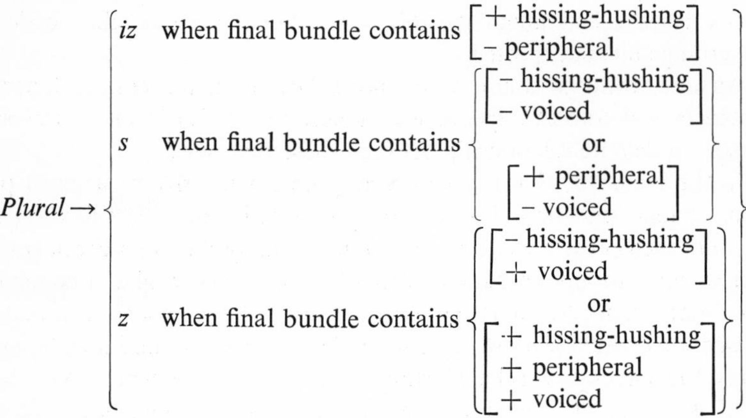


The greater complexity of this rule is self-evident.

The role of ordering in the "secret" language of the 4- and 5-year olds is similar. As an example, consider the English words *died* and *dies* which the children pronounced, respectively, *di?e* and *dide*. The glottal stop rule (Rule 7) is applied first, changing standard English *died* to the children's *di?e*. The standard *dies* is untouched by this rule because it does not contain two identical noncontinuing consonants. Then Rule 6, which replaces all "continuing" sounds by the

$$\begin{bmatrix} - & \text{back} \\ - & \text{continuing} \\ - & \text{hissing-hushing} \end{bmatrix}$$

complex, changes standard English *dies* to the children's *dide*.

But suppose the rules are applied in reverse order? The replacement, by Rule 6, of all "continuing" sounds with the

$$\begin{bmatrix} - & \text{continuing} \\ - & \text{hissing-hushing} \\ - & \text{back} \end{bmatrix}$$

complex will leave standard English *died* untouched, while changing standard English *dies* to *dide*. But then the glottal stop rule will apply, changing not only the standard English *died* but also the children's *dide,* yielding *di?e* for both words. This result is wrong. Therefore the glottal stop rule must be applied first to yield the correct results.

A model that matches the linguistic behavior of human beings, then, must not only be able to manipulate symbols and words and sentences, but it must also be able to order these manipulations with respect to one another. The ordering of the reflexive rule before the imperative rule turned out to be the only possible ordering of these two rules that would produce sentences which English speakers consider correct. Hence the model must also order the rules in this way if it is to produce correct sentences in English.

But what is the significance of this model which, based on the view of language as the manipulation of symbols, has proved so successful? For one thing the model suggests that it may be useful to take a second look at the mental capacities of human beings themselves. For to describe a model capable of performing analyses, manipulating symbols, and establishing an order among these manipulations is to describe in essence what the human brain is capable of. For where else does man's linguistic ability reside if not in the brain?

Furthermore, to realize that children of the age of three are capable of manipulating symbols, grasping regularities, performing abstract analyses, and establishing order among manipulations is to realize something startling about the innate capacities of the human brain. That 3-year-olds can even begin to master the manipulations characteristic of language — with only the barest minimum of guidance — suggests that they are prepared at birth for these manipulations. After all, when faced with considerably simpler manipulations such as those of elementary mathematics, most children are at a loss. The only explanation possible is that children are born with the predisposition to speak and need merely to be exposed to a language. With mathematics, and several other disciplines as well, mere exposure is not nearly enough, and we are forced to provide them with rigorous and long periods of training.

Finally, studies of languages which are quite familiar to everyone, such as German, French, and Russian, and of unfamiliar ones as well, such as Hidatsa, Mohawk (American Indian), Turkish, Japanese, and Mundari (a language of east-central India) have shown that in all of these diverse languages essentially the same kinds of manipulations of abstract symbols are performed that characterize the plural, reflexive, and imperative rules in English. This is exactly what one would expect if these manipulations are, in fact, characteristic of an innate ability of the human brain and not simply of the English language. Since these manipulations are at the heart of every living language, it follows that in a much deeper sense than ever before realized, man throughout the earth speaks what is fundamentally the same language.

## Acknowledgment

Preparation of this paper was supported in part by the U.S. Air Force (ESD Contract AF 19(628)–2487) and the National Institutes of Health (Grant MH-13390–01) through the Research Laboratory of Electronics, M.I.T., and in part by the U.S. Air Force (Contract AF 19(628)–5524) through Brandeis University.

## Bibliography

Chomsky, N. *Syntactic Structures.* The Hague: Mouton, 1957.

Chomsky, N., and G. A. Miller. Introduction to the formal analysis of natural languages. In R. D. Luce, R. Bush, and E. Galanter (Editors), *Handbook of Mathematical Psychology.* New York: Wiley, 1963. Vol. II, pp. 269–322.

Halle, M. Phonology in generative grammar. *Word,* 1962, *18,* 54–72.

Jakobson, R., M. Halle, and C. G. M. Fant. *Preliminaries to Speech Analysis: The Distinctive Features and Their Correlates.* Cambridge, Mass.: M.I.T. Press, 1963. 2nd ed.

*Dr. Chung has written a scholarly review of recent work on the electrophysiology of visual nervous systems. Note the plural form, for one point the author makes is that responses from different species to the same visual presentation are themselves different. The result raises an interesting question for those who wish to simulate a visual system, namely, which system? The frog's? The cat's? Man's? Yet even though they differ in details, the various systems do have certain notable similarities. Chief among these are the recoding and transforming of responses to visual presentations as the electrochemical impulses travel along nerve fibers inward from the receptor. There is no simple transmission system for visual perception.*

*A second point he makes is that it has recently been found that responses tend to be specific to stimuli rather than only transformations of energy. The contours, the movement and its direction, and the size of the stimulus seem to be responded to directly by different parts of nervous systems; and these responses cannot be understood as reactions only to light flux. This discovery of stimulus-specific cells (sometimes called analyzers) is probably the most significant event in recent work in electrophysiology.*

*Shin-Ho Chung, trained in psychology and physiology, works on the electrophysiology of the visual system, usually the frog's, on the research staff of the Neurophysiology Group at the Research Laboratory of Electronics, M.I.T.*

# 3. Neurophysiology of the Visual System

*Shin-Ho Chung*

In his lucid essay on the brain, von Neumann (1958) points out that the operations of the nervous system in processing information are fundamentally different from those a computer would perform in a similar situation. The operations the nervous system performs (or the "language of the brain") lack logical precision and arithmetical depth. Nevertheless, the brain performs its exceedingly complicated tasks with an efficiency unmatched by any known automaton, using its own logic and its own arithmetic. Herein lies the profound and fundamental problem in neurophysiology: In what manner does the nervous system process information?

The way in which vision is handled by the nervous system has long been a topic of intense interest in neurophysiology. From evidence brought forth thus far it is clear that incoming visual information undergoes drastic modification as it proceeds along the pathways of the nervous system, the degree of modification increasing as messages proceed further centrally. The further centrally one goes through the chain of neurons, the more complex and specific become the stimulus parameters to which the cell responds. The action of a particular cell deep in the visual system is then best described as invariant with respect to the stimulus rather than with respect to a measure of quantity and distribution of light.

The present chapter is a brief survey of what is known to date about the electrophysiology of the visual system. On the whole, it is a summary of factual findings rather than interpretation and speculation.

## The Visual Pathway

The nerve cells and fibers constituting the retina of vertebrates are arranged in several distinct layers parallel to its surface. Between the first layer, the photoreceptors, and the last, that of the ganglion cells, lie successive layers of neurons (horizontal, bipolar, and amacrine cells). The bipolars connect the photoreceptors to the ganglion cells. The horizontal cells interconnect photoreceptors, and the amacrines interconnect bipolar cells (see Fig. 3.1). Everywhere the connection is many-to-many; that is, each neuron is fed by many others, and in turn feeds many others.

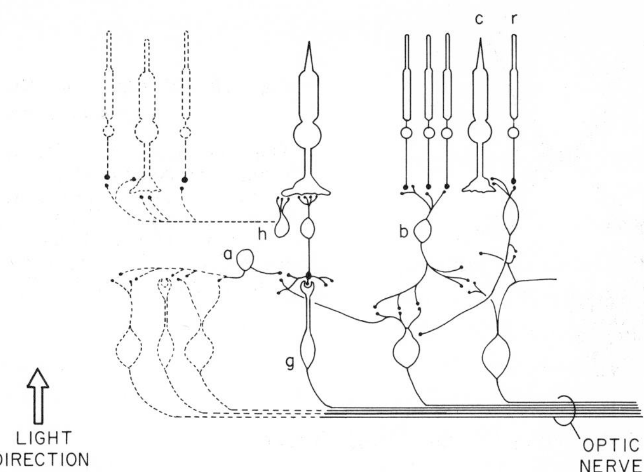


**Fig. 3.1** A schematic diagram, illustrating neuron constituents of the retina. Rods and cones (*r*, *c*) are connected to ganglion cells (*g*) via bipolar cells (*b*). Photoreceptors are interconnected by horizontal cells (*h*), and bipolar cells are interconnected by amacrine cells (*a*). Axons of the ganglion cells form the optic nerve. (Modified from Polyak, 1957, plate following p. 286.)

Axons of the ganglion cells form the optic nerve. In man and other primates, those fibers which originate in the nasal half of each retina pass through the optic chiasma to join the optic tract on the opposite side, while the fibers coming from the temporal half of each retina do not decussate but stay in the optic tract on the same side. The terminals of optic nerve fibers end in the layered structure known as the lateral geniculate body. All the cells in a given layer receive projections from a single eye, the ipsilateral or contralateral, depending on the layer. In the frog the optic nerve originating from one eye crosses over to the other side, and the majority of the fibers terminate in each of the four superficial layers of the tectum, the chief visual center in amphibians.

All the axons originating in the lateral geniculate body, as far as is known, go to the striate cortex. This region has neurons of various shapes, sizes, and synaptic relationships. As in the retina and the lateral geniculate body, the nerve cells of the striate cortex are arranged in distinct horizontal layers. Some layers contain small cells, and others, large cells; cells are densely packed in some layers and more thinly in others. The functional significance of this architectonic organization is not known at present. The fibers from the striate cortex project to adjoining structures, the parastriate and peristriate areas. A schematic illustration of the visual pathway for the mammals is shown in Fig. 3.2. For a detailed anatomy of the visual system, see Polyak (1957).

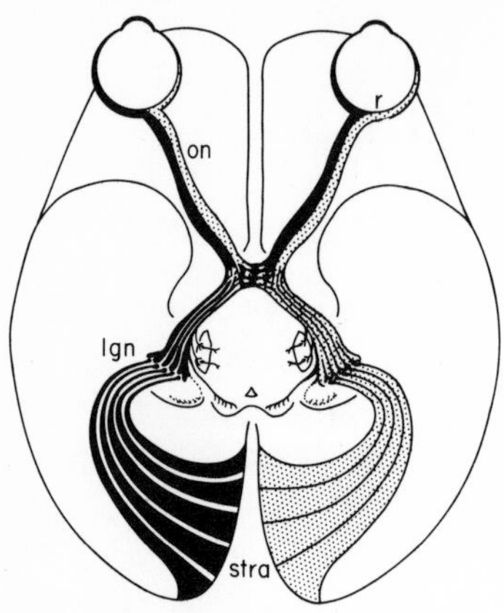


**Fig. 3.2** Diagram of the human visual pathway.

The optic nerve (*on*) after leaving the retina (*r*) decussates and terminates at the lateral geniculate body (*lgn*) of each hemisphere. The axons originating from the lateral geniculate body project to the striate cortex (*stra*). (Modified from Polyak, 1957, p. 408.)

## Electrical Activities in the Optic Nerve

In 1927 Adrian and Matthews succeeded in recording the electrical activity in an eel's optic nerve. The record from a large number of optic nerve fibers showed a sudden burst of impulses when the retina was illuminated, followed by a continuing discharge at a lower rate as the light remained on. Upon cessation of light there was a renewed burst, which gradually subsided. Subsequently, Hartline (1938) demonstrated that this composite response originates from the contribution of many individual optic nerve fibers. Records obtained from single fibers of the frog's optic nerve fell into three distinctly different patterns of discharge. Approximately 20 per cent of the fibers which Hartline observed responded briskly at the onset of illumination and discharged at somewhat lower frequency throughout the duration of illumination. When the light was turned off, this discharge stopped ("on" fiber). At least 50 per cent of the fibers responded only briefly when the light was turned on and again when the light was turned off ("on-off" fiber). In a third type no impulses appeared during illumination, but there was a vigorous discharge of impulses at the cessation of illumination ("off" fiber).

For each optic fiber, according to Hartline (1940a, 1940b), there was a certain restricted area on the retina which, when stimulated, evoked a discharge. The sensitivity of the fiber to its particular stimulus was found to be greatest in the center of the area and fell off steadily with increasing distance from this center, to become insignificant outside an area approximately one millimeter in diameter. The area of retina containing receptors which influence the discharge of a single optic fiber was referred to as the *receptive field* of that fiber. Hartline observed that the receptive field of most of the fibers in the frog was roughly circular. The extent of each receptive field, however, varied with the size and intensity of the light spot used to explore it as well as the state of adaptation of the eye.

### *Lateral inhibition*

The anatomical complexity of the retinal organization makes it no more surprising that there are "on," "off," and "on-off" fibers in the optic nerve than if there were any other arrangement. Receptor cells in a receptive field are connected through intermediate neurons to the ganglion cells in such a way that some of the intermediate neurons exert excitatory, and others inhibitory influences on the activity of the ganglion cell. Therefore, the firing of a particular optic nerve fiber may be increased or decreased depending on which cells are activated by the stimulus. It is exceedingly difficult to record from these connector cells in the vertebrate retina. Evidence from studies on single sense cells of *Limulus,* to which the excellent works of Hartline and Ratliff (1957, 1958; Ratliff and Hartline, 1959) have contributed, has revealed the precise quantitative mode of the excitatory and inhibitory interactions between adjoining receptor units. The lateral eye of *Limulus,* the horseshoe crab, is a compound eye, composed of approximately 1000 single sense cells or ommatidia, whose axons form the optic nerve. These cells are interconnected by small lateral branches of nerve fibers.

A single fiber of the optic nerve was dissected from the bundle, and the activity of the fiber in response to illumination of the ommatidium from which it arises (test ommatidium) was recorded. At the onset of illumination the fiber discharged at a relatively high frequency. Subsequently, the frequency of discharge subsided to a low steady level, which was maintained for long periods of time. Illumination of other ommatidia near the test ommatidium produced an inhibitory effect. The frequency of discharge, when adjoining receptor units were illuminated, decreased, and the discharge could even be stopped altogether by increasing the intensity of illumination on adjoining receptor units.

The magnitude of the inhibitory effect exerted by adjoining units on the activity of the nerve fiber from the test ommatidium was found to be a function of such variables as intensity of illumination, area illuminated, and location of adjoining units in relation to the test ommatidium. The details of the findings obtained by Hartline and Ratliff are not relevant here, but it is worth noting that a mutual inhibitory interaction of two receptor units generates a discharge pattern similar to that of "off" responses. In Fig. 3.3, the discharge patterns of two interacting ommatidia are plotted. One receptor unit (lower curve) was steadily illuminated throughout the period, while the intensity of illumination of the other unit (upper curve) was increased suddenly to a new level and returned to its original level 2 seconds later. During the added illumination on the second ommatidium, the discharge frequency in the steadily illuminated ommatidium was inhibited; the subsequent discharge in il-

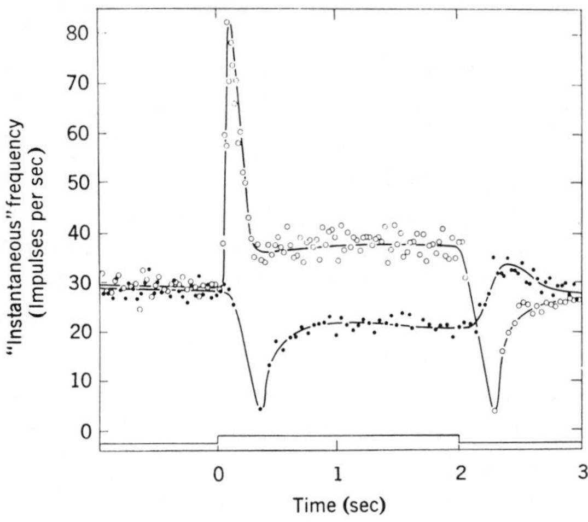


**Fig. 3.3** Discharge frequencies of two adjoining ommatidia.
(From Ratliff, 1961, p. 197.)

lumination on the second ommatidium produced a marked release from inhibition in the steadily illuminated ommatidium, thereby giving a discharge pattern similar to that of "off." Ratliff and Mueller (1957) showed that by adjusting the duration of the stimulus and the relative state of adaptation of various receptors, pure "on-off" and "off" responses could be synthesized in individual fibers. This demonstration supplies an analogy to the "on-off" and "off" responses obtained from a frog's optic nerve and suggests that a similar interplay of excitatory and inhibitory influence may account for the responses observed.

The experimental evidence obtained by Tomita (1958) indicates that the inhibitory action in the lateral eye of *Limulus* is mediated by a plexus of nerve fibers that lies just back of the receptor units. In Tomita's experiment the activity of a single optic nerve fiber elicited by a spot of light on its ommatidium was inhibited by antidromic impulses in the remaining optic nerve fibers in a manner similar to the lateral inhibition produced by illuminating nearby ommatidia. Volleys of antidromic impulses evoked in the optic nerve were found to reduce the frequency of the sensory discharge from the illuminated ommatidium, and the slowing of the sensory discharge was very similar to the inhibition produced by illumination of other ommatidia. Tomita showed that antidromic volleys were reaching the origin of the illuminated ommatidium's nerve fiber with a correspondence of one impulse to one shock. The findings suggest that lateral inhibition is the result of suppression of the impulse-generating mechanism near the origin of the fiber. The impulses spreading through the plexus compete with excitation by repolarizing the membrane of the nerve fiber at its origin, where it had been depolarized by illumination.

It is clear then that the pattern of optic activity does not correspond to the pattern of stimulation on the receptor mosaic. For instance, if one half of the receptor mosaic is dimly illuminated while the other half is brightly illuminated, the boundary between the two regions will be accentuated in its neural representation. As a result of the inhibitory influence exerted by the adjoining units, which are brightly illuminated, a unit lying at the edge of the dimly illuminated field will have a lower frequency of discharge than units equally illuminated but further away from the boundary. Similarly, a unit lying at the edge of the brightly illuminated field will have a higher frequency of discharge than other equally illuminated units that are located further away from the edge. Inhibitory interaction, resembling but more complex than that observed in the lateral eye of *Limulus,* was inferred by Barlow from his studies on the frog's retina (1953a, 1953b). He extended Hartline's observation by showing that receptor elements at the center of a receptive field interact with those at the periphery of the field. For an "off" fiber, for instance, the response always occurred to the offset of illumination at both the center and periphery of the receptive field. However, upon the cessation of illumination at the center, the "off" response was enhanced when the receptor elements at the periphery were not illuminated. Likewise, a discharge from an "on-off" fiber at the onset of illumination in the center diminished if the light was turned on in the periphery. The same interaction occurred on reversing the stimulus.

### *Detectors in the frog*

All these findings indicate that a considerable reorganization of the visual image is performed by the retina. Lettvin and his associates (Lettvin, et al., 1959, 1961; Maturana, et al., 1960) have demonstrated that each nerve fiber detects selected features of the whole distribution of light in an area of the receptive field. They categorized responses from the frog's optic nerve fibers into four distinct classes.

The first class of optic nerve fibers responded mainly to the sharp edge of an object either lighter or darker than the background. The discharge was sustained as long as the edge remained in the receptive field.

The sustained discharge could be interrupted by turning off the light, and renewed by turning the light on. The fibers of this type, called the "sustained contrast detectors," along with the color-sensitive fibers which project to the diencephalon (Muntz, 1962), are the "on" fibers of Hartline. By illuminating the retina with a small spot of light, Hartline furnished a sharp contrast within the receptive field.

The second class of fibers, the "net convexity detectors," discharged briskly to a small dark object passing through the field. These fibers responded for a long time if the object was brought into the receptive field and left there, but the responses ceased when the background illumination was briefly decreased. No responses were obtained when the straight edge of a dark object was moved through the receptive field, but there were sustained discharges when the corner of the object was brought into the field.

The "event detectors," the third class, probably correspond to the "on-off" units of Hartline. Diffuse illumination of the receptive field and its surroundings, as well as partial illumination of the receptive field by means of a small spot of light, elicited a short burst of discharges at "on" and "off." The fibers responded optimally to any distinguishable edge moving through their receptive field, whether a black object against a white background or the reverse. The frequency of discharge increased with the velocity of movement, within certain limits.

Finally, there were fibers which responded only at the offset of illumination. These "dimming detectors" are Hartline's "off" fibers. The frequency with which these units discharged depended on the intensity and duration of illumination, as well as the state of the eye's dark adaptation.

The significance of Lettvin's findings can hardly be overemphasized. The findings showed that a remarkable amount of data processing is performed by the retina, and a highly specific message is transmitted through the optic nerve fibers. Lettvin characterized the receptive fields of optic nerve fibers as sensitive to attributes of a stimulus rather than to spatial and temporal changes in light flux. The degree of specialization of nerve cells, furthermore, undoubtedly increases as the message is transmitted through successive synapses. It is conceivable, therefore, that there are scores of different types of neurons in the higher visual center, each devoted to detecting exceedingly specific patterns or changes of illumination.

### *Receptive fields in mammals*

Another group of investigators, notably Kuffler, Hubel, and Wiesel, explored the neural organization in the visual system of mammals. Kuffler (1952, 1953) found that the type of response elicited from the cat's ganglion cell depended on a specific portion of the area within its receptive field. When a small spot of light was moved from one position to another within a receptive field, either "on" responses or "off" responses could be recorded from the ganglion, depending on the area which was illuminated. Kuffler concluded that, within the receptive fields of single ganglion cells, there exist areas which evoke different kinds of responses. The receptive fields generally were organized in a regular concentric manner, as shown in Fig. 3.4.

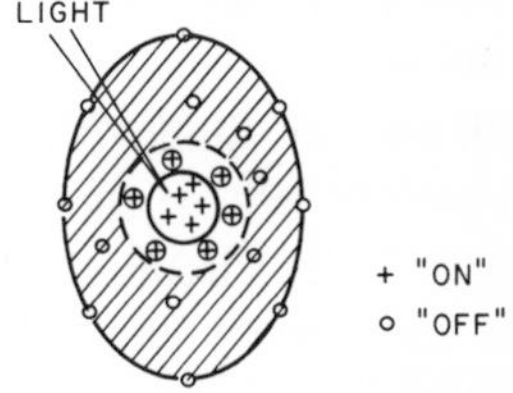


**Fig. 3.4** Organization of a receptive field.

Illumination of the center evoked "on" responses from the ganglion cell, while "off" responses were elicited when the surround was illuminated. "On-off" responses were obtained from the intermediate region. (Modified from Kuffler, 1952.)

Each receptive field had an inner concentric region of greatest sensitivity in which either the "on" or "off" responses predominated. In the outer annulus only the "off" discharge (or "on" discharge if the inner concentric region evoked an "off" discharge) occurred. The receptive field is not, however, a fixed anatomical unit. Kuffler (1953) noted that the size of the field increased or decreased as the background illumination was varied. With a given intensity of the test spot, the receptive fields were shown to expand when the background illumination was lowered and shrink when it was raised. When the background light was completely eliminated and the eye was well dark-adapted, the response which was characteristic of an inhibitory surround disappeared, and the characteristics of the center predominated (Barlow, FitzHugh, and Kuffler, 1957). But the center-surround organization of the field could always be found by using a dim background and a moderate-intensity test spot.

### *Differences among species*

It should be emphasized that findings obtained from one species are not to be generalized across different species. The responses of Lettvin's "sustained contrast detector," "convexity detector," and "event detector," for example, cannot be explained by means of the excitatory and inhibitory subdivisions within the receptive field, even if some kind of asymmetry in the receptive field is assumed (Grüsser-Cornehls, Grüsser, and Bullock, 1964).

The differences between the cat's visual system and the frog's may be due to differences in neuronal interconnections between rod and cone layers on the one hand and ganglion cells on the other. The structural difference in the retina between various species probably accounts for the difference in results obtained from various species. Barlow and his coworkers (Barlow and Hill, 1963; Barlow, Hill, and Levick, 1964; Barlow and Levick, 1965) have found a class of ganglion cells in the rabbit that responds selectively to movements in particular directions. An illuminated spot or black spot moving in one direction evoked responses from the ganglion cell, whereas the same spot moving in the reverse direction (the "null direction") was ineffective. Maintained discharges from these cells could be suppressed by motion in the null direction. A report of similar directional selectivity has been made on the retinal ganglion cell of the pigeon (Maturana and Frenk, 1963). The cell's sensitivity to direction of motion cannot be explained satisfactorily, if at all, with the center-surround pattern of receptive field described by Kuffler (1953). In the cat's retinal ganglion cells, however, units which responded selectively to one direction of movement have not been convincingly demonstrated. All receptive fields of ganglion cells are subdivided into excitatory center and antagonistic surround. A similar concentric arrangement of receptive fields was found in the ganglion cell of a spider monkey (Hubel and Wiesel, 1960) and of a rat (Brown and Rojas, 1965). In addition to cells with the center-surround receptive field, there were, in the rat, units which had no demonstrable surround (Brown and Rojas, 1965).

It may appear strange that no general law holds across species with respect to the visual system. But there is no reason why the world should look the same to a frog as it does to a human. The view that different animal species have different "perceptual worlds" was proposed by von Uexküll (1909), who coined the term *Umwelt* to express the view of the environment transformed into the animal's particular perceptions.

### *Maintained discharges*

Before describing the findings obtained from the lateral geniculate body, mention should be made of "maintained discharges" in the nervous system. Most visual cells in the mammal show a maintained activity in the absence of specific visual stimulation, even when no light impinges on the retina. It has been suggested that incoming visual messages are coded by modulation of this maintained discharge. Kuffler, FitzHugh, and Barlow (1957) investigated the discharge patterns of the maintained activity in the cat's retinal ganglion cells. Maintained activities, it was noted, were present whether the animal was in total darkness or in light. The average frequency of maintained discharge appeared to be approximately constant over a wide range of illumination, but transient enhancement or suppression of the discharge frequency could always be noted when the intensity of background illumination was raised or lowered. The discharge pattern of maintained activity is also noteworthy. It was shown that there was a tendency for short intervals to be followed by long intervals and vice versa (Kuffler, FitzHugh, and Barlow, 1957), and the distributions of the interspike intervals commonly show distinct peaks, a tall peak in the short interval range and one or two more peaks in the long range (Bishop et al., 1963; Levick and Williams, 1964; Fuster, Herz, and Creuzfeldt, 1965). The physiological significance of these findings is not thoroughly understood, but it is conceivable that different bands of interspike interval convey different kinds of information in a manner similar to a system which multiplexes information by frequency modulation.

## Electrical Activities in the Lateral Geniculate Body

In mammals the lateral geniculate body is the only synaptic center on the direct path between the retina and the visual cortex. Each lateral geniculate body as a whole receives input either from the ipsilateral or contralateral eye. A small number of cells in the interlaminar regions of the lateral geniculate body, however, receive fiber terminations from both eyes (Hayhow, 1958). There is little information at present about the morphology of the synapses in the geniculate body, or their efferent and afferent projection system. Interest in the lateral geniculate body has been spurred by speculation that the preliminary mechanisms concerned with binocular interaction would be located there.

### *Receptive fields in the cat*

Early experiments showed, in accordance with anatomical findings, that cells in the two layers, A and B, of the cat's geniculate body responded to contralateral eye stimulation, while those in the intermediate layer, $A_1$, responded to ipsilateral eye stimulation (Bishop and Davis, 1953; Erulkar and Fillenz, 1960; Bishop et al., 1962). Evidence for bilateral interaction in some cells has been provided by various investigators (Bishop and Davis, 1953; Erulkar and Fillenz, 1958, 1960; Bishop, Burke, and Davis, 1959). A particular cell could be activated by stimulating either eye, although responses from one eye were generally greater than those from the other. There was also a group of cells that responded to stimulation of only one eye, but responses were modified by the stimulation of the other eye. The modifications of response pattern took various forms. The latency of responses, frequencies of discharge, or duration of response could be increased or decreased by simultaneously stimulating the other eye.

The receptive fields of single cells in the cat's lateral geniculate body were shown to resemble those of retinal ganglion cells, having a center and antagonistic surround (Hubel and Wiesel, 1960, 1961). "On"-center units and "off"-center units existed in all three layers. Cells found in the two dorsal layers had similar patterns of firing, and showed no systematic differences in the size or organization of their receptive fields. In the ventral layer, however, receptive fields of single geniculate cells were several times larger than those of dorsal layers. When the retina was illuminated with diffuse light, responses evoked in the geniculate cell were much weaker than would be expected from a retinal ganglion cell. For some cells the inhibitory effect of the annulus on the concentric center was so effective that they did not respond to diffuse light. The findings reported by Hubel and Wiesel (1961) suggest that no profound reorganization of receptive fields takes place at the geniculate level.

### *Receptive fields in the rabbit*

The organization of the receptive fields of the rabbit's geniculate cells is more complex than that in the cat. Arden (1963a, 1963b) has shown that it is difficult to detect the center-and-surround organization from the rabbit's geniculate cells. The receptive fields mapped appeared to be the resultant of two or more simple ganglion cell-type receptive fields, which overlapped. When a dim test spot was used, the shape of receptive fields generally appeared to be circular or oval, giving either pure "on" or "off" responses. But when the stimulus light intensity was increased, the receptive field increased in size and the responses became more complex. One border of the field, for instance, would give pure "on" responses, the other "off" responses, while the large intermediate region gave mixed responses. A dim test spot did not always disclose a simple receptive field. Just-suprathreshold stimuli disclosed a long, narrow field that contained pure "on" and pure "off" edges and an intermediate mixed zone. When the light intensity was increased, the receptive field became very much longer and its organization pattern remained unchanged. Arden's finding can be explained by assuming, despite the lack of support of histological findings, that a lateral geniculate cell is activated by the combined activity of many optic nerve fibers.

### *Reticulo-genicular interactions*

The lateral geniculate body is believed to receive a second input from the brain-stem reticular formation, which by some is thought to be the structure responsible for "attention" or "wakefulness." The evidence for this second input depends on the fact that maintained discharge remains active long after section of the optic tracts (Chavez and Spiegel, 1957). It has also been shown that electrical activity in the geniculate body in response to a visual stimulus could be modified by "attention" and "habituation" (Arden and Söderberg, 1961; Hernández-Peón, 1961). A similar finding was reported by Hubel and Wiesel (1960). The pattern of maintained discharge, when the animal was in sleep, consisted of high-frequency bursts of two to eight spikes, followed by a relatively long pause. The clustered firing disappeared when the animal was alert. Stimuli which elicited strong responses in the awake animal, tended to eliminate the clustered activity, whereas those which suppressed firing in the awake animal tended to increase the clusters in a sleeping animal. More recently Bizzi (1966) has demonstrated that the activity of geniculate cells in the sleeping cat was strongly affected during the period when the eyes move, and showed a definite phasic relation between the eye movements and the changes in the maintained discharges of the geniculate cells. The clustered firing was accentuated during the rapid eye movement in the majority of geniculate cells, while a small portion of the geniculate units decreased their firing rate during this period. Interpretation of these findings must remain speculative until the efferent and afferent projection systems of the geniculate body, along with the source of maintained electrical activity in the brain, are clearly known.

## Electrical Activities in the Visual Cortex

The nerve cells of the striate cortex are arranged in several more-or-less distinct horizontal layers parallel to the cortical surface. Axons stemming from the lateral geniculate body, or optic radiation, end on tiny 4th-layer granule cells of the striate cortex. There seems to be a fair amount of vertical connectivity from these cells to other neurons and from these neurons to yet others. The enormous complexity of cortical connections suggests that the structure is performing elaborate data processing through successive synapses. In view of the complexity of the system, it is not surprising to find that very little is known about this region, either anatomically or physiologically.

### *Simple cells*

Most of what is known to date about the electrophysiology of the visual cortex stems from the work of Hubel and Wiesel (1959, 1962, 1965). When an attempt was made to record the response of a single cell in the visual cortex of the cat, the investigators were faced with a new problem, namely, finding an optimal stimulus to which cortical cells respond. While circular spots were the most effective stimuli for activating ganglion cells and lateral geniculate cells, they were ineffective at the cortical level. Therefore, the shape of the stimulus, its orientation and position, and its direction and velocity of movement were found to be the important variables for an optimal discharge.

The receptive field of a cortical cell does not have a simple concentric arrangement, but varies from one cell to another. Hubel and Wiesel (1962) divided cells of the striate cortex into two physiologically distinct groups: "simple" and "complex." Like retinal ganglion and geniculate cells, cortical cells with simple fields possess conspicuous excitatory and inhibitory subdivisions. Illumination of an excitatory region increased the maintained discharge of the cell, whereas illumination of an inhibitory region suppressed the discharge and evoked "off" responses. The two regions were antagonistic; that is, illumination of both excitatory and inhibitory regions evoked responses similar to that of "on-off." The spatial arrangement of these regions, however, differed markedly from those of retinal ganglion cells and geniculate cells. All had a side-by-side arrangement of excitatory and inhibitory areas with separation of areas by parallel straight-line boundaries rather than circular ones. Two examples of cortical cells' simple fields are shown schematically in Fig. 3.5.

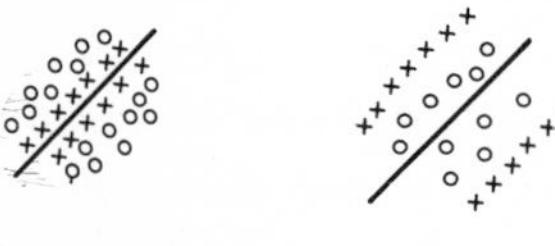

**Fig. 3.5** Receptive field organization of the simple cells.

The area outlined by the cross marks (x) evoked "on" responses from the cortical cells, and "off" responses were obtained from the area outlined by the circles (o). (Modified from Hubel and Wiesel, 1962.)

### *Complex cells*

Complex receptive fields, as the name implies, possess far more intricate and elaborate properties. The cortical cells which have complex receptive fields respond to variously shaped stationary or moving forms in a way that cannot be predicted from maps made with a small circular test spot. In the striate cortex, these complex cells are found intermixed with simple ones. However, receptive fields of complex cells, unlike those of simple cells, cannot be subdivided into excitatory and inhibitory areas. Furthermore, the exact position of a stimulus within the receptive field was found not to be critical for a complex cell. The first of the four types of complex cells described by Hubel and Wiesel (1962) responded optimally to a horizontally oriented slit, ⅛ degree wide and 3 degrees long at the eye. A vigorous "off" response was obtained when the stimulus was placed anywhere above the center of the receptive field, and "on" responses were obtained throughout the lower half. Both "on" and "off" responses were obtained in an intermediate position. The second type of complex cell also responded optimally to a slit, but the orientation was crucial. When the stimulus was placed in a 10-o'clock orientation, the cell responded maximally, especially when the target was moving slowly. There was a group of cells that responded selectively to an edge oriented at a specific angle. Excitatory or inhibitory responses were produced depending on whether the brighter area was to the left or the right, irrespective of the position of the edge separating light from darkness. The last type of complex cell showed a directional selectivity. A dark rectangle, oriented horizontally, was the optimum stimulus. A slow downward movement evoked a strong discharge, but upward or left-right movement had little or no effect on the cell's activity.

The stimulus parameters which determine the optimum discharge of the parastriate and peristriate cells (the cells immediately adjacent to the area receiving fibers from the lateral geniculate) were found to be far more specific than those for the striate cells. The great majority of cells in the parastriate area and half of the cells in the peristriate area had complex receptive fields. Besides the complex cells, these regions contained a second type which Hubel and Wiesel (1965) called "hypercomplex." Like complex cells, a hypercomplex cell unit is most affected by stimuli with line-like properties, such as a slit, an edge, or a dark bar. Unlike complex cells, however, a hypercomplex unit responded optimally only when a line stimulus was limited in length at one or both ends. A slit of proper size and orientation would, for instance, evoke vigorous responses from a hypercomplex cell. When the length of the slit was increased, responses could not be evoked from the same cell.

Mention has already been made of the binocular interaction in the lateral geniculate cells. It was noted that only a small minority of the total geniculate cells appear to be binocularly influenced. In the cortex the great majority of cells were influenced by both eyes. The receptive fields of all binocularly influenced cortical cells occupied corresponding positions on the two retinas and were similar in their organization. When each of the two receptive fields was stimulated in identical fashion, their effects combined. Likewise, when antagonistic regions in the two receptive fields were stimulated, the responses tended to cancel. Identical stimuli to the two eyes did not always evoke equally strong responses from a given cell. Stimulation of the contralateral eye in some cases evoked much more effective discharge than stimulation of the ipsilateral eye, and vice versa. There were a few cells that did not respond to stimulation of either eye alone but only to stimulation of both eyes simultaneously.

## Color Mechanisms

Before concluding this review, some of the experiments performed with monochromatic light should be briefly summarized. In the discussion of single-cell electrophysiology of vision thus far, color as a stimulus variable has been completely ignored. Both the cat and the frog appear to have poorly developed color vision, and no additional information is likely to be attained by adding this stimulus variable. With animals with well-developed color vision, such as the primates and certain fishes, it can be shown that the majority of cells respond differentially to different wavelengths of light.

Wagner, MacNichol, and Wolbarsht (1960) reported an experiment in which responses from the ganglion cell of a goldfish were recorded. When the retina was illuminated with white light, the discharge pattern of the cell was "on-off." The use of monochromatic light, however, revealed a dramatic wavelength dependency of the "on-off" pattern. Light of wavelengths 400 m$\mu$ through 550 m$\mu$ evoked an "on" response only, while illumination with wavelengths longer than these evoked pure "off" responses. Similar findings in monkeys have been reported (De Valois, et al., 1958; De Valois, 1960; Wiesel and Hubel, 1966). A monkey's lateral geniculate cell, which gave "on-off" response to white light, either gave pure "on" or pure "off" responses to monochromatic stimulation, depending on the wavelength of the light. This result occurred because the center and periphery of a receptive field are in general sensitive to different wavelengths. The center of a receptive field, for instance, would be sensitive to red while the periphery responded optimally to green. The cells which discharged at the onset or offset of a small white light responded to only a relatively narrow band of wavelengths, different cells responding to different portions of the spectrum. At present it is not known what becomes of these color-coded messages when they reach the cortex.

### *Concluding remarks*

This survey has described various ways in which the nervous system processes some of its incoming visual information. It was pointed out that the pattern of luminance distribution impinging on the retina is not faithfully represented by neurons but rather that certain features of the visual stimuli themselves are accentuated in their neural representation.

Each neuron, it appears, detects specific features of visual stimuli, and the specificity of the stimulus parameter to which a neuron responds increases as messages proceed further centrally.

There are a number of superficial resemblances between neurophysiological findings and some of the known psychophysical phenomena. For instance, changes in sensitivity of the retinal ganglion cell, when plotted against time in darkness, yield curves that are fairly similar to the dark-adaptation curves obtained in human psychophysical experiments. Likewise, one finds neurophysiological counterparts of such phenomena as brightness contrast, Mach bands, the Purkinje shift, and others. Nevertheless, it is impossible to conclude that the neurophysiology is translatable into the perceptual experience. Such a conclusion makes assumptions about psychological processes that are not tenable on either behavioral or philosophical grounds.

**Overview**

There remain two distinct questions that an engineer who proposes to build a pattern recognizer might consider. The first is whether an analogue of a living pattern recognizer can be designed in the foreseeable future. Before one can seriously contemplate this possibility, a series of problems must be solved.

It was pointed out earlier that the elements in the visual system form a hierarchical organization. The response of a photoreceptor can be described perhaps most simply in terms of the quantity of light falling upon it, as well as the immediate history of its response to light that has fallen upon it. The anatomical and physiological connections of the bipolar cells and cells at deeper levels are many-to-many. Thus the deeper one goes in the visual system, the wider is a cell's receptive field and the more complex is its behavior, although it preserves a behavioral identity that allows one to characterize groups of similar cells. The problem enters not in forming such hierarchies but rather in characterizing the particular operations performed by the elements at each level. The successive steps taken by the nervous system in processing information are not likely to be describable with simple mathematical transformations, such as the Laplacian.

One of the remarkable features of the nervous system is its ability to vary an element's operating characteristics. The dimming detectors in the frog, for instance, normally discharge steadily in the dark and respond to the offset of a light against a background of moderate intensity, and they will also fire vigorously when the background illumination is intense. Analogously, certain cells in the cat's spinal cord that ordinarily respond to cutaneous input (that is, touch) respond primarily to proprioceptive inputs (that is, signals from internal joints) when descending impulses from the brain stem are present (Wall, 1967). In addition, it is not certain what constitutes a meaningful signal for the nervous system. In studying the behavior of the visual cells, for example, a unit has been considered to be responsive to a stimulus if the maintained discharge rate increases or decreases. Frequently, however, one observes that the firing pattern changes upon the presentation of a certain stimulus even though the average frequency of discharge remains relatively unchanged. This complicates the description of the receptive field to the point where one can no longer talk about the message on the axons in the optic nerve simply as a correlate to variations in stimulus intensity. If what succeeding cells do is to correlate the information carried by various fibers rather than simply transform some arbitrary combination of average frequencies into a new frequency, then the task of building a model is indeed complex. In summary, the nervous system appears to be, even at the simplest levels, a multidimensional, nonlinear coupling system, the "output language" of which has not yet been fully decoded. This is not to say that it is impossible to build an analogue of an animal's visual system. Such a project seems, however, somewhat premature given the present state of knowledge of the complexity of the living system.

The second question to be raised is whether a "seeing" machine that uses a strategy unrelated to the biological one will help elucidate the biological processes. While important properties of an image may be extracted and combined by a machine built to recognize patterns, we must not assume that its performance can be taken as a model for another system that also extracts and combines different features. One cannot assume that all complexities are reducible to the same complexity. Thus, all of the ancient models, from the Pandemonium of Selfridge to the feature extractors of Minsky, are not necessarily relevant to the neurophysiological work on the visual system, nor helpful in understanding it; nor are they even remote models of the biological system one actually observes.

The purpose of modeling a visual system, however, need not be to represent slavishly a frog where one does not want a frog, as for example, in the nose cone of a missile. Almost certainly the specification of what one wants a machine to see will determine the strategy underlying the machine's seeing, and this need not necessarily be a strategy in the least relevant to the biological one. It may be that what one finds in an animal may be useful to engineers who build machines to see, but even this is doubtful, since the purposes for which one builds a machine and for which an animal possesses eyes are notably disparate. Perhaps all that is shared by those who would build seeing machines and those who investigate existing biological perceivers is a respect and admiration for any system that works.

**Acknowledgment**

Preparation of this paper was aided by support from the U.S. Air Force (Aerospace Medical Division) under Contract AF 33(615)–3885 and by a grant from Bell Telephone Laboratories, Inc., to the Research Laboratory of Electronics, M.I.T.

## References

Adrian, E. D., and R. Matthews. The action of light on the eye. I. Impulse in optic nerve. *J. Physiol.,* 1927, *63,* 378–414.

Arden, G. B. Types of response and organization of simple receptive fields in cells of the rabbit's lateral geniculate body. *J. Physiol.* 1963a, *166,* 449–467.

Arden, G. B. Complex receptive fields and responses to moving objects in cells of the rabbit's lateral geniculate body. *J. Physiol.,* 1963b, *166,* 468–488.

Arden, G. B., and U. Söderberg. The transfer of the optic information through the lateral geniculate body of the rabbit. In W. A. Rosenblith (Editor), *Sensory Communication.* Cambridge, Mass.: M.I.T. Press, 1961. Pp. 521–544.

Barlow, H. B. Action potentials from frog's retina. *J. Physiol.,* 1953a, *119,* 58–68.

Barlow, H. B. Summation and inhibition in the frog's retina. *J. Physiol.,* 1953b, *119,* 69–88.

Barlow, H. B., R. FitzHugh, and S. W. Kuffler. Change of organization in the receptive fields of the cat's retina during dark adaptation. *J. Physiol.,* 1957, *137,* 338–354.

Barlow, H. B., and R. M. Hill. Selective sensitivity to direction of motion in ganglion cells of the rabbit's retina. *Science,* 1963, *139,* 412–414.

Barlow, H. B., R. M. Hill, and W. R. Levick. Retinal ganglion cells responding selectively to direction and speed of image motion in the rabbit. *J. Physiol.,* 1964, *173,* 377–407.

Barlow, H. B., and W. R. Levick. The mechanism of directionally selective units in rabbit's retina. *J. Physiol.,* 1965, *178,* 477–504.

Bishop, P. O., W. Burke, and R. Davis. Activation of single lateral geniculate cells by stimulation of either optic tract. *Science,* 1959, *130,* 506–507.

Bishop, P. O., and R. Davis. Bilateral interaction in the geniculate body. *Science,* 1953, *118,* 241–243.

Bishop, P. O., W. Kozak, W. R. Levick, and G. J. Vakkur. The determination of the projection of the visual field on to the lateral geniculate nucleus of the cat. *J. Physiol.,* 1962, *163,* 503–539.

Bishop, P. O., W. H. Levick, and W. O. Williams. Statistical analysis of the dark discharge of lateral geniculate neurons. *J. Physiol.,* 1963, *170,* 598–612.

Bizzi, E. Discharge patterns of single geniculate neurons during the rapid eye movements of sleep. *J. Neurophysiol.,* 1966, *29,* 1087–1095.

Brown, J. E., and J. A. Rojas. Rat retinal ganglion cells: Receptive field organization and maintained activity. *J. Neurophysiol.,* 1965, *28,* 1073–1090.

Chavez, M., and E. A. Spiegel. The functional state of sensory nuclei following deafferentation. *Confin. Neurolog.,* 1957, *17,* 144–152.

De Valois, R. L. Color vision mechanisms in the monkey. *J. gen. Physiol.,* 1960, *43 Suppl.,* 115–128.

De Valois, R. L., C. J. Smith, S. T. Kitai, and A. J. Karoly. Response of single cells in monkey lateral geniculate nucleus to monochromatic light. *Science,* 1958, *127,* 238–239.

Erulkar, S. D., and M. Fillenz. Pattern of discharge of single units of the lateral geniculate body of the cat in response to binocular stimulation. *J. Physiol.,* 1958, *140,* 6P–7P.

Erulkar, S. D., and M. Fillenz. Single-unit activity in lateral geniculate body of cat. *J. Physiol.,* 1960, *154,* 206–218.

Fuster, J. M., A. Herz, and O. K. Creutzfeldt. Interval analysis of cell discharge in spontaneous and optically modulated activity in the visual system. *Arch. ital. Biol.,* 1965, *103,* 160–177.

Grüsser-Cornehls, H., O. J. Grüsser, and T. H. Bullock. Unit responses in the frog's tectum to moving and non-moving stimuli. *Science,* 1964, *141,* 820–822.

Hartline, H. K. The response of single optic nerve fibers of the vertebrate eye to illumination of the retina. *Amer. J. Physiol.,* 1938, *121,* 400–415.

Hartline, H. K. The receptive fields of optic nerve fibers. *Amer. J. Physiol.,* 1940a, *130,* 690–699.

Hartline, H. K. The effects of spatial summation in the retina on the excitation of fibers of the optic nerve. *Amer. J. Physiol.,* 1940b, *130,* 700–711.

Hartline, H. K., and F. Ratliff. Inhibitory interaction of receptor units in the eye of *Limulus. J. gen. Physiol.,* 1957, *40,* 357–376.

Hartline, H. K., and F. Ratliff. Spatial summation of inhibitory influences in the eye of *Limulus,* and the mutual interaction of receptor units. *J. gen. Physiol.,* 1958, *41,* 1049–1066.

Hayhow, W. R. The cytoarchitecture of the lateral geniculate body in the cat in relation to the distribution of crossed and uncrossed optic fibers. *J. comp. Neurol.,* 1958, *110,* 1–64.

Hernández-Peón, R. Reticular mechanism of sensory control. In W. A. Rosenblith (Editor), *Sensory Communication.* Cambridge, Mass.: M.I.T. Press, 1961. Pp. 497–520.

Hubel, D. H. Single unit activity in striate cortex of unrestrained cats. *J. Physiol.,* 1959, *147,* 226–238.

Hubel, D. H. Single unit activity in lateral geniculate body and optic tract of unrestrained cats. *J. Physiol.,* 1960, *150,* 91–104.

Hubel, D. H., and T. N. Wiesel. Receptive fields of single neurones in the cat's striate cortex. *J. Physiol.,* 1959, *148,* 574–591.

Hubel, D. H., and T. N. Wiesel. Receptive fields of optic nerve fibers in the spider monkey. *J. Physiol.,* 1960, *154,* 572–580.

Hubel, D. H., and T. N. Wiesel. Integrative action in the cat's lateral geniculate body. *J. Physiol.,* 1961, *155,* 385–398.

Hubel, D. H., and T. N. Wiesel. Receptive fields, binocular interaction and functional architecture in the cat's visual cortex. *J. Physiol.,* 1962, *160,* 106–154.

Hubel, D. H., and T. N. Wiesel. Receptive fields and functional architecture in two nonstriate visual areas (18 and 19) of the cat. *J. Neurophysiol.*, 1965, *28*, 229–289.

Kuffler, S. W. Neurons in the retina: organization, inhibition, and excitation problems. *Cold Spring Harbor Sympos. quant. Biol.*, 1952, *17*, 281–292.

Kuffler, S. W. Discharge patterns and functional organization of mammalian retina. *J. Neurophysiol.*, 1953, *16*, 37–68.

Kuffler, S. W., R. FitzHugh, and H. B. Barlow. Maintained activity in the cat's retina in light and darkness. *J. gen. Physiol.*, 1957, *40*, 683–702.

Lettvin, J. Y., H. R. Maturana, W. S. McCulloch, and W. H. Pitts. What the frog's eye tells the frog's brain. *Proc. Inst. Radio Engr.*, 1959, *47*, 1940–1951.

Lettvin, J. Y., H. R. Maturana, W. H. Pitts, and W. S. McCulloch. Two remarks on the visual system of the frog. In W. A. Rosenblith (Editor), *Sensory Communication*. Cambridge, Mass.: M.I.T. Press, 1961. Pp. 757–776.

Levick, W. R., and W. O. Williams. Maintained activity of lateral geniculate units in darkness. *J. Physiol.*, 1964, *170*, 582–597.

Maturana, H. R., J. Y. Lettvin, W. S. McCulloch, and W. H. Pitts. Anatomy and physiology of vision in the frog. *J. gen. Physiol.*, 1960, *43 Suppl.*, 129–171.

Maturana, H. R., and S. Frenk. Directional movement and horizontal edge detectors in pigeon retina. *Science*, 1963, *142*, 977–979.

Muntz, W. R. A. Microelectrode recordings from the diencephalon of the frog (Rana pipiens) and a blue-sensitive system. *J. Neurophysiol.*, 1962, *25*, 699–711.

Polyak, S. L. *The Vertebrate Visual System*. Chicago: University of Chicago Press, 1957.

Ratliff, F. Inhibitory interaction and detection and enhancement of contours. In W. A. Rosenblith (Editor), *Sensory Communication*. Cambridge, Mass.: M.I.T. Press, 1961. Pp. 183–203.

Ratliff, F., and H. K. Hartline. The responses of *Limulus* optic nerve fibers to patterns of illumination on the receptor mosaic. *J. gen. Physiol.*, 1959, *42*, 1241–1255.

Ratliff, F., and C. Mueller. Synthesis of "on-off" and "off" responses in a visual-neural system. *Science*, 1957, *126*, 840–841.

Tomita, T. Mechanism of lateral inhibition in the eye of *Limulus*. *J. Neurophysiol.*, 1958, *21*, 419–429.

von Neumann, J. *The Computer and the Brain*. New Haven: Yale University Press, 1958.

von Uexküll, J. J. *Umwelt und Innenwelt der Tiere*. Berlin: Springer, 1909.

Wagner, H. G., E. F. MacNichol, and M. L. Wolbarsht. The response properties of single ganglion cells in the goldfish retina. *J. gen. Physiol.*, 1960, *43*, 45–62.

Wall, P. D. The laminar organization of dorsal horn and effects of descending impulses. *J. Physiol.*, 1967, *188*, 666–687.

Wiesel, T., and D. Hubel. Spatial and chromatic interactions in the lateral geniculate body of the rhesus monkey. *J. Neurophysiol.*, 1966, *29*, 1115–1156.

*Another approach to electrophysiological aspects of pattern recognition is found in the following paper, which deals with auditory nervous systems. The author is concerned with some of the transformations and recodings of the electrical signals that can be measured in auditory nerves; he does not worry about measuring them, however, but with formulating a model to account for them. The model is essentially a probabilistic one.*

*In various places in this collection, a bias is expressed against statistical approaches to pattern recognition. The bias is not against the use of statistics but against their wholesale application as a sophisticated disguise for ignorance. Statistics, it can be argued, are appropriately applied only* after *the basic problem of classification or identification of parameters is made. The use of statistics in the following paper represents a method of describing phenomena that are themselves stochastic, rather than an effort to partition some undefined data space as the result of what the statistical mill grinds out.*

*William M. Siebert is a professor of electrical engineering whose interest in electrical properties of nervous systems is expressed in the Communications Biophysics Laboratory of the Research Laboratory of Electronics at M.I.T.*

# 4. Stimulus Transformations in the Peripheral Auditory System

*William M. Siebert*

A central connotation of the words "pattern recognition" is a division of some more-or-less continuous stimulus space into a set of discrete regions. Presumably this continuous-to-discrete transformation preserves the basic "meaning" of the stimulus, but it is nevertheless generally irreversible. Every pattern-recognition scheme is thus fundamentally an information-destroying process. There appear, however, to be important differences between man-made and natural pattern-recognition systems in the way in which this information destruction is carried out.

In man-made systems pattern recognizing typically begins with the replacement of the original pattern either by a small set of "characteristic features" or by a projection of the stimulus vector into a restricted subspace. The designers of these systems attempt to justify this immediate drastic destruction of data by pointing out that the original pattern clearly contains much "inessential detail" and that in any event their computers have very limited processing capacity.

Suppression of inessential information is, of course, a basic feature of every information-processing system. But if the purpose of the system is not rigidly prescribed — in other words, if it is not known in advance precisely what information is inessential — then it is obviously desirable to preserve as many as possible of the original stimulus details through at least the early stages of the data-processing system. Natural information-processing systems are characterized by great diversity of purpose and by relatively large data-handling capacity. Thus we might expect that their "designer" would have avoided the information losses associated with any attempt to replace the stimulus early in the system by a set of characteristic features, and would instead have tried to construct a more-or-less continuous, analog, information-preserving type of system, at least in its more peripheral parts. And indeed, it does seem to be true (as we shall try to show for one system, at least) that a successful description of the functioning of a sensory system often takes the form of a succession of smooth transformations of the original stimulus with the bulk of the information-destroying decisions taking place only in the later stages.

One should not, however, conclude either that transformations that are approximately information preserving are consequently unimportant or that the only "interesting" parts of sensory systems are the "higher centers." The variability and fluctuations (noise) present in every system, physical or biological, introduce some information losses at every stage of processing. As a result, stimuli that are physically quite distinct may be nearly indistinguishable to the organism. Of course, stimuli that the organism may ultimately recognize as belonging to the same pattern category are not necessarily indistinguishable, but local distance measures are at least the beginnings of a geometry of the stimulus space. By noting the kinds of distinctions that the organism preserves as contrasted with those it sacrifices, we may obtain valuable insights into the way in which the over-all system organizes information. By studying the methods employed to carry out these preliminary transformations, it may be possible to deduce design principles that would contribute to our understanding of other parts of the system. To be sure, a detailed knowledge of the principles and functioning of a natural pattern-recognition system may not help directly in the design of an artificial system — the component constraints are likely to be totally different in both quality and quantity — but the indirect benefits may well be substantial. And, of course, studies of natural sensory systems are interesting for their own sake.

Among sensory systems, the mammalian auditory system has a number of advantages for the type of study projected here. We have all had personal experience with a number of the behavioral properties of this system; many of these behavioral properties have been studied extensively and quantitatively; the experimental techniques have been elaborately refined; and the data show great uniformity and stability. But most important perhaps is the fact that, in large part as a result of recent progress in recording and data processing of the electrical activity in single neurons, the physiology of the peripheral mammalian auditory system is probably as well or better understood than any other sensory system of comparable interest and complexity.

The organization of this chapter will be the following. First, a summary of the main physiological features of the peripheral auditory system (as now understood) will be presented in the form of a quantitative model relating the total pattern of neural activity in the auditory nerve to the acoustic stimulus. As already suggested, this neural activity pattern is inherently stochastic, in that an identical repetition of the stimulus will not produce an identical repetition of the neural activity.

Conversely a particular pattern of neural activity may have been produced, with various probabilities, by any one of a number of stimuli. This random aspect of the neural coding inherently limits the discrimination performance of the over-all system. These discrimination limits can be computed by standard statistical methods for a variety of simple acoustic stimuli. In most of these cases the computed limits turn out to be only slightly better than the observed psychophysical behavior of trained subjects; that is, in these simple cases the more central parts of the auditory nervous system can be effectively almost "optimum," and we may legitimately claim that the psychophysical results are "explained" by the character of the peripheral neural coding. Although there are many nearly equivalent ways in which the central nervous system could function and yield an over-all optimum performance, one of these is particularly attractive, as we shall see, and suggests a principle that may be important in the recognition of more elaborate auditory patterns such as those of speech and music.

## Model for the Neural Coding in the Auditory Nerve

A schematic diagram of the peripheral parts of the auditory system that are of importance to this discussion is shown in Fig. 4.1. Briefly,

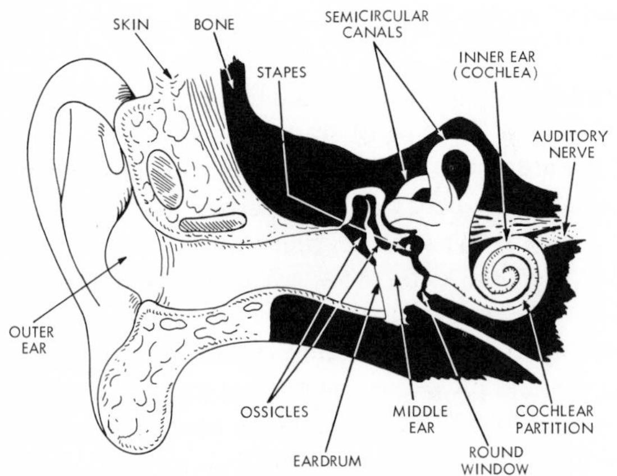


**Fig. 4.1** Schematic diagram of the ear.

(After a drawing by Alfred Feinberg.)

sound energy impinging on the outer ear is coupled through the eardrum and the small bones (ossicles) in the middle ear to the stapes. The stapes acts roughly as a piston in the wall of a fluid-filled spiral tubelike cavity in the bone — the inner ear or cochlea. The cochlea is divided longitudinally into two tubes by the cochlear partition, the stapes being on one side and the round window on the other. The fluid in the cochlea is virtually incompressible, so that a displacement of the stapes produces an equal (net) displacement of the cochlear partition which, in turn, produces a compensating displacement of the round window. The elastic properties of the cochlear partition vary radically from one end to the other. As a result, sinusoidal displacements of the stapes at a low frequency (~20 *Hz*) produce displacements of the partition primarily at the apical end (remote from the stapes), whereas high-frequency stapes displacements (~20 *kHz*) produce partition displacements at the basal end (near the stapes). The vibrations of the cochlear partition stimulate hair cells in the partition, which in turn stimulate the 30,000 or so fibers of the auditory nerve. The resulting activity in each fiber is a time pattern of essentially identical electrochemical spikes, or firings, that propagates along the fiber at a fixed velocity. By this means, information about the original stimulus is conveyed to the brain.

The model of these portions of the auditory system that I shall attempt to justify and analyze is shown in Fig. 4.2. Although the struc-

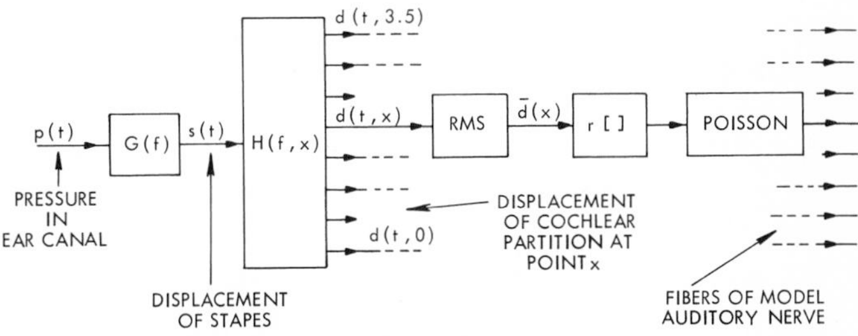


**Fig. 4.2.** Model of the peripheral auditory system.

tures and variables in this model have definite anatomical and physiological names and associations with corresponding structures in Fig. 4.1, these must not be taken too literally because in many cases details have been ignored, simplified, or combined into a single "black box." Of course, this model, like all models, is an idealization. It contains only those features that I believe are important to the over-all functioning of the auditory system under simple monaural quasi-steady-state stimulation. Nevertheless, I believe that it does contain *all* important features, in the sense that if the actual pattern of activity in the auditory nerve were to be replaced by that generated by the model, only certain details of the over-all behavior of the organism would be influenced; presumably all behavioral trends would be unaltered in their essentials over the full dynamic range of the stimulus variables, at least for the class of stimuli dealt with here. Clearly, this is a substantial claim and one that cannot be directly supported in full. Evidence to justify my faith will accumulate in the course of this chapter.

The first block, labeled $G(f)$ in Fig. 4.2, is a linear time-invariant system with frequency-response magnitude $G(f)$, modeling the transformation from acoustic pressure $p(t)$, as measured, say, in the external ear canal, to the volume displacement $s(t)$ of the stapes in the middle ear. All of the available physiological evidence suggests that this is an excellent model for this part of the ear, combining the effects of the external ear canal, the eardrum, and the ossicles (Békésy, 1960, chapter 5; Guinan and Peake, 1964). "Linearity" has the same meaning here as in the characterization of a Hi-Fi amplifier, that is, except for a few per cent distortion. This deviation may be behaviorally significant under some circumstances, but its effects will be ignored here. The transfer characteristic of the middle ear also seems to adapt to the intensity of the stimulus — much like an automatic gain control in a radio. But this effect appears to be both relatively small and slow-acting, so that in the interests of simplicity we shall ignore it. Measurements show that $G(f)$ has roughly the characteristics of a low-pass filter with a cutoff frequency $\approx 1$ *kHz*, falling smoothly ($\sim 30$ *dB*/decade) for higher frequencies. Only the magnitude of the frequency response of this system will enter into our calculations, so it is this that we have denoted by $G(f)$. Since $G(f)$ will not appear in any of our answers, we shall not attempt to provide an explicit definition in terms of a formula or graph.

The second block in Fig. 4.2, labeled $H(f,x)$, also represents a linear time-invariant system, or rather a distributed system or collection of systems, as suggested by the multiple outputs shown in the figure. For each $x$, $H(f,x)$ is the magnitude of the frequency response relating $s(t)$, the volume displacement of the stapes, to $d(t,x)$, the "volume displacement of the cochlear partition" at a point $x$ cm from the stapes. Our knowledge of the dynamic behavior of the inner ear is almost entirely due to G. von Békésy (1960, Chapters 11 and 12) and, for our present purposes, can be simplified and summarized as follows:

a. For a unit sinusoidal displacement of the stapes at a frequency $f$, the amplitude of the volume displacement of the partition (which is simply $H(f,x)$) is maximum at a point $x_0(f)$ that is approximately given by

$$x_0(f) \ln 10 = \ln \frac{10^5}{f}, \tag{4.1}$$

where $f$ is measured in $Hz$ and $x_0(f)$ in cm. Thus high frequencies stimulate the basal part of the partition near the stapes ($x = 0$) and low frequencies the opposite end ($x = 3.5$ cm). A fixed distance between maximum responses corresponds approximately to a fixed *ratio* of frequencies. The shape of the volume displacement of the partition, except for a shift of origin, is almost independent of frequency; that is, $H(f,x)$ is a function of $x - x_0(f)$.

b. At a fixed point $x$ along the partition, the response to a unit displacement of the stapes has a maximum at a frequency $f_0(x)$ that is approximately the inverse of $x_0(f)$; that is,

$$f_0(x) = 10^5 e^{-x \ln 10}. \tag{4.2}$$

The shape of $H(f,x)$ on a logarithmic frequency scale, except for a choice of origin, is almost independent of $x$; that is, $H(f,x)$ is a function of $f/f_0(x)$.

c. Specifically, we shall choose

$$H(f,x) = \begin{cases} (f/f_0(x))^{10}, & 0 < f < f_0(x), \\ (f/f_0(x))^{-20}, & f_0(x) < f < \infty. \end{cases} \tag{4.3}$$

These equations are illustrated in Fig. 4.3. A comparison of this figure with Békésy's observations will show fair agreement in all respects ex-

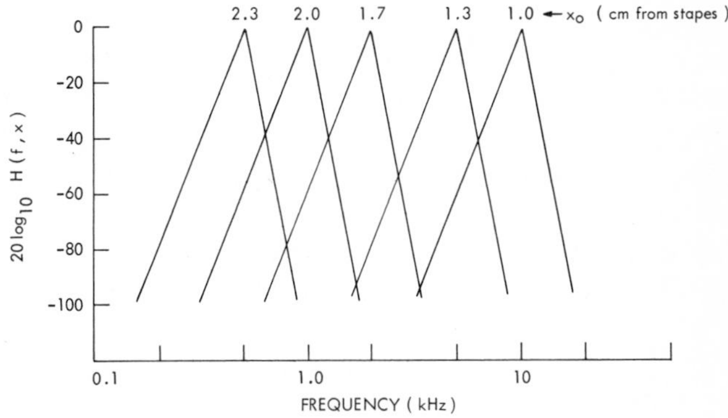


**Fig. 4.3** Plot of $H(f,x)$ from Eq. 4.3.

cept one — the frequency responses at a fixed point are substantially narrower than Békésy observed. There would be no difficulty in matching his observations rather well with a different choice of exponents in Eq. 4.3. But the values that have been selected will provide a better fit (as will be seen) to the "tuning curves" or isorate contours measured for primary auditory neurons. In other words, $H(f,x)$ combines in a single block both the mechanical behavior of the inner ear and certain not very well understood "sharpening" effects that are presumably of neural origin. It is for this reason that quotation marks were put around the phrase "volume displacement of the cochlear partition" for $d(t,x)$.

The remaining blocks in Fig. 4.2 also represent an attempt to combine in a few functional black boxes a number of little-understood phenomena. They will only be described; any attempt at justification will be postponed until the over-all properties of the model are considered. The first set of blocks, labeled "RMS" in Fig. 4.2, have outputs equal to the short-time root-mean-square value of the input, $d(t,x)$, where "short time" is about 10 msec. Analytically, the output might be written as

$$\left[\frac{1}{10^{-2}}\int_{t-10^{-2}}^{t} d^2(\tau,x)d\tau\right]^{1/2},$$

and it would be at most a slowly varying function of time whose spectrum would have little energy at frequencies greater than about 100 *Hz.* For the signals of present interest, however, the output will be substantially constant over the relevant intervals; consequently the time variable has been suppressed and the output of each *RMS* block in Fig. 4.2 has been designated simply $\bar{d}(x)$ independent of time.

The next set of blocks, labeled "$r[\ ]$," is a nonlinear no-memory transformation. The details are not critical, except for a few to be discussed later; an appropriate choice, which in spite of its apparent complexity will lead to simple results, is

$$r[\bar{d}(x)] = \frac{1}{4}\left[20 - \frac{6}{\sqrt{1 + \bar{d}(x)}}\right]^2. \tag{4.4}$$

This equation is plotted as the dashed curve in Fig. 4.5.

The last set of blocks, labeled "POISSON" in Fig. 4.2, are intended to generate sample functions from independent Poisson processes (see, for example, Parzen, 1962) characterized by the corresponding rate function $r[\bar{d}(x)]$. Since $r[\bar{d}(x)]$ will in general be a slowly varying function of time, these processes will in general be nonstationary. The sample functions generated by these blocks in response to a pressure wave $p(t)$ are our simplified model of the time pattern of firings that would be observed at some fixed point along the auditory nerve of a man listening to the same acoustic waveform.

## Comparison of the Model with Firing Patterns Experimentally Observed in the Auditory Nerve

The structure and parameters of the model of Fig. 4.2 have been so chosen that the output will have quantitative and qualitative similarity to data obtained with microelectrodes in the auditory nerve. The most comprehensive studies of activity in single fibers of the auditory nerve are those of Kiang and his associates (1965; Kiang's experiments were done with cats, but it is reasonable to assume that data on humans would be similar). A comparison of Kiang's observations with corresponding properties of our model shows the following:

a. All auditory nerve fibers are spontaneously active in the absence of any apparent acoustic input. The rate of spontaneous firing varies from a few per second to as many as 100/sec — a typical value being perhaps 50/sec — and is essentially a constant for any one fiber. The time pattern of spontaneous firings is irregular. Simple statistical tests show that it is reasonable to assume that successive intervals between firings are statistically independent random variables. A histogram of the intervals between spontaneous firings for a typical fiber is shown in Fig. 4.4. Except for a "refractory interval" much shorter than the mean

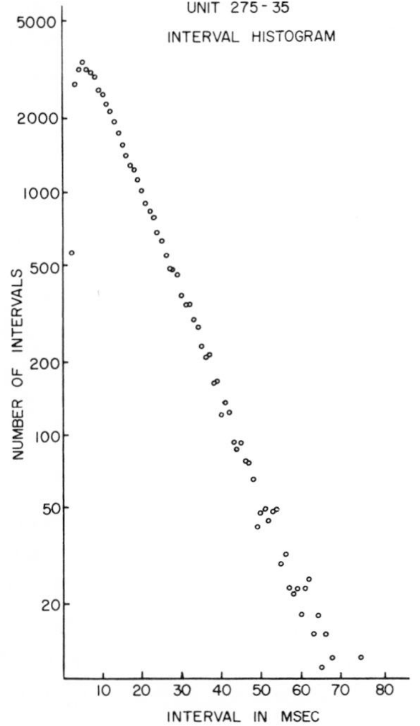


**Fig. 4.4** Interval histogram for spontaneous firings.
(From Kiang, et al., 1965, p. 98.)

interval between firings, all spontaneous interval histograms are well fitted by an exponential distribution.

For $p(t) = 0$ the model will have $\overline{d}(x) = 0$ for all $x$. From Eq. 4.4, $r[0] = 49$. Thus each spontaneous output of the model will be a Poisson impulse process with a rate of 49/sec. Successive intervals between firings are independent and the interval distribution is exponential.

b. If the acoustic input is a steady sinusoid or noise, the firing rate of an auditory nerve fiber will increase. Except for a short (~10 msec) transient at the beginning of the stimulus the rate of firing is nearly constant, fading only a little over periods of many minutes. Some typical rate versus stimulus-intensity curves are shown in Fig. 4.5. The maximum firing rate is typically only several times the spontaneous rate. Notice also that auditory nerve fibers show no very strong evidence of a threshold: small inputs produce small but proportional changes in rate. Of course, not all fibers are equally sensitive or respond equally well to all stimuli; the unit stimulus in Fig. 4.5 has been selected differ-

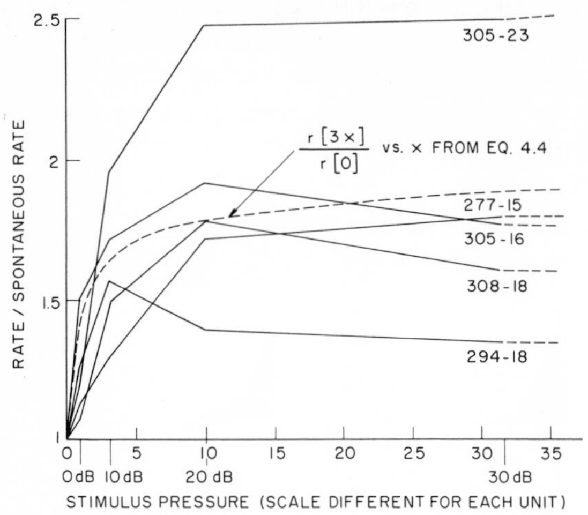


**Fig. 4.5** Experimental rate functions compared with $r[\ ]$ from Eq. 4.4. (Data derived from Kiang, et al., 1965.)

ently for each fiber to permit comparison of the shapes of the rate functions. For high frequency stimuli (say $>4$ $kHz$) the firing patterns are similar to the spontaneous patterns — successive intervals may be well modeled as independent almost exponentially distributed random variables (Fig. 4.6). At lower frequencies the interval histograms are grossly similar, but there is a tendency for firings to occur during only one half of each cycle, so that the interval between firings tends to be roughly quantized into multiples of the stimulus period (Fig. 4.7).

For steady sinusoidal stimulation, $\overline{d}(x)$ in the model will be proportional to the stimulus intensity and independent of time (except possibly at very low frequencies) so that the rate of firing of each model fiber will increase with intensity as shown by the dashed curve in Fig. 4.5. Successive intervals in the firing pattern of one fiber will be independent exponentially distributed random variables, and will show none of the stimulus-locking effects of real nerve fibers (again except at very low frequencies). For noise stimuli whose spectra are restricted to medium and high frequencies, the average value of the output of the *RMS* block will be large compared with the fluctuations about the

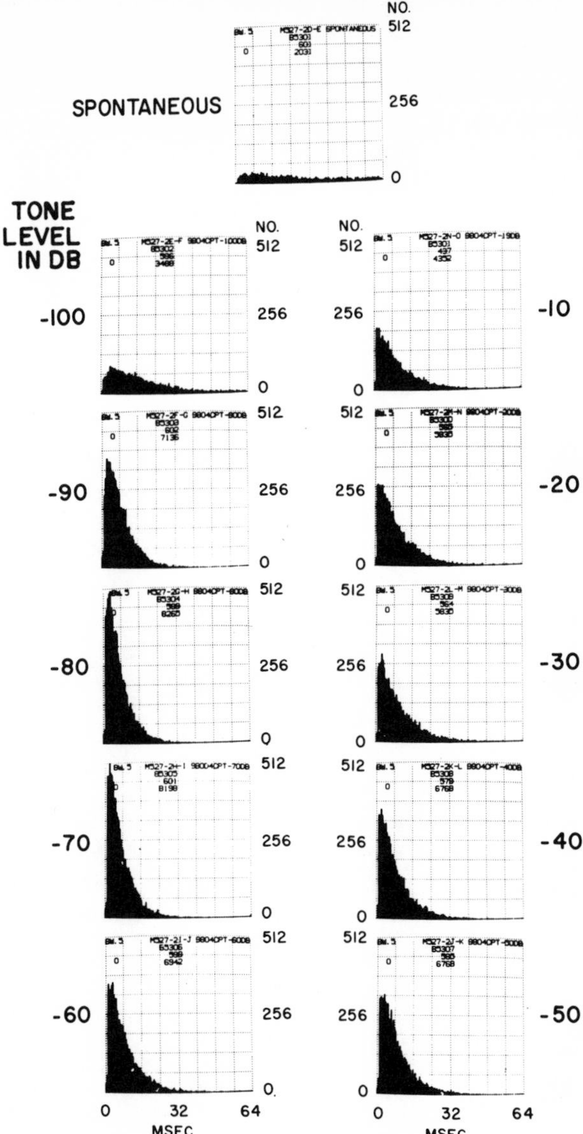


**Fig. 4.6** Interval histogram for steady sinusoidal stimulation (9.8 $kHz$). (From Kiang, et al., 1965.)

UNIT 415 - 2

INTERVAL HISTOGRAMS

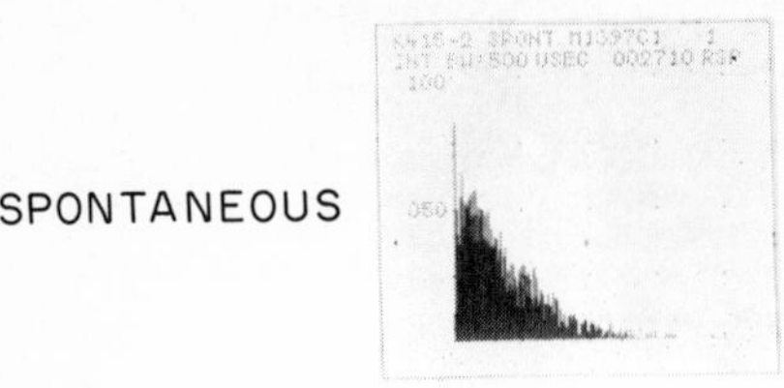


CONTINUOUS
TONE INTENSITY
IN dB

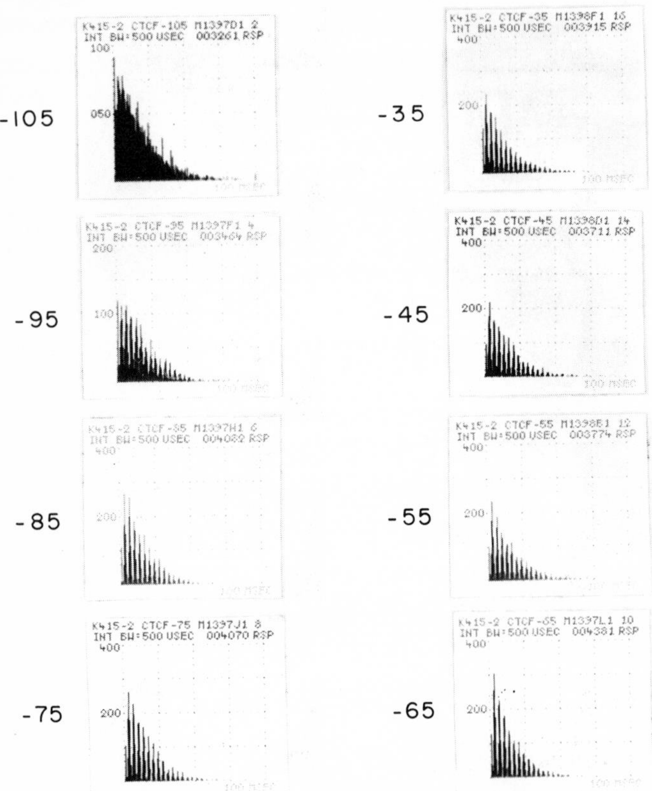


**Fig. 4.7** Interval histogram for steady sinusoidal stimulation (0.26 *kHz*). (Data supplied by N. Y.-S. Kiang.)

average, because the bandwidth of $H(f,x)$ at points sensitive to higher frequencies is substantially larger than the reciprocal of the averaging time of the *RMS* block. Thus the firing pattern of the model fibers will approximate a Poisson process with firing rate largely determined by the long-time *rms* value of the output of $H(f,x)$. Actually this conclusion is more nearly correct than our argument[1] might indicate; to the extent that our model accurately reflects the important attributes of the firing pattern in the auditory nerve, it would seem to be true that the *randomness* of a noise waveform has only a small effect on the over-all performance of the auditory system. This conclusion, incidentally, is directly counter to the assumption usually made by the detection-theory psychologists (Swets, 1964), who attribute all, or at least most, of the observed variabiilty in behavior to the randomness of the stimulus. In

[1] A better argument is as follows. An important and characteristic feature of a Poisson process is that the expected value and variance of the number of firings occurring in an interval $T$ are equal. We can show that this property holds approximately for the pattern of firings in each model fiber when $p(t)$ is a noise waveform. Let $\bar{d}(x)$ be replaced for a particular $t$ by $n(t) = m + \eta(t)$, where $m = E[n(t)]$ and we assume $\eta(t)$ is relatively small compared with $m$; that is, $E[\eta^2(t)] = \overline{\eta^2}$ is a fraction of $m^2$. Assume further that we may write $r[n(t)] = r[m] + \dot{r}[m]\eta(t)$. For a fixed $n(t)$, let $r[n(t)]$ be the rate of a nonstationary Poisson process. Let $N$ be the number of events occurring in this process in a time $T$. Conditional on a known $n(t)$ it follows that

$$E[N|n(t)] = \int_0^T r[n(t)]dt = Tr[m] + \dot{r}[m] \int_0^T \eta(t)dt$$

and

$$\begin{aligned} E[N^2|n(t)] &= \int_0^T r[n(t)]dt + \left[\int_0^T r[n(t)]dt\right]^2 \\ &= Tr[m] + \dot{r}[m] \int_0^T \eta(t)dt + T^2r^2[m] \\ &\quad + 2Tr[m]\dot{r}[m] \int_0^T \eta(t)dt + (\dot{r}[m])^2\left[\int_0^T \eta(t)dt\right]^2. \end{aligned}$$

Next carry out the average over $n(t)$:

$$\begin{aligned} E[N] &= Tr[m], \\ E[N^2] &= Tr[m] + T^2r^2[m] + (\dot{r}[m])^2\left[\iint_0^T E[\eta(t)\eta(\tau)]dt\, d\tau\right]. \end{aligned}$$

It is easy to show that

$$\iint_0^T E[\eta(t)\eta(\tau)]dt\, d\tau \approx T\frac{\overline{\eta^2}}{W},$$

where $W$ is roughly the bandwidth of $\eta(t)$, that is, $\sim 100$ *Hz*. Thus

$$\begin{aligned} \sigma^2[N] &= E[N^2] - (E[N])^2 \\ &= Tr[m]\left[1 + \left\{\frac{m^2(\dot{r}[m])^2}{r[m]}\right\}\frac{\overline{\eta^2}}{m^2}\frac{1}{W}\right]. \end{aligned}$$

Finally, it can be shown that the quantity in braces (later defined as $R[m]$) has a maximum value (when $r[m]$ is given by Eq. 4.4) of 4/3, so that within less than 1 per cent

$$\sigma^2[N] = E[N],$$

which is precisely the result that would be obtained if $\eta(t) = 0$.

our view the random (Poisson) character of the way the stimulus is coded in the auditory nerve — which is a form of what the psychologists call "internal noise" — is more important, and indeed by itself accounts rather well for the over-all behavior, as will be shown.

c. For sinusoidal stimulation the sensitivity of a given fiber in the auditory nerve depends markedly on frequency. Some typical examples of isorate contours — plots of the intensity required at each frequency to induce a given rate of firing — are shown in Fig. 4.8 for a number of different fibers and a rate of ~20 per cent greater than the spontaneous rate for each fiber. Contours for higher rates would be approximately parallel to those shown. Both the physiological and anatomical evidence suggest that the density of fibers with a particular most-sensitive frequency is approximately uniform on a logarithmic frequency scale.

For the model the isorate contours will be identical in shape to $H(f,x)$ for fixed $x$. Comparison of Fig. 4.3 and Fig. 4.8 shows that the fit is fairly good at least at intermediate frequencies. For fibers with high most-sensitive frequencies the model has somewhat too wide a bandwidth; for low-frequency fibers the reverse is true.

To summarize, there are many ways in which the performance of the model deviates from the observed activity in auditory nerve fibers. Some

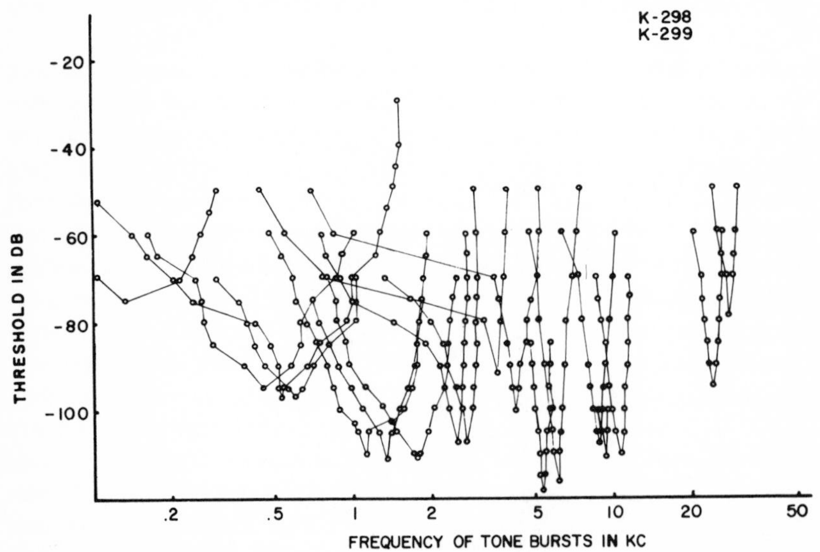


**Fig. 4.8** Isorate contours for a number of fibers at a rate slightly greater than spontaneous.

(From Kiang, et al., 1965, p. 87.)

of these, such as the difference in bandwidth of the isorate contours, could be easily accounted for by changes in parameter values or function shapes; these changes might make the model more unwieldy analytically but clearly would not modify its essential character. Other differences, such as the influence of refractory effects or the fact that all model fibers are identical in spontaneous rate and sensitivity whereas real nerve fibers vary considerably in these parameters, could also be corrected by substantial changes in the model. But I believe that these deviations are not particularly significant, in that it seems likely that they influence only details of behavior rather than gross trends. Another kind of difference is a result of the fact that there is significant evidence that under appropriate circumstances various sorts of complicated interactions between stimuli occur in auditory nerve fibers that have no direct reflection in our model. For example, two sinusoids of slightly different frequency and appropriate amplitudes may interact in such a way as to produce together a smaller firing rate in a given fiber than is produced by either acting alone. It is not easy to assess the importance of such effects; conditions have to be just right to make them stand out. It seems probable that the mechanisms responsible for these "inhibition" effects may also cause the "neural sharpening" mentioned earlier and reflected in our choice of $H(f,x)$. Except for their possible effect on $H(f,x)$, however, no attempt has been made here to include these complicated interactions in the model. Indeed the experimental evidence is still too incomplete to make such an attempt worthwhile.

Finally, however, there is one way in which the available data from the auditory nerve differ markedly from the performance of the model. This is in the time structure of the firing pattern for middle and low frequencies; the model shows no tendency toward locking of the firing pattern to the detailed time structure of the stimulus, whereas such locking is clearly evident in the auditory nerve responses up to frequencies greater than 3 *kHz*. This failure of the model represents a deliberate choice; other models can be postulated that more-or-less accurately mirror this time structure as well as that corresponding to initial transients and to click responses (Weiss, 1964; Siebert, in preparation). I believe, however, that any detailed time structure varying faster than 1–200 *Hz* is not in fact exploited by the more central parts of the auditory nervous system (at least for monaural stimulation). There are several kinds of evidence which can be put forward to support this belief. Physiologically, observations of single neurons in higher parts of the brain such as the cortex show no locking to any components of the stimulus or its modulating envelope varying faster than approximately 200 *Hz* (Goldstein, Kiang, and Brown, 1959). Tonotopic organization of stimuli in the cortex seems to be on a spectral rather than a periodicity basis (Goldstein, 1957). Psychologically, subjects have great difficulty in matching the pitch of a periodically modulated noise at modulating frequencies in excess of 200 *Hz.*[2] Finally, it can be shown by methods similar to those of this chapter that if the more central parts of the nervous system do make effective use of the time structure of medium-frequency sinusoidal signals, the system would be capable of much finer frequency discriminations than in fact it seems to be able to make (Siebert, in preparation). Moreover, the just noticeable difference in frequency under these conditions would show a quite different dependence on the duration, intensity, and frequency of the tones that are being discriminated than is psychophysically observed. On the other hand, the frequency discrimination performance of the organism, on the assumption that it paid no attention to the detailed timing of the firings in the auditory nerve fibers but made optimum use of other (place) information relating to frequency, mirrors the actual psychophysical performance, as we shall see.

In the final analysis, no comparison with physiological data of a model for a system as complex as the peripheral auditory system is likely to prove totally convincing. The available data inevitably represent a very modest sample of the system (Kiang by an intense effort over 5 years has managed to examine about 5000 individual fibers subject to a limited set of stimuli — there are 30,000 fibers in one human auditory nerve and the set of possible stimuli is endless), and there is no clear physiological method to prove that proposed idealizations and simplifications are legitimate. We must then turn to the deductions that can be drawn from our model for the final justification.

## A General Scheme for Computing Discrimination Limits

The "noisy" character of the coding of the acoustic stimulus in the firing pattern in the auditory nerve sets limitations on the discrimination and detection performance of the organism in precisely the same way that the noise present at the input to a radar or communication receiver limits the performance of those devices. And we can compute these limits in the same way, that is, by discovering the form of an optimum system for carrying out the desired discriminations and then computing its performance. A simpler procedure is to compute, directly from standard theorems in statistics, bounds on the performance of any dis-

[2] These are the classical results of Miller and Taylor (1948). More recent studies (for example, Harris, 1963) show that some periodicity information is present up to frequencies at least as high as 1000 *Hz.*

crimination system and then to show that we can in fact approach these bounds with at least one system.

The key theorem that we shall need is the Cramér-Rao inequality (Cramér, 1951). Suppose that we have some data, represented by a vector $\mathbf{x}$, which is a sample from a probabilistic mechanism whose statistics depend in a known way upon the value of some parameter $\alpha$. In particular we assume that we know the form of the probability density $p(\mathbf{x}|\alpha)$ of getting the sample $\mathbf{x}$, given $\alpha$. Our problem is to estimate the value of $\alpha$, given $\mathbf{x}$. Let $\hat{\alpha}(\mathbf{x})$ be any particular proposed estimate and assume that it is conditionally unbiased; that is,

$$E[\hat{\alpha}(\mathbf{x})|\alpha] = \int \hat{\alpha}(\mathbf{x})p(\mathbf{x}|\alpha)d\mathbf{x} = \alpha.$$

Then it can be shown that the conditional variance $\sigma^2[\hat{\alpha}(\mathbf{x})|\alpha]$ of the estimate $\hat{\alpha}(\mathbf{x})$ is bounded by

$$\sigma^2[\hat{\alpha}(\mathbf{x})|\alpha] \geq \frac{1}{-\int \left[\frac{\partial^2 \ln p(\mathbf{x}|\alpha)}{\partial \alpha^2}\right] p(\mathbf{x}|\alpha)d\mathbf{x}}. \tag{4.5}$$

Under certain conditions (which will always be met at least in an asymptotic sense in our applications) there exists an optimum estimator $\hat{\alpha}(\mathbf{x})$ for which the expression 4.5 is satisfied with an equality sign.

In order to see how we shall apply this expression to the problem at hand, consider a two-alternative forced-choice psychophysical experiment for determining the just noticeable difference (jnd) in the intensity of a sine wave. A sine wave of amplitude $\alpha$ is presented for $T$ seconds. A moment later, the sine wave is repeated with amplitude $\alpha + \Delta\alpha$ for $T$ seconds and the subject is required to guess which interval contained the tone of larger amplitude. The order of presentation is randomized from trial to trial, and $\Delta\alpha$ is adjusted until, after extensive training, the subject is correct in his judgments, say, 75 per cent of the time. This value of $\Delta\alpha$ is reported as the jnd in intensity at the intensity $\alpha$.

Now consider a mechanical device presented with the outputs from our model of the peripheral auditory system and required to perform the same task. During the first interval of $T$ seconds a certain pattern of firings would result in the model fibers. A device could be designed that would work from this pattern of firings to give an estimate of the sine-wave intensity during that interval. Similarly, from the pattern of firings in the second interval the device could give another estimate of the sine-wave amplitude during that interval. Finally, the device could be designed to compare these estimates and announce the interval that had the larger estimate as the one during which the larger sine wave was presented. If these are optimum estimates in the sense previously defined, then it is easy to show that this is an optimum decision procedure; on the average no other device will make fewer errors.

We can analyze the performance of this decision device in a little more detail as follows. Consider intervals in which the signal strength is actually $\alpha$. For such intervals the distribution of our estimates (assuming our estimator is conditionally unbiased) will be centered on $\alpha$ and will have a variance $\sigma^2$ (see Fig. 4.9). Similarly, for intervals in

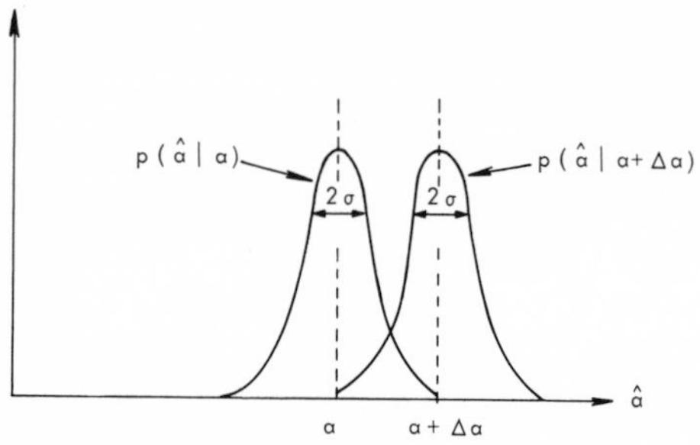


**Fig. 4.9** Distribution of estimates.

which the signal strength is actually $\alpha + \Delta\alpha$, the distribution of our estimates will be centered on $\alpha + \Delta\alpha$ but will have nearly the same variance $\sigma^2$ when $\Delta\alpha << \alpha$, as it usually will be. The probability of an incorrect identification is simply the probability that a sample from the left-hand distribution in Fig. 4.9 is *larger* than an independent sample from the right-hand distribution. This probability is easily computed if for example we assume the distributions are normal. (This assumption will later be justified.) The result of these computations is that the decisions will be approximately 75 per cent correct when $\Delta\alpha = \sigma$. Thus when we apply 4.5 to the firing pattern in the auditory nerve, the minimum value of $\sigma$ from that inequality is approximately equal to that jnd for $\alpha$ which would be implied by the random nature of the coding in the auditory nerve if the more central parts of the auditory system could be arranged to operate optimally for this discrimination. Clearly the value of $\sigma$ sets a limit on the jnd in any case. If this limit is close to the observed psychophysical performance, then as we have suggested we may legitimately infer that the more central parts of the system are effectively optimum for this task, and we may further claim to have "explained" or accounted for the value of the jnd.

To calculate $\sigma$, we must determine the form of $p(\mathbf{x}|\alpha)$ where $\mathbf{x}$ is the set of quantities required to specify the total pattern of activity in the model of the auditory nerve, and where $\alpha$ is the intensity of the acoustic stimulus (or any other parameter whose discrimination limits we might seek to compute). The activity pattern during an interval of $T$ seconds is completely specified by the set of numbers $K_i$ (where $K_i$ is the number of firings in the $i$th fiber) together with the times at which the firings occurred. It is easy to show, however, that if the firing pattern is generated by stationary Poisson processes, then the joint probability of the $K_i$'s and the firing times actually depends only upon the $K_i$'s. In other words, knowledge of the actual instants at which the firings occurred adds nothing to our ability to estimate $\alpha$; knowledge simply of the total number of firings in each fiber is sufficient. Thus $p(\mathbf{x}|\alpha)$ can be expressed explicitly as

$$P[K_1, K_2, \cdots, K_M|\alpha] = \prod_1^M \frac{(Tr[\bar{d}(x_i;\alpha)])^{K_i}}{K_i!} e^{-Tr[\bar{d}(x_i;\alpha)]}, \tag{4.6}$$

where $x_i$ is the value of $x$ corresponding to the $i$th fiber, and $\bar{d}(x)$ has been replaced by $\bar{d}(x;\alpha)$ to show explicitly the dependence on $\alpha$. In Eq. 4.6, it is assumed that the firing patterns of all of the $M$ fibers are statistically independent so that the joint probability is simply the product of $M$ Poisson distributions. (There is no experimental evidence either to support or refute this assumption of independence.)

Substituting $P(K_1K_2, \ldots, K_M|\alpha)$ for $p(\mathbf{x}|\alpha)$ in Eq. 4.5 we obtain directly

$$\sigma^2 \geq \frac{1}{T\sum_1^M \frac{(\dot{r}[\bar{d}(x_i;\alpha)])^2}{r[\bar{d}(x_i;\alpha)]}\left[\frac{\partial}{\partial\alpha}\bar{d}(x_i;\alpha)\right]^2}, \tag{4.7}$$

where $\dot{r}[\xi] = dr[\xi]/d\xi$. Since the number of fibers is large, the sum can be well approximated by an integral, so that we obtain for the optimum system

$$\sigma^2 = \frac{1}{\frac{TM}{3.5}\int_0^{3.5} R[\bar{d}(x;\alpha)]\left[\frac{\partial \ln \bar{d}(x;\alpha)}{\partial\alpha}\right]^2 dx}, \tag{4.8}$$

where we have defined

$$R[\xi] = \frac{\xi^2(\dot{r}[\xi])^2}{r[\xi]}. \tag{4.9}$$

For $r[\xi]$ given by Eq. 4.4,

$$R[\xi] = \frac{9\xi^2}{(1+\xi)^3}. \tag{4.10}$$

This equation is plotted in Fig. 4.10; $R[\xi]$ is, as we shall see, a measure of the sensitivity for indicating change of a point on the cochlear partition vibrating with amplitude $\xi$. Accordingly, we shall call $R[\xi]$ the *sensitivity function.* These equations, together with the fact that the jnd

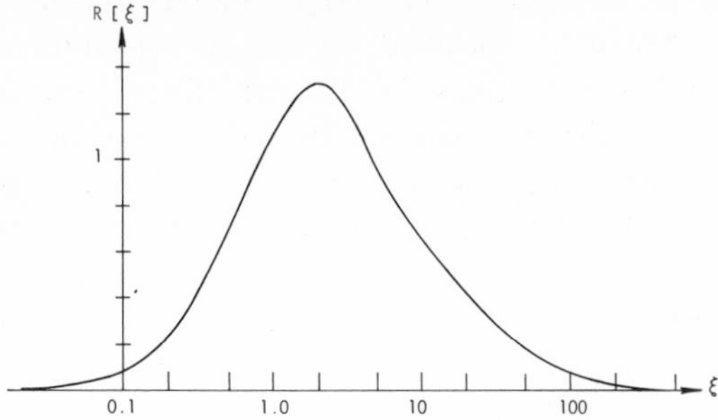


**Fig. 4.10** Plot of sensitivity function $R[\xi]$, from Eq. 4.10.

in $\alpha$ is approximately given by $\Delta\alpha = \sigma$, represent our major theoretical results, which we shall apply to a variety of situations.

## Discrimination Limits for Various Psychophysical Situations

### *Jnd in intensity for a sine wave*

Let $p(t) = A\sqrt{2}\cos 2\pi ft$. Then $\bar{d}(x;A) = AG(f)H(f,x)$, and, from Eq. 4.8,

$$\frac{\sigma^2}{A^2} = \frac{1}{\dfrac{TM}{3.5}\displaystyle\int_0^{3.5} R[AG(f)H(f,x)]dx}. \tag{4.11}$$

For very small values of $A$, $R[AG(f)H(f,x)] \approx 9A^2G^2(f)H^2(f,x)$ and

$$\sigma^2 \approx \frac{1}{\dfrac{9TM}{3.5}\,G^2(f)\displaystyle\int_0^{3.5} H^2(f,x)dx}. \tag{4.12}$$

The value of $\sigma$ given by Eq. 4.12 essentially defines the threshold intensity, $A_0$, for a sine wave of frequency $f$. The integral in Eq. 4.12 can be approximately evaluated, by using Eq. 4.3, as

$$\begin{aligned}\int_0^{3.5} H^2(f,x)dx &= \int_0^{x_0(f)} \left[\frac{f}{10^5\exp(-x\ln 10)}\right]^{20} dx \\ &\quad + \int_{x_0(f)}^{3.5} \left[\frac{f}{10^5\exp(-x\ln 10)}\right]^{-40} dx \\ &\approx 0.033\end{aligned} \tag{4.13}$$

if the frequency is neither too high nor too low so that end effects can be ignored. Thus

$$A_0 \approx \frac{1}{CG(f)}, \tag{4.14}$$

where

$$C^2 \approx 0.085TM, \tag{4.15}$$

which suggests, as is not unreasonable, that the shape of the threshold-of-hearing curve is largely determined by the frequency response of the external and middle ear. The approximations involved in writing Eq. 4.12 are clearly justified for $A \leq A_0$ if, say, $M \approx 30{,}000$ and $T \approx 0.2$ sec so that $C^2 \approx 500$.

Measuring intensity in units of $A_0$, that is, in terms of sensation level, and setting $\sigma = \Delta A$, Eq. 4.11 can be written

$$\left(\frac{\Delta A}{A}\right)^2 = \frac{1}{3.4C^2 \displaystyle\int_0^{3.5} R\left[\frac{A}{A_0}\frac{H(f,x)}{C}\right] dx}. \tag{4.16}$$

Again the integral can be approximated by using Eq. 4.3 and a method similar to that used to obtain Eq. 4.13, as

$$\int_0^{3.5} R\left[\frac{A}{A_0}\frac{H(f,x)}{C}\right] dx \approx 0.065 \int_0^{A/A_0C} R[\xi]\,\frac{d\xi}{\xi}$$

$$= \frac{0.29\left(\dfrac{A}{A_0C}\right)^2}{\left(1+\dfrac{A}{A_0C}\right)^2}. \tag{4.17}$$

Thus, finally, we get

$$\frac{\Delta A}{A} = \frac{A_0}{A} + \frac{1}{C}, \tag{4.18}$$

which is a form that has often been suggested as an empirical fit to experimental measurements of the Weber fraction as a function of sensation level. $\Delta A/A$ vs. $A/A_0$ is plotted as the upper dashed curve in Fig. 4.11 for $C^2 = 500$ (corresponding to $M \approx 30{,}000$, $T \approx 0.2$ sec). For comparison, some psychophysical measurements of the Weber fraction are also shown in Fig. 4.11; these were taken by several different investigators under a variety of conditions and experimental paradigms (none of which, however, precisely matches our assumptions).

For large sensation levels, Eq. 4.18 and Fig. 4.11 show that $\Delta A/A$ tends to a constant. This is "Weber's Law." By tracing this effect back-

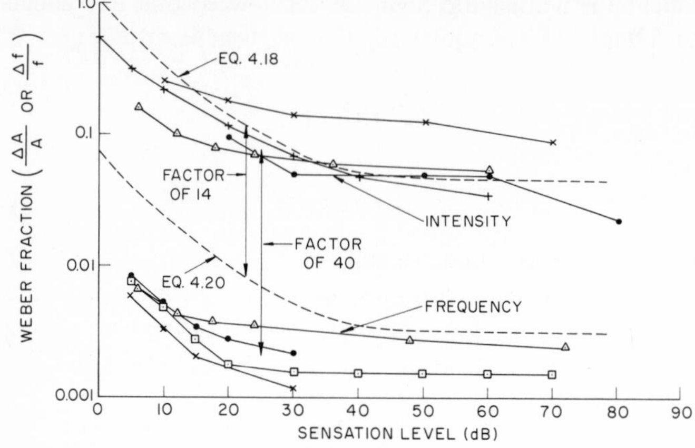


**Fig. 4.11** Weber function versus sensation level.

Experimental results from R. R. Riesz, *Phys. Rev.*, 1928, *31*, 867–875; B. G. Churcher, A. J. King, and H. Davies, *Phil. Mag.*, 1934, *18*, 927–939; V. O. Knudsen, *Phys. Rev.*, 1923, *21*, 84–102; S. S. Stevens, C. T. Morgan, and J. Volkmann, *Amer. J. Psychol.*, 1941, *54*, 315–335; J. D. Harris, *J. Acoust. Soc. Amer.*, 1952, *24*, 750–755; E. G. Shower and R. Biddulph, *J. Acoust. Soc. Amer.*, 1931, *3*, 275–287.

ward through our derivation, it is seen to be a result of the fact that, for large $A/A_0$,

$$\int_0^{3.5} R\left[\frac{A}{A_0}\frac{H(f,x)}{C}\right] dx$$

is independent of intensity. How this comes about is illustrated in Fig. 4.12. For moderate sensation levels, the regions of the cochlear parti-

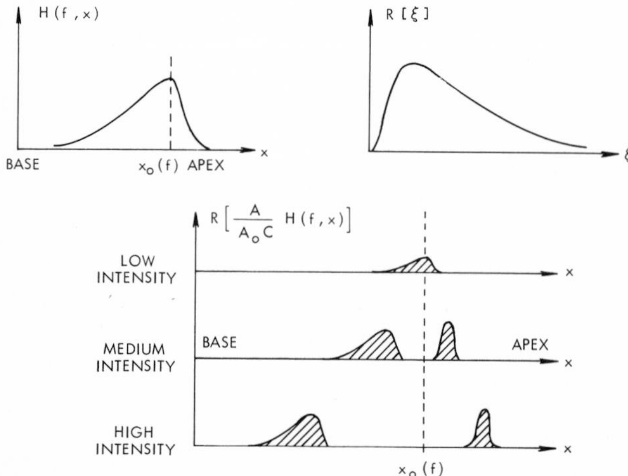


**Fig. 4.12** Illustration of a mechanism for Weber's law.

tion that are sensitive to changes in intensity are those that are moderately stimulated but not saturated, that is, those on the edges of the stimulated region where

$$R\left[\frac{A}{A_0}\frac{H(f,x)}{C}\right]$$

is large. As $A/A_0$ is increased, these regions move apart but their areas (loosely the number of sensitive fibers) remain roughly invariant. If the "tails" of the response region, that is, the tails of $H(f,x)$ vs. $x$, had an arbitrary shape, then the shape of $R[\xi]$ would have to be carefully chosen in order to achieve this invariance. But if the tails of $H(f,x)$ are exponential in $x$, then it can be shown that *any* shape of $R[\xi]$ such that

$$\int_0^\infty R[\xi]\frac{d\xi}{\xi}$$

is finite will lead to Weber's Law (Siebert, 1965). For exponential tails of $H(f,x)$, it is unnecessary to assume anything special about the way in which the neural firing rate varies with intensity (beyond some form of saturation so that $R[\xi]$ vanishes as $\xi \to \infty$). This is an explanation of Weber's Law (for at least this modality) which is especially appealing because of its lack of sensitivity to particular, often *ad hoc,* assumptions.

*Jnd in frequency for a sine wave*

As before, we shall let $p(t) = A\sqrt{2}\cos 2\pi ft$, but now we shall let $f$ be the variable and attempt to compute the discrimination limit for frequency. Simpler results can be obtained, however, if we vary $f$ at a constant sensation level rather than at a constant intensity, that is, if we write (using Eq. 4.14)

$$p(t) = \frac{A}{A_0}\frac{\sqrt{2}}{CG(f)}\cos 2\pi ft \quad \text{so that} \quad \bar{d}(x;f) = \frac{A}{A_0}H(f,x).$$

Holding $A/A_0$ fixed, we obtain

$$\frac{\partial}{\partial f}\ln \bar{d}(x;f) = \frac{\partial}{\partial f}\ln H(f,x) = \begin{cases} 10/f, & 0 < x < x_0(f), \\ -20/f, & x_0(f) < x < 3.5. \end{cases} \tag{4.19}$$

Thus from Eq. 4.8, we obtain

$$\left(\frac{\Delta f}{f}\right)^2 = \frac{1}{3.4C^2\left\{100\int_0^{x_0(f)} R\left[\frac{A}{A_0C}H(f,x)\right]dx + 400\int_{x_0(f)}^{3.5} R\left[\frac{A}{A_0C}H(f,x)\right]dx\right\}}. \tag{4.20}$$

Paralleling Eq. 4.17, the integral can be evaluated, and we get finally

$$\frac{\Delta f}{f} = \frac{1}{14}\left(\frac{A_0}{A} + \frac{1}{C}\right),$$

which is also plotted in Fig. 4.11 as the lower dashed curve. A selection of psychophysical results on the jnd for frequency is also shown.

One should not attempt too detailed a comparison between the dashed and solid curves of Fig. 4.11; the specific shapes of the dashed curves and the absolute values of the Weber fractions can be altered somewhat by minor changes in some of our assumptions. Such an exercise in curve-fitting is not likely to be very rewarding. Nevertheless it is both possible and reasonable to draw at least the following conclusions from our analysis.

1. Plots of $\Delta f/f$ and $\Delta A/A$ vs. $A/A_0$ should be parallel and separated by a factor of the order of 20.
2. Both curves should be essentially independent of $f$, and at moderate intensities $\Delta f/f$ and $\Delta A/A$ should be proportional to $1/\sqrt{T}$ for times neither so short that the steady-state assumption is violated nor so long that "memory limitations" become the limiting factor.

Both of these deductions from the model are in general agreement with the available psychophysical data.

### *Jnd in intensity for noise*

A result similar to those just obtained can be derived for the jnd in intensity for noise if we assume that for any one fiber noise is equivalent to a steady signal of the same filtered rms value. Thus if the noise power spectral density is $NS(f)$ on a single-sided basis we assume that

$$\bar{d}^2(x;\sqrt{N}) = N \int_0^\infty S(f)G^2(f)H^2(f,x)df. \tag{4.21}$$

The results for $\Delta N/N$ depend in part on the shape of $S(f)$. For simple low-pass and band-pass spectra, $\Delta N/N$ can usually be evaluated approximately in the form

$$\frac{\Delta N}{N} \approx \frac{k_1 N/N_0}{\left(1 + \frac{k_2}{C}\sqrt{\frac{N}{N_0}}\right)^2}, \tag{4.22}$$

where $k_1$ and $k_2$ are constants the order of 1, and $N_0$ is the threshold value of $N$,

$$N_0 = \frac{1}{C^2 \int_0^\infty S(f)G^2(f)df}. \tag{4.23}$$

Thus plots of $\sqrt{\Delta N/N}$ vs. $\sqrt{N/N_o}$ should be similar to the corresponding plots for sine waves, as in fact the psychophysical data show them to be.

*Jnd in intensity for a sine wave in a noise background*

As a final example, we consider a masking problem. Let $p(t)$ be a sine wave $A\sqrt{2}\cos 2\pi ft$ in a background of white noise with spectral density $N$. Then

$$\bar{d}^2(x;A) = N\int_0^\infty G^2(\eta)H^2(\eta,x)d\eta + A^2G^2(f)H^2(f,x)$$

$$\approx 0.15f_0(x)NG^2[f_0(x)] + A^2G^2(f)H^2(f,x), \tag{4.24}$$

where we have assumed that for each $x$, $G^2(\eta)$ is approximately constant at the value $G^2(f_0(x))$ over the region in frequency where $H^2(\eta,x)$ is large. Now,

$$\frac{\partial \ln \bar{d}(x;A)}{\partial A} = \frac{AG^2(f)H^2(f,x)}{\bar{d}^2(x;A)} \tag{4.25}$$

as a function of $x$ is small except in the vicinity of $x_0(f)$. Hence in the integral (Eq. 4.8) slowly varying functions of $x$ may be replaced by their value at $x_0(f)$. Thus we obtain

$$\sigma^2 \approx \frac{1}{\dfrac{TM}{3.5}\displaystyle\int_0^{3.5} R[k^2 + A^2G^2(f)H^2(f,x)]\,\frac{A^2G^4(f)H^4(f,x)}{[k^2 + A^2G^2(f)H^2(f,x)]^2}\,dx}, \tag{4.26}$$

where $k^2 = 0.15fNG^2(f) = 0.15fN/C^2A_0^2$ (and $A_0$ is the threshold for a pure tone of frequency $f$). Assuming that $k >> 1$, we may approximate $R[\xi]$ by $9/\xi$ and evaluate Eq. 4.26 by methods similar to those that we have already used to obtain

$$\frac{1}{\sigma^2} \approx \frac{2C^2}{3A^2K}\left\{2 - \frac{2 + (3A^2/0.15fN)}{[1 + (A^2/0.15fN)]^{3/2}}\right\}. \tag{4.27}$$

Pfafflin and Mathews (1962) have studied the corresponding psychophysical situation. Their procedure was to present a pair of tone bursts of amplitudes $A$ and $A + \Delta A$ in random order in a forced-choice experiment against a background of white noise. They plotted the probability of being correct as a function of the "pedestal" height $A$. Some of their results are shown in Fig. 4.13. The interesting feature is that as the pedestal is increased, the probability of being correct first increases and then ultimately decreases. This effect (the "pedestal effect") was first discovered by Green (1960) and explained by him in terms of the theory of an ideal observer; the pedestal was assumed to provide the listener with an accurate description of the signal and thus to make it easier to detect the increment. Pfafflin and Mathews suggested instead that the ear works as an energy detector so that as the pedestal is reduced the well-known "small-signal suppression" effect acts to reduce

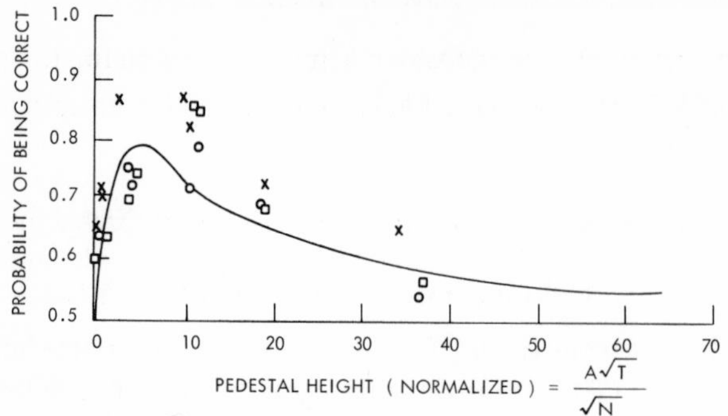


**Fig. 4.13** Probability of being correct versus pedestal height — solid curve from Eq. 4.29.

Data for three subjects from Pfafflin and Mathews (1962).

the probability of being correct. Neither Green's theory nor that of Pfafflin and Mathews explains directly why the probability of detection reaches a maximum and ultimately decreases as $A$ is increased.

Equation 4.27 can be altered to compare with Pfafflin and Mathews' data by multiplying both sides by $(\Delta A)^2$ to obtain

$$\left(\frac{\Delta A}{\sigma}\right)^2 = \frac{2C^2}{3K}\frac{(\Delta A)^2}{N}\frac{N}{A^2}\left\{2 - \frac{2 + (3A^2/0.15fN)}{[1 + (A^2/0.15fN)]^{3/2}}\right\}. \tag{4.28}$$

The values that Pfafflin and Mathews used were

$$K^2 \approx 5000$$

$$\frac{(\Delta A)^2}{N} = 160 \text{ sec}^{-1}$$

$$f = 1000 \; Hz.$$

Setting $C^2 = 500$ gives

$$\left(\frac{\Delta A}{\sigma}\right)^2 = 800\frac{N}{A^2}\left[2 - \frac{300 + (3A^2/N)}{(150 + A^2/N)^{3/2}}\sqrt{150}\right]. \tag{4.29}$$

For each value of $\Delta A/\sigma$, the probability of being correct can be calculated assuming two normal distributions with variances $= \sigma^2$ and difference of the means $= \Delta A$. The resulting curve is shown in Fig. 4.13 and clearly matches the data at least in general trends. The rising part of the curve is, much as in Pfafflin and Mathews, due to the small-signal suppression effect of our *RMS* blocks. The decrease for large $A^2/N$ in our model is a result of the built-in "internal noise" and is essentially the same effect that led to Weber's law.

## A Model for the Ideal Central Detector

The parameters of our model were by and large selected for their fit to the physiological data. The extent to which the model fits the psychophysical data, both qualitatively and quantitatively, strongly suggests that, at least in such simple tasks as we have explored, the noisy character of the stimulus coding at the periphery is a strong constraint on the over-all performance. Or in other words, given the nature of the peripheral coding, the more central parts of the auditory nervous system can apparently behave in ways that are nearly optimum. Under these conditions, it becomes worth while to consider what functional forms the optimum system might take. It is important to understand, however, that there is not just one optimum system — or at least there is not just one nearly optimum system. Indeed the class of very good systems is probably very large, so we cannot expect to learn too much by this exercise. Nevertheless, it will prove interesting.

Perhaps the simplest system which reaches decisions on the basis of the auditory nerve data and which has some potential for being fairly good is as follows. Count the number of events $K_i$ during each trial in each fiber, weight these counts by factors $\lambda_i$, and compute the test statistic

$$\Lambda = \sum_{1}^{M} \lambda_i K_i. \tag{4.30}$$

If the experiment involves a comparison of trials, compute $\Lambda$ also for the counts during the second trial (using the same factors $\lambda_i$) and announce that trial having the larger value of $\Lambda$ as the one corresponding to the larger value of $\alpha$. The performance of this system obviously depends upon a judicious choice of the $\lambda_i$.

For almost any choice of the $\lambda_i$, $\Lambda$ will be nearly normal by the central limit theorem, and hence the performance of this system will be characterized by the means and variances of $\Lambda$ under each hypothesis. For small $\Delta\alpha$, $\sigma^2[\Lambda|\alpha] \approx \sigma^2[\Lambda|\alpha + \Delta\alpha]$ and a measure of performance is

$$Q = \frac{\{E[\Lambda|\alpha + \Delta\alpha] - E[\Lambda|\alpha]\}^2}{\sigma^2[\Lambda|\alpha]} \approx T \frac{\left[\sum_{1}^{M} \lambda_i \dot{r}_i[\bar{d}] \dfrac{\partial \bar{d}}{\partial \alpha} \Delta\alpha\right]^2}{\sum_{1}^{M} \lambda_i^2 r_i[\bar{d}]}. \tag{4.31}$$

Maximizing this ratio with respect to $\lambda_i$, we find that an optimum choice is

$$\lambda_i = \frac{\dot{r}_i[\bar{d}]\,\dfrac{\partial \bar{d}}{\partial \alpha}}{r_i[\bar{d}]} \tag{4.32}$$

and

$$Q_{\max} = (\Delta\alpha)^2 \sum_1^M R[\bar{d}(x_i;\alpha)] \left[\frac{\partial \ln \bar{d}(x_i;\alpha)}{\partial \alpha}\right]^2 \tag{4.33}$$

which is precisely equal to the maximum possible value of $Q$ from the Cramér-Rao inequality. In other words, a simple weighted sum of the firings in the entire nerve is an optimum way (if the weights are properly chosen) to carry out any discrimination. This is a particularly appealing result, since a weighted count is commonly believed to be well within the functional capacities of a neural net. Presumably the function of the training or learning phase of the experiment would be to discover and to establish the appropriate weights for the task at hand.

There are other forms that an optimum decision system could take. One that has some intellectual interest is the following. We begin with a set of devices, one for each model fiber, which take the square root of the count $K_i$. (This result could be realized with a saturating counter in which the increment added to the "count" became successively smaller for each input firing.) The reason for this operation is that, whereas the variances of the quantities $K_i$ increase with the means, the variances of the quantities $\sqrt{K_i}$ are nearly independent of the means. To show this, assume that $E[K_i] = r_i[\bar{d}]T$ is large so that $K_i - r_i[\bar{d}]T$ is probably small compared with $r_i[\bar{d}]T$. Then

$$\sqrt{K_i} = \sqrt{r_i[\bar{d}]T\left\{1 + \frac{K_i - r_i[\bar{d}]T}{r_i[\bar{d}]T}\right\}} \approx \sqrt{r_i[\bar{d}]T}\left[1 + \frac{K_i - r_i[\bar{d}]T}{2r_i[\bar{d}]T}\right]. \tag{4.34}$$

Hence $E[\sqrt{K_i}] \approx \sqrt{r_i[\bar{d}]T}$ and $\sigma^2[\sqrt{K_i}] \approx 1/4$. The set of numbers $\sqrt{K_i}$ can thus be thought of as composed of a "signal," $\sqrt{r_i[\bar{d}]T}$, plus an independent additive "white noise" (in the sense of independent values from one fiber to the next). The problem of the best possible method for detecting a signal in an additive white-noise background is a classical one and leads to a matched filter or correlation detector. In particular, if we wish to test which of two signals, $s_1(t)$ or $s_2(t)$, is present together with noise in a received waveform, $f(t)$, classical theory tells us that we should form the quantity

$$\int f(t)[s_1(t) - s_2(t)]dt$$

and compare it with an appropriate threshold. Correspondingly if we wish to determine which of two rate-function "signals," $\sqrt{r_i^{(1)}[\bar{d}]T}$ or $\sqrt{r_i^{(2)}[\bar{d}]T}$, is present in a set of $\sqrt{K_i}$, we should form the quantity

$$\Lambda = \sum_1^M \sqrt{K_i}\{\sqrt{r_i^{(1)}[\bar{d}]T} - \sqrt{r_i^{(2)}[\bar{d}]T}\} \tag{4.35}$$

and compare $\Lambda$ with a threshold. The performance of the matched filter system depends upon the energy in the difference of $s_1(t)$ and $s_2(t)$ divided by the noise power density. Similarly, the "distance" between two rate functions (the square of the difference of the means of $\Lambda$ divided by the variance) is

$$Q = 4\sum_1^M \{\sqrt{r_i^{(1)}[\bar{d}]T} - \sqrt{r_i^{(2)}[\bar{d}]T}\}^2. \tag{4.36}$$

For $r_i^{(1)}[\bar{d}]T = T\ \{r_i^{(2)}[\bar{d}] + \dot{r}_i^{(2)}[\bar{d}](\partial d/\partial\alpha)\Delta\alpha\}$, it is easy to show that

$$Q = (\Delta\alpha)^2 T \sum_1^M \frac{\{\dot{r}_i^{(2)}[\bar{d}]\}^2 \left[\frac{\partial\bar{d}}{\partial\alpha}\right]^2}{r_i^{(2)}[\bar{d}]}, \tag{4.37}$$

which is precisely what we should expect from the Cramér-Rao inequality. In this case $\Lambda$ becomes

$$\Lambda = \sqrt{T}\sum_1^M \sqrt{K_i}\frac{\dot{r}_i^{(2)}[\bar{d}]\frac{\partial\bar{d}}{\partial\alpha}}{\sqrt{r_i^{(2)}[\bar{d}]}}, \tag{4.38}$$

which is a (nearly) optimum discrimination system equivalent to Eqs. 4.30 and 4.32.

Equation 4.36 provides an easy way of visualizing the "distance" between two acoustic waveforms. Compute the "spectrum" of each waveform, that is, $\bar{d}(x)$; pass this spectrum through a heavily saturating nonlinearity, that is, $\sqrt{r[\bar{d}(x)]}$; and compute the energy in the difference. Note that as a result of the square-root operation the saturation is even more severe than that of $r[\quad]$ alone; there is some evidence that such additional saturation does in fact occur in more central parts of the auditory nervous system (Whitfield, 1956). The principal consequence of this small dynamic range is apparently that intensity in the auditory system is primarily coded in terms of the spread of activity rather than the amount at any one place. As applications of this principle we briefly mention two. If loudness corresponds to the total amount of activity, then, except at low intensities, loudness should be primarily proportional to spread which (for a sine wave at least) would imply that it grows roughly logarithmically with intensity because of the exponential tails of $H(f,x)$. (If this argument is indeed correct, then both the loudness function and Weber's law would depend upon the same phenomena and thus would be related, although not in quite the way that Fechner suggested. I have no desire here to get involved in an argument as to whether loudness is better approximated by a logarithmic or power function of intensity.) For a second application we observe that a great deal of effort in speech research has gone into "formant tracking," that is, determining the loci of spectral maxima as a function of time. If our saturated spectrum principle is correct, then perhaps the ear is less interested in the spectral maxima than in the loci of the edges of the strong spectral regions. One speech analyzer based on this idea has apparently been highly successful (Martin, Nelson, and Zadell, 1964). The saturated spectrum principle may also explain why the sonograph, with its very limited dynamic range, nevertheless seems to reflect many of the important characteristics of auditory stimuli.

## Conclusion

I have had little to say here about the classic problems of auditory pattern recognition: I have barely mentioned speech and have said not a word about music. My concerns have been rather more mundane. By analyzing the peripheral transformations in the auditory system, I have tried to account for a few auditory phenomena. Some of these — notably the detection of a sine wave in a background of noise — might legitimately be called the recognition of an auditory pattern. Similarly, some speech and music problems — such as the recognition of a vowel or the identification of a chord — do not seem to me to be very different from the problems that we have been discussing. Similar methods should contribute to their understanding. But some of the other classical problems — the identification of consonants or of a rapidly articulated musical instrument, the recognition of unsegmented speech or of a melody — appear to be problems of a quite different sort. In fact the strictly auditory aspects of these problems, although undeniably important, seem not to be part of their essential core. Many of the neural mechanisms involved in speech recognition, for example, are equally concerned with other tasks, such as reading, writing, and speaking. Indeed, most recent studies conclude that speech recognition can be understood only in a broader, linguistic context (Halle and Stevens, 1962).

## Acknowledgment

This work was supported in part by the National Institutes of Health (Grant 1 PO1 GM-14940-01), and in part by the Joint Services Electronics Program (Contract DA 28-043-AMC-02536(E)).

## References


Békésy, G. v. *Experiments in Hearing.* New York: McGraw-Hill, 1960.

Cramér, H. *Mathematical Methods of Statistics.* Princeton: Princeton University Press, 1951. Chapter 32.

Goldstein, M. H., Jr. Neurophysiological Representation of Complex Auditory Stimuli. Technical Report 323, Res. Lab. Electronics, M.I.T., Cambridge, Mass., February 19, 1957.

Goldstein, M. H., Jr., N. Y.-S. Kiang, and R. M. Brown. Responses of the auditory cortex to repetitive acoustic stimuli. *J. acoust. Soc. Amer.,* 1959, *3,* 356–364.

Green, D. M. Psychoacoustics and detection theory. *J. acoust. Soc. Amer.,* 1960, *32,* 1189–1202.

Guinan, J. J., Jr., and W. T. Peake. Motion of middle-ear bones. Quart. Prog. Rep. No. 74, Res. Lab. Electronics, M.I.T., July 15, 1964, pp. 219–221.

Halle, M., and K. Stevens Speech recognition: a model and a program for research. *IRE Trans. on Information Theory,* IT–8, 1962, 155–159.

Harris, G. G. Periodicity perception by using gated noise, *J. acoust. Soc. Amer.,* 1963, *35,* 1229–1233. (Harris shows that some periodicity information is present up to frequencies at least as high as 1000 Hz.)

Kiang, N. Y.-S., T. Watanabe, E. C. Thomas, and L. F. Clark. *Discharge Patterns of Single Fibers in the Cat's Auditory Nerve.* Cambridge, Mass.: M.I.T. Press, 1965.

Martin, T. B., A. L. Nelson, H. J. Zadell. Speech Recognition by Feature-Abstraction Techniques. Tech. Doc. Report AL TDR 64–176, AF Avionics Lab., W-P AFB, Ohio, August 1964.

Miller, G. A., and W. B. Taylor. The perception of repeated bursts of noise. *J. acoust. Soc. Amer.,* 1948, *20,* 171–182.

Parzen, E. *Stochastic Processes.* San Francisco: Holden-Day, 1962. Chapter 4.

Pfafflin, S. M., and M. V. Mathews. Energy detection model for monaural auditory detection. *J. acoust. Soc. Amer.,* 1962, *34,* 1842–1852.

Siebert, W. M. Some implications of the stochastic behavior of primary auditory neurons. *Kybernetik,* 1965, *2,* 206–215.

Siebert, W. M. Signals and noise in primary auditory neurons. (In preparation.)

Swets, J. A. *Signal Detection and Recognition by Human Observers.* New York: Wiley, 1964.

Weiss, T. F. A model for firing patterns of auditory nerve fibers. Technical Report 418, Res. Lab. Electronics, M.I.T., Cambridge, Mass., March 2, 1964.

Whitfield, I. C. Electrophysiology of the central auditory pathway. *Brit. med. Bull.,* 1956, *12,* 105–109.

# PART II: AUTOMATIC SYSTEMS

*The transition in this volume from descriptions of living systems to automatic ones occurs with the next paper. The author describes some efforts to get a machine to recognize and create a uniquely human product — cursive script. The means by which this is accomplished can be called "generative." That is to say, a small set of abstract objects (components of cursive letters, such as loops, hooks, and arches) is isolated and a set of rules is specified for combining them. Their proper combination produces the equivalent of handwriting. The complexities of this production, and the complexities of handwriting recognition, are suggested by the fact that even a powerful computer takes far longer to accomplish these tasks than a moderately skilled human; but it does accomplish them.*

*Murray Eden is a physical chemist-turned-engineer and is a professor of electrical engineering at M.I.T. His research interests are principally in the interface region that uses machines to simulate human behavior and studies human behavior in part to make better machines.*

# 5. Handwriting Generation and Recognition

*Murray Eden*

When humans communicate with one another, they use patterns produced by one individual that are recognized in the intended sense, that is, understood, by certain others. Some of the principal forms of this communication are speech, gesture, writing, drawing, singing, and dancing. Speech may be the most important communication pattern in this class. In certain ways, however, speech is a very difficult pattern to study. It is ephemeral, it leaves no visible trace. As a consequence, the research worker has no object which he can look at while he thinks about it; nor can he concentrate his attentions on one aspect or portion of it as he formulates his working hypotheses. Further, no single currently available mode of visual display of the speech sound is suitable for studying all of its relevant properties. It has not yet been found possible to characterize speech sounds simply.

Writing is a more tractable pattern to study. It is reasonably permanent and, of course, is its own visual display. Moreover, it permits people to communicate through the sense of sight essentially the same information they would communicate by sound.

Written language must be regarded as a derived communication form. There is, in general, no grammar for a written language different from that of its equivalent spoken language. For most written languages there are precise rules relating the phonemes of speech to the graphemes of the written language. In fact, there exist a large number of very close analogies between the concepts, structures, and problems of speech and their counterparts in handwriting. It is for these reasons that one may expect to find new insights concerning the production and recognition of speech from studies of reading and writing.

We may regard the task of the study described here as that of providing a complete and simple description for any specimen which can be taken to be handwriting. An adequate description must satisfy the facts of handwriting — the shapes of the letters and words, and the manner in which these shapes are formed by the writer. It must also take into account our intuitive judgments about writing: the existence of variations within the corpus of any given writer, the variations from one hand to another, the effects of haste in writing, and so on. Such a description has two distinct parts. The first provides a formalism with which to characterize any handwritten text as a sequence of abstract elements. The second uses the abstract representation to characterize the physical form of the text.

Once descriptions have been devised for the production of handwritten text, one may ask whether the process can be reversed; that is, whether one can discover the sequence of abstract elements (or even better, the sequence of letters or words in the natural language) from the handwritten text. Of course, this is the central concern of any pattern recognition problem. In this case, as in many other pattern recognition problems, it is clear that humans can perform this task with remarkable ease and accuracy. Furthermore, it is not at all certain that humans make important use of the algorithms by which they generate handwriting, in order to recognize handwriting. Nevertheless it is worth while to ask whether a connection can be made between the descriptions of the process of production and the process of recognition. The recognition schemes to be described later depend heavily on the notions associated with procedures in which a generative algorithm provides the parameters by which one makes a judgment concerning the goodness of the recognition.

A formal model for the abstract description of English cursive script has been given by Eden and Halle (1961) in some detail. Only a brief and somewhat modified account of this model will be presented here.

## The Formal Model

The primitive constituents of English cursive script[1] are four distinct *line segments* which generate a set $\Sigma$ of elements of the form:

$$\sigma_j = [(\alpha_{j_1},\beta_{j_1}), (\alpha_{j_2},\beta_{j_2}), \theta_j].$$

The alphas and betas define the *neighborhoods* within which the end points, called nodes, are located. We interpret $\alpha_{j_1} > \alpha_{j_2}$ to mean that the first node *must* be above the second node. In like manner, we interpret $\beta_{j_1} > \beta_{j_2}$ to mean that the first node of the line segment must be

[1] Of course, the same primitive elements suffice for any language written in the Roman alphabet. A few trials with Cyrillic, Hebrew, Arabic, Old German, and Armenian scripts suggest that the primitive elements suffice for their description as well, but the lower level rules involve a greater or lesser modification. The only major rule change required in Hebrew and Arabic is the obvious one that prescribes the sequence as proceeding from right to left since Semitic languages are read and written in that direction. Cursive Chinese scripts such as "grass writing" also seem to fit the formalism reasonably well, but non-cursive symbol systems, for example, block letters, are not usefully characterized in this way.

to the right of the second. The $\theta_j$ refers to the sense of rotation from the first to the second node; positive if the sense of rotation is clockwise and negative if counterclockwise. We need to specify two values for the ordering along the horizontal line. We shall refer to them as $\epsilon$ and 1; $\epsilon$ is interpreted as any value greater than 0 and less than 1, and 1 is an arbitrary unit displacement in either the $x$ or $y$ direction. As will be seen, the motive for this distinction lies not so much in the character of the stroke as in the concatenation rule which needs to be applied.

The four generators of $\Sigma$ we shall call *bar, hook, arch,* and *loop,* respectively (Fig. 5.1).

$$\sigma_1 = [(1,0), (0,0), +] \quad \text{“bar”}$$
$$\sigma_2 = [(1,1), (0,0), +] \quad \text{“hook”}$$
$$\sigma_3 = [(0,0), (0,1), +] \quad \text{“arch”}$$
$$\sigma_4 = [(1,\epsilon), (0,0), +] \quad \text{“loop”}$$

The four basic line segments can be transformed by changing the sign of $\theta$, or by reflection about the horizontal or vertical axis, in this way

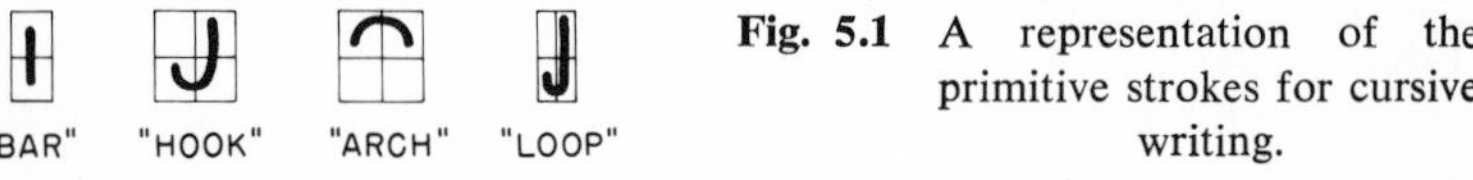


**Fig. 5.1** A representation of the primitive strokes for cursive writing.

generating the elements[2] of $\Sigma$. To each element we shall associate a class of directed curves with the following properties. Each curve is to connect the first node with the second node; the curve is to be continuous and have no points of inflection (except perhaps at the end points); the initial direction is either "up" or "down," the specific direction for a curve being determined in an obvious way from $\theta$ and the ordering of the two points. We call each class of curves corresponding to an element of $\Sigma$ a *stroke class.* One additional feature must also be taken into account.

To this point in the formalization, the two strokes of a miniscule "e" and miniscule "l" would be classified as identical. At first sight, the feature distinguishing "l" from "e" is vertical extent. However, there is no absolute scale for the physical dimensions of any letter in the alphabet. Size measures can only be made either by comparing certain dimensions of a letter, say "height" and "width," or by comparing dimensions of two or more contextually related letters. Since in most cases letters are connected to their neighbors, the notions of "height" and "width" of individual letters are themselves difficult to define in a natural way. Clearly it is the contextual character of writing that is crucial in making

[2] Although these transformations yield 28 strokes (because of symmetry the arch generates only four strokes), only nine of them are of interest in the English script commonly used in the United States.

such distinctions.[3] In other words, letters can be assigned dimensions only when they are written in a cluster of several letters.

Accordingly, we have introduced the notion of a *field* to represent the location and the vertical extent of a stroke. Note that the fields have meaning only as relative measurements, that is, the location and extent of one stroke relative to its neighbors. The three fields to which a stroke may be assigned are equivalent to the rule known by every writer that some strokes occur entirely within a middle field, as between the top and bottom of an "a" or "s"; that others may extend from the bottom of this middle field to considerably above it, as in "d" and "k"; and that still others extend from the top of the middle field to a point considerably below it, as in "g" and "y." [4]

A word is completely specified — as far as our model is concerned — by the stroke sequence (with field designations) comprising its letters. A word is represented by the image of a mapping of a finite sequence of strokes into the set of continuous functions, the mapping being specified by concatenation and tracing rules applied in a specific order. The functions however are not necessarily continuous in their derivatives.

Only two concatenation rules are required. The first specifies stroke locations *within* a letter. The rule prescribes that two consecutive strokes are concatenated by identifying the abscissa of the neighborhood containing the terminal node of the first stroke with that of the initial node of the second stroke. The second rule states that across a letter boundary, the leftmost node of the stroke following the boundary is placed so as to be to the right of the rightmost node of the penultimate stroke before the letter boundary.[5] The simple cursive strokes of the word "globe" are shown in Fig. 5.2 and their concatenation in Fig. 5.3.

These concatenation rules are not sufficient to specify all sequences of English letters unambiguously. Ambiguities of this character, however, do not represent any failure of the theory. The ambiguities are intrinsic to the writing system, even in careful handwriting. So, for example, the script sequence in "bi" can be read as "lr." The number of ambiguities of strokes increases rapidly when the writing is not done

[3] The *line* width is one of the physical dimensions. However, it is intuitively obvious that line width is irrelevant to the description of the process, although it may play an important aesthetic role, as it does in italic script.

[4] The smallest linguistically meaningful unit in handwriting that contains more than one stroke is the letter. There is no letter consisting of a single stroke. However, as the case mentioned shows, the context is too small to assign an unambiguous field to a two-stroke letter *standing by itself.* It is clear that a much more useful unit therefore is the word.

[5] Note that the leftmost node is not necessarily the initial node. Further, we have no cogent explanation for the necessity for defining the concatenation rules in terms of the next-to-last stroke before the boundary; however, it clearly indicates that serious contextual influences extend beyond "nearest neighbor" strokes.

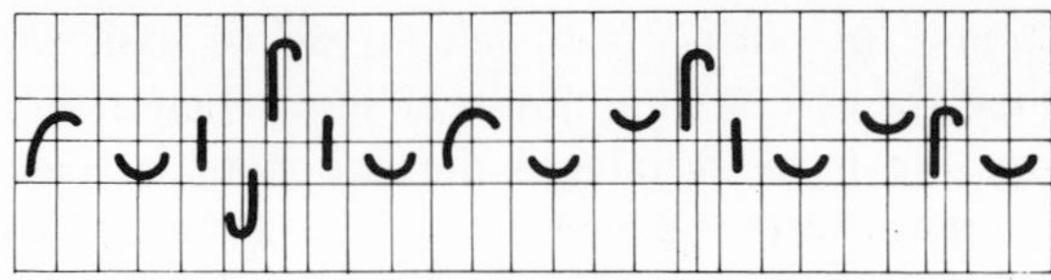

**Fig. 5.2** Sequence of strokes corresponding to the English word "globe."

carefully, even though the word can still be read. Such ambiguities are common in most other cursive languages. In each case the ambiguities appear to be resolved by certain adventitious marks. These conventions in English include the dots on "i" and "j," the cross on the "t," and certain stylistic flourishes and marks in majuscules.

**Fig. 5.3** Stroke sequence of Fig. 5.2 after application of the concatenation rules.

So far in the analysis, the strokes have been regarded as abstract objects. We apply to the strokes certain *tracing rules* that serve to produce a handwritten word.

Tracing rule 1a. The strokes are traced in the order in which they appear in the sequential representation of the word.

Tracing rule 1b. Each stroke is traced from the initial node with the direction and sense provided by the stroke description.

The last step to describe is the manner in which strokes are joined.

Tracing rule 2. The terminal node of the first of two consecutive strokes is joined to the initial node of the following stroke.

Tracing rule 3a. If these two nodes are in a single neighborhood, they are to be identified as the same point.

Tracing rule 3b. If the nodes are in different neighborhoods and the sense of rotation is the same for both strokes, the nodes are joined in a smooth curve.

Tracing rule 3c. If the nodes are in different neighborhoods and the senses of rotation are different, a curve with a single point of inflection is to connect the two strokes.

In English, there is one important convention that deviates from these rules; ligatures (the connection between letters) must not cross hooks,[6]

[6] This convention is equivalent to prescribing two points of inflection between sequential strokes when a letter such as "a" is preceded by another letter with a counterclockwise final stroke such as in "ea."

for example *ea*." Except for this limitation, ligatures are the shortest curves joining two strokes consistent with the rules just given.[7]

The script generated by these rules is an idealized norm. Obviously individual scripts deviate from this norm. However, the description for writing given in these rules provides too few constraints on the curves that may be generated by following these rules. The actual curves that practiced writers draw are quite different from, say, the labored script of an illiterate or a child in the early years of his training, even though the rules will include these types of production as well as well-practiced script. The second task, therefore, is to provide a characterization of the curves that experienced human writers produce.

## Physical Characterization of Scripts

Very little attention has been paid to the dynamics of the trajectory — in space and time — that the point of the pen traces out as it moves across the paper under the guidance of a skillful writer. Early analysis was attempted using measurements taken from motion picture frames but they proved to be inadequate for a detailed characterization of the process. Recently a number of workers have investigated the motion of a pencil point during writing as a function of time. We are not now concerned with the details of these studies. It is sufficient to point out here that the several models, although different in form, all provide fits to handwritten words that are quite good.

Three models will be briefly considered here; Model I (Eden, 1962), Model II (Mermelstein and Eden, 1964), and Model III (Van der Gon, Thuring and Strackee, 1962; MacDonald, 1964). All three models assume that the motion of the pen is controlled by a pair of orthogonal forces, as if one pair of muscles controls the vertical displacement and another the horizontal.

Model I is the simplest of the three in the sense that it requires the fewest parameters. Its basic equation may be written as

$$\left.\begin{aligned} \dot{x}(t) &= \alpha \sin\left[\omega_x(t - t_0) + \phi\right] + \gamma \\ \dot{y}(t) &= \beta \sin \omega_y(t - t_0) \end{aligned}\right\} \qquad t_0 < t \leq t_2.$$

Subject to the constraint

$$t_2 - t_0 = \frac{\pi}{\omega_y}.$$

Figure 5.4 illustrates the trajectories generated by the equation.

[7] It is worth noting that the rapid writer violates this convention; that is, rule 3b is followed, for example, "*ea*." However, for the letters "*ec*" it is clearly improper to write "*ee*."

Model II is an extension of Model I and allows for the fact that velocity is not symmetric in vector rotations of 180 degrees. Two ranges

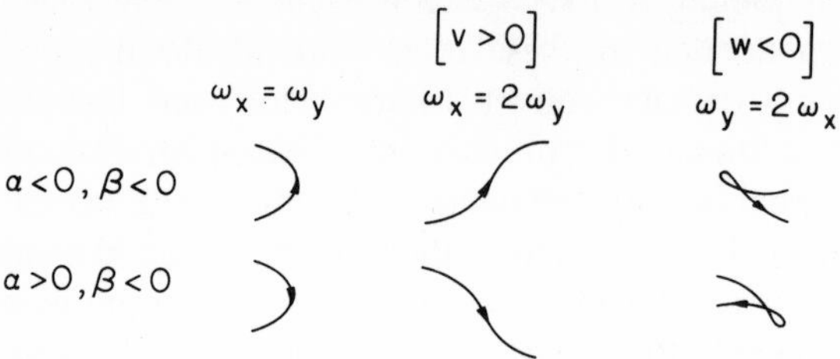


**Fig. 5.4** A representation of the primitive strokes in the simplest form of the model for continuous handwriting generation.

are chosen instead of one, so that the $x$-velocity amplitude, the frequency and the phase shift between $x$ and $y$ velocities, are allowed to take on different values over the two ranges. The equations are

$$\begin{aligned} \dot{x}(t) &= \alpha_1 \sin[\omega_1(t - t_0) + \phi_1] + \gamma, && t_0 < t \leq t_1, \\ &= \alpha_2 \sin[\omega_2(t_2 - t) + \phi_2] + \gamma, && t_1 < t \leq t_2, \\ \dot{y}(t) &= \beta \sin[\omega_1(t - t_0)], && t_0 < t \leq t_1, \\ &= \beta \sin[\omega_2(t_2 - t)], && t_1 < t \leq t_2. \end{aligned}$$

The additional constraints for this model are

$$\omega_2 = \frac{\pi}{2}(t_2 - t_1),$$

$$\omega_1 = \frac{\pi}{2}(t_1 - t_0),$$

$$\alpha_1 \cos\phi_1 = \alpha_2 \cos\phi_2 \quad \text{(ensures continuity at } t = t_1\text{)},$$

$$\omega_1\alpha_1 \sin\phi_1 = \omega_2\alpha_2 \sin\phi_2 \quad \text{(ensures continuous derivative at } t = t_1\text{)}.$$

Model III is based on a description of force rather than velocity. A force applied in the $x$ or $y$ direction rises linearly from rest to some specific value, maintains this value for some interval, and then falls linearly back to zero. The slopes of the initial and final segments, corresponding to the rate of change of muscular force per unit time, are considered invariant as a first approximation. Since frictional forces are negligible, the displacement can be assumed to be proportional to the second integral of the forces.

Mermelstein compared the three models by fitting handwritten words to them. The criterion of deviation from perfect fit was the ratio of least root-mean-square difference between the analytic curve and the handwritten word (experimental function), to the root-mean-square of the handwritten word. When the functions were fitted in the time domain, that is, in three dimensions, the value of the criterion of difference between the experimental specimen and the analytic approximation was between 10 and 20 per cent. Model I was the poorest of the three. However, when the fit was made in the $x,y$ plane only, that is, when time was eliminated, the difference between experiment and analytic form was barely visible to the naked eye, the value of the difference criterion being about 4–5 per cent for all three models.

It may appear surprising that a theory based on a sinusoidal description of a curve is empirically indistinguishable from one based on quadratic sections. However, it is a simple exercise in calculus to fit a parabola to a sine function from 0 to 180 degrees so that the value of the fit criterion will be less than 5 per cent. Accordingly any preference for one model over another must be justified on other grounds than the closeness of fit to the experimental functions. At this time, there is neither physiological nor psychological evidence that facilitates distinguishing between the models.

Models I and II are obviously compatible with the notions of stroke-sequence characterization discussed earlier. It is not at all clear how to provide an equivalent characterization of Model III. The model does not furnish a sequence of discrete symbols from which one might reproduce the written word. Further, note that the derivative of the function described in Model III comprises sequences of impulses which can be regarded as discrete entities. However, the timing of the pulses is critical, and the preliminary attempts we have made to quantize this variable were inadequate in furnishing unique characterizations of arbitrary letter sequences.

The kind of description that has been given for the production of handwriting is known as a generative model, that is, one in which a prescription is given that generates any specimen of the pattern class under study. It is important to point out that it is not at all the case behaviorally that the act of recognizing a pattern is necessarily one in which the observer proceeds to generate the pattern in his mind's eye, as it were. Even if in some abstract sense it is supposed that the competent observer compares aspects of sensory input to an internalized model of the possible patterns, he almost certainly does not "synthesize" the pattern in a prescribed, structured, and hierarchically ordered way.

Evidence for such a theory of human recognition of patterns (usually called "analysis-by-synthesis") is not very persuasive in handwriting, nor for that matter in any other perceptual process. Nevertheless, experience in our group and elsewhere with a variety of linguistic processes strongly suggests that a successful generative procedure can shed light on the converse task of recognition.

## Experiments on Recognition

Although a very great deal of recent work has been done on block letter recognition and on isolated cursive letters, it will not be discussed here because these tasks are much more appropriately considered as similar to printed character recognition. Curiously enough, very little research has been done on the recognition of cursive writing. Frischkopf and Harmon (1961) have reported on two approaches to cursive writing recognition. Aside from these reports and the experiments to be described here, I am aware of no other published work on this problem.

Two recognition experiments, quite different in method of attack but each depending on a stroke analysis and the generative procedures, already discussed are worth describing in some detail. Both methods can be said to have attained respectable performance levels in recognizing English script words. They represent different strategies for recognition, although the common elements in these methods are in large measure a consequence of the work on script generation discussed previously.

### *Earnest*

Earnest (1963) used the formal model given by Eden and Halle (1961) to derive a set of criteria or properties by which to identify strokes or stroke classes.

One of the most popular methods for pattern recognition research might be called the "property list" procedure. Each element of the universe of objects to be classified is described in terms of a set of properties chosen by the investigator either explicitly or implicitly. Some properties, such as height, width, or ratios for various dimensions, may be assigned numerical values. Other properties may be described either by their presence or absence, for example, intersections and discontinuities. In any case, the properties serve as the basis for making the classification decisions. They are chosen largely *ad hoc* and are tested and retained or discarded depending on performance. While intuition certainly entered into Earnest's choices, the criteria he chose may be regarded as derived properties of the formal theory, that is, properties that would always succeed with handwriting formed "correctly."

The first property Earnest identified was field location.[8] Our usage of the word "field" has already been discussed. The computational prob-

[8] The handwriting was introduced into the computer by requiring the subject to write on the face of a cathode-ray tube with a "light pen." The time information was not saved, and the handwritten specimen was stored as a matrix of zeros and ones. The "line thickness" was in general several matrix elements in extent.

lem is to assign the boundaries of each field on a particular handwritten word using arbitrary but reasonable criteria. The assignment is made by examining some property of the word as a whole. Bounding was accomplished by counting the intersections of the handwritten word with a line parallel to the horizontal for all relevant values of the ordinate. These counts furnish the basis for a histogram that will exhibit large changes in slope at the field boundaries. In principle, this procedure should work well. (Uneven writing or certain words such as "tilt" or "gypsy," which have many extensions into the upper or the lower fields, may be incorrectly bounded however. Nonetheless, the field bounds can be adequately set for most words.) When this test is correctly performed, certain strokes, that is, those in either the upper or lower field, may be coded by a symbol. Earnest tagged these "L" and "J," respectively.

Since the "t" in English is indistinguishable in all but the most meticulous scripts from the comparable stroke in "k," "d," "h," "f," and so on, Earnest applied a test to detect a "horizontal" line in the upper field which intersected an "L." Such a stroke was labeled "T."

The next criterion tested for was "boundedness" in the middle field. It is obvious that the letter "e" has a loop in the middle field. In reasonably careful handwriting the "a," "o," and "s." have also. In poor hands these may be open; for that matter, the "e" may be written as an "i." All such stroke constellations are labeled "O." [9]

The fifth criterion attempts to locate strokes in the middle field which are clockwise in sense. In typical English scripts these strokes will be found in the letters "h," "k," "m," "n," "p," "r," "s," "v," "x," "y," "z." However, the clockwise stroke in "p" and "s" and possibly "k" will already have been labeled "O." The program introduces a horizontal midline into the middle field and applies the "boundedness" test between the midline and the upper portion of the handwritten word. For reasonably well-written words the letters listed above would supply a stroke constellation to satisfy this criterion and it would then carry the label "R."

Earnest's program examined only those regions that had not already been labeled. This characteristic enabled him to apply a final test which identified any remaining continuous segment as an "I" if its highest node was near the top of the middle field and its lower point was near the bottom of the middle field and to the right of the highest point.

In this way a code word in six distinct symbols was generated for any handwritten specimen. The order of the code symbols was simply the order in which the specific symbol criterion was located in the

[9] Obviously, the stroke sequences in "e," "a," "o," and "s" are quite distinct, but they share this property of permissive boundedness.

specimen. In some cases there is an unavoidable ambiguity. For example, the minuscule "f" might be coded "LJ" or "JL."

At the same time, twenty-six code lists were prepared, one for each English letter. Thus, for example, under the heading "a" there might be the entries *II, O, OI;* under the heading "d" there might be the entries OL, IL. The leftmost symbols of the code word can be compared with the letter dictionaries for permissible starting letters. The procedure continues from left to right until the code word is identified as an English word or as several.[10]

At first, it seems surprising that a six letter code word can be used to identify words in a twenty-six letter code. Even when we account for the fact that each English letter takes an average of 1.5 symbols in this code, we have about 3.5 bits per code symbol compared with about 4.5 for normal English. However, the redundancy of English is so great that the code designed by Earnest will identify a word uniquely in a surprisingly high number of cases.[11]

Of course the method fails to provide uniqueness, especially with short words. What is particularly disconcerting about the errors is that they do not appear to be the ones humans would make. For example, "toll," "tell," and "tall" are ambiguous, as are "slide" and "elide," and "also," "else," and "eke."[12] It is possible to resolve many of these ambiguities by devising new criteria to partition the troublesome "o," "a," "e," and "s" class. However, after a while the marginal benefit derived from additional tests becomes small and the elegance of a small symbol-set is lost.

There is an obvious interplay between the entries in the word dictionaries and the number of word ambiguities the program will produce. If the entries in the "a" dictionary were simply restricted to O, then an "a" written without a closure at the upper right would be consistently misidentified. On the other hand, if II is included in this list, then any occurrence of "u" could also be interpreted as an "a."

Earnest's recognition scheme was in very large measure built on the results of the generative description but did not itself attempt to generate a replica of the handwritten specimen. Mermelstein in his thesis (1964) and elsewhere (1963; Mermelstein and Eden, 1964) described an ex-

[10] The computer used was Lincoln Laboratory's TX-2, a very large and rapid device constructed in 1958 (65,000 36-bit words in the principal core memory; a cycle time of about 5 microseconds). The identification time depended primarily on the word length, the average time being about 15 seconds for all machine operations.

[11] Earnest used a glossary of about 10,000 English words.

[12] However, the usefulness of such approaches can be illustrated by the illuminating sidelights they cast. Note that if one writes "else" and "eke" without taking special care, the specimens look quite similar.

periment to investigate whether the generative model could be used explicitly as the basis for analysis by synthesis.[13] Since his methods and results are well documented in the publications cited, only a brief description will be given here.

### *Mermelstein*

The critical feature of Mermelstein's approach was taking instances of strokes as points in a continuous space whose dimensions corresponded to the parameters of Model II (or Model I), for most strokes executed in the same positions within a given letter or between two letters exhibit some clustering in this space.[14] The fact that the strokes cluster as one would intuitively expect them to, can serve as the basis for partitioning the stroke space into a number of stroke classes sufficient to achieve identification of the word.

Partitioning the stroke space is not an easy task. If it is assumed that each stroke is independent of the others in a sequence, that is, is not being influenced by neighboring strokes, the problem becomes equivalent to one that has been considered extensively in classification theory, but classification theory is not our main interest here. Suffice it to say that there are statistical procedures that prescribe how to partition a set of points in some finite dimensional space so that a particular statistic of the partitioned subsets is optimized. If multivariate probability distributions of the parameters are available for each stroke class, then an optimal assignment rule exists. But the distributions are not available, and estimates of the required statistics would necessitate an unacceptably large amount of sampling. Mermelstein assumed the strokes to have multivariate normal distributions. In order to save computing time, he also assumed that the intrastroke parameters were statistically independent.[15] He first identified the stroke class of highest likelihood for

[13] There is a certain terminological confusion in the linguistic literature — particularly in that portion dealing with speech — which can perhaps be avoided here. By analogy to Halle and Stevens (1962) on speech, the method employed by Mermelstein should be called "analysis-by-synthesis." Thus, recognition using analysis-by-synthesis requires a generative description, but generative descriptions do not prescribe any class of recognition procedures.

[14] Unlike Earnest, who had no time information, Mermelstein made explicit use of the time course of writing. This might be called recognition of cursive writing-in-progress. It is a different kind of recognition task from, and possibly a little easier than, recognition in two dimensions only. The "line" was stored as a set of points and each point was identified by the three coordinates $x$, $y$, and $t$.

[15] Clearly, there are no theoretical justifications for such assumptions. The practical fact remains, however, that simplifying assumptions must nonetheless be made, for otherwise further study of problems of this character becomes impossible. It is a melancholy consideration that one can never place much reliance on the "statistical verification" of a classification scheme.

each stroke in the specimen. Next, the strokes were taken in pairs proceeding from left to right. There are very many interstroke constraints in English writing which can be used to help identify the letter sequence in the specimen word. These operations are equivalent to tracing out the branches of a tree.

In this problem, as in others that involve tree search, the explosive rapidity with which the number of paths increases with depth in the tree requires that certain *ad hoc* rules be used to delimit the tree search.

Mermelstein found that with his methods the probability of correct recognition of a single stroke independent of contextual constraints was less than 65 per cent. Obviously, the likelihood is rather high that at least one stroke in a word will be misidentified. To overcome this difficulty, Mermelstein chose a small set of stroke classes for each stroke (those with likelihoods above a certain threshold) and repeated the process of tree search for permissible letter sequences for each possible stroke sequence whose strokes exceeded this likelihood threshold.

In this way he obtained a set of letter sequences each of which was permissible in that it exhausted the stroke sequence without violating some interstroke constraint. The criterion for each permissible letter sequence was the product of the likelihoods of the assigned stroke classes for the stroke sequence of elements of a particular word. Finally, the words were ordered by this likelihood criterion.

An even more powerful set of constraints was also employed. As in the Earnest experiment, a dictionary was used.[16] Mermelstein points out that the power of this set of constraints is illustrated by the observation that in the word list used, only 32 per cent of all possible English letter pairs actually occurs as the first and second letters of any word. Since the letter sequence was generated from the stroke sequences, the letter sequence was checked against the dictionary to determine whether or not it was the initial subsequence of some English word.

Mermelstein performed two series of experiments. In the first, the vocabulary was restricted to 12 words chosen for their ambiguity. In the second, the full dictionary was used.

In series A, twelve four-letter words, each beginning with "f" and ending with "l" were written by four subjects. Another set, used for identification, comprised 59 words, the 12 sample words, and a group of other possible ambiguous ones.[17] Stroke statistics were compiled from

[16] In fact, the dictionary was identical in both experiments, being the set of words, taken from the Thorndike-Lorge word list, whose frequency of occurrence is greater than two instances per million text words.

[17] This particular series was designed to minimize contextual constraints, so that misidentification of a particular stroke more frequently led to an incorrect word than would be expected with an unselected word list.

all specimens, and on the basis of the statistics, the program was used to identify the same specimens. The results are shown in Table 5.1.

Certain conclusions are quite striking: (1) The prediction made by Eden and Halle (1961) that only downstrokes carry information is verified. (2) The five-parameter set is not as accurate as the eleven-parameter set in providing correct recognition. (3) A partitioning of the parameter space based on one set of subjects is more accurate when it is tested on a set of specimens written by the same subjects than when it is tested on specimens from other subjects.

**Table 5.1** Results of Recognition Experiments — Experimental Series A

| *Experiment Number* | *Learning Set* | *Test Set* | *Strokes Used for Recognition* | *Percentage Recognized* |
|---|---|---|---|---|
| 1A | all strokes | all strokes | all strokes | 91 |
| 1B | all downstrokes | all downstrokes | all downstrokes | 91 |
| 1C | all downstrokes | all downstrokes | all downstrokes 5 parameters only | 68 |
| 2A | 2 subjects | other 2 subjects | all strokes | 69 |
| 2B | 2 subjects | other 2 subjects | all downstrokes | 78 |
| 2C | 2 subjects | sequence from different subject | all downstrokes | 78 |
| 3 | 50 samples—all subjects and words | 50 different samples — all subjects and words | all downstrokes | 83 |

In experimental series B, words were again written by four subjects. Of the total of 254 samples, 249 were successfully segmented into stroke sequences. In the other five cases, as a result of the smoothing of the normal direction changes in certain contexts under conditions of rapid writing, the last upstroke-downstroke pair of a letter and the following ligature were found to be inseparable by the segmentation algorithm used, as illustrated by writing on instead of on. In two other cases the words, as segmented by the program, were not recognizable with the aid of downstrokes alone because the last downstroke of the last letter of the word was not explicitly executed, for example row instead of row.

Recognition was attempted on the remaining 247 words by using a stroke representation of the letters based on downstrokes only and compiled from the strokes constituting those words. The stroke partition used consisted of 22 downstroke categories; one of these corresponded to downstrokes found at the beginning and end of words which did not form part of the first or last letter, and was therefore assigned to the null letter. The stroke classification was carried out by using all 12 computed parameters and treating them as if they were independent. Eighty per cent of the words on which recognition was attempted were correctly identified. Of the 49 samples incorrectly identified, 14 had the correct word selected as the second choice, 7 as choices lower than the second, and 26 did not give the correct word as one of the 20 possible choices in the threshold range. Recognition of 2 samples had to be terminated when no result was obtained after 20 minutes of processing.

The experimental strategy for word recognition, namely, repeated attempts with successively lower stroke-likelihood thresholds, does not eliminate the possibility that if some lower initial threshold setting were used, a previously incorrect decision might be corrected or a correct decision upset. In order to observe the frequency of this phenomenon, 12 word samples for which the correct word was not selected initially were reprocessed by using a value for the initial threshold setting that permitted consideration of strokes having likelihoods down to half the previous minimum likelihood. Six of these words were now correctly selected as first choices in the recognition output. The reason for this improvement in performance is that in certain cases the correct category may lie just beyond the likelihood threshold value and therefore be missed, while all of the other strokes are correctly recognized. We may, of course, process samples with the higher threshold value initially, but this frequently results in an undesirable increase in the required processing time for word recognition.

Next, the mean and variance of the parametric values were computed for each subject, and recognition was attempted on the previously incorrectly recognized samples by using the parameters derived in each case from the test subject's own handwriting. Forty-three of the previous 49 errors were now recognized correctly. Since 40 of the 198 samples correctly recognized previously were correctly recognized now as well, and none was misrecognized, we may assume that all of the 198 samples would have been correctly recognized, thereby resulting in a subject-dependent recognition rate of 98 per cent. Time requirements for recognition in this experiment fell to an average of 9 seconds on the IBM 7094 computer, as compared to 30 seconds for the subject-independent recognition.

One may gain insight into the magnitude of the contribution made by contextual information from the fact that in the set of strokes, when considered individually in the subject-independent experiment, the calculated most likely category was in fact the correct category in only 58 per cent of the cases. Hence, the probability that none of a sequence of say ten strokes was in error was $(0.58)^{10}$ or 0.0043.

These studies of handwriting recognition suggest certain conclusions. The formal model seems adequate not only for handwriting production but also (although with certain reservations) for handwriting recognition. A properly chosen set of features or properties provides a basis for fairly accurate recognition of words. The analysis-by-synthesis approach leads to even better results, most strikingly because it can learn to recognize the idiosyncrasies of a particular subject's hand. It improves its performance much as does a human when reading a text written by a stranger.

However, the results to date are not as good as human performance with the same samples. In addition, one should note that Mermelstein depended upon time information. It would appear to be a somewhat more complicated problem to attempt analysis-by-synthesis without time information. In truth, it is not difficult to provide excellent curve-fitting for the $x$-$y$ plane presentation without time information but with a knowledge of the sequence of strokes based on the experimenter's experience with the language. Attempts have been made to provide curve-following programs that will reconstruct the time ordering of strokes. To date the attempts have not been very successful. Indeed one may doubt whether even a human observer with no knowledge of Roman script could correctly specify the sequence of strokes in a poorly written "p" or "k" or "q."

While there are several ways in which the recognition procedures may be improved, there seem to be intrinsic limitations to machine recognition. In the last analysis there are always ambiguities in reading script which cannot be resolved even by the person who wrote the specimen, if they are presented to him as unrelated words, particularly if some days have elapsed since he wrote them. One would not expect a computer to resolve such ambiguities. A more significant difference from human performance is that the machine context in the experiments previously discussed is limited to a word. One can anticipate programs which might provide certain syntactic constraints for text that represents a natural-language word sequence, but it is not known how to provide to the computer the linguistic constraints that are available to a human when, for example, he reads a letter written in a difficult script. He can reconstruct it with the help of his knowledge of the grammar of the language, the meaning of the text he has been able to read, the character of the subject matter, and, perhaps, the state of mind of the writer. There is now, alas, no hint of how to embody such knowledge of the world and its ways in the computer.

## Acknowledgment

This work was supported principally by the National Institutes of Health (Grant 1 PO1 GM-14940-01), and in part by the Joint Services Electronics Program (Contract DA 28-043-AMC-02536(E)).

## References

Earnest, L. D. Machine recognition of cursive writing. In C. M. Poplewell (Editor), *Information Processing, Proceedings of the IFIP Congress, 1962*. Amsterdam: North Holland Publishing Co., 1963. Pp. 462–466.

Eden, M. Handwriting and pattern recognition. *IRE Trans. on Information Theory,* IT–8, 1962, 160–166.

Eden, M. On the formalization of handwriting. *Proc. Symposia in Applied Mathematics,* 1961, *12,* 83–88.

Eden, M., and M. Halle. The characterization of cursive writing. In C. Cherry (Editor), *Proceedings of the 4th London Symposium on Information Theory*. London: Butterworth, 1961. Pp. 287–299.

Eden, M., and P. Mermelstein. Models for the dynamics of handwriting generation. In *Proc. 16th Ann. Conference Engr. Med. Biol.,* 1963, 12–13.

Fluckinger, F. A., C. A. Tripp, and G. H. Weinberg. A review of experimental research in graphology, 1933–1960. *Perception and Motor Skills,* 1961, *12,* 67–90.

Freeman, F. N. The handwriting movement, a study of the motor factors of excellence in penmanship. *Supplementary Educational Monographs,* 1918. Vol. 2, No. 3.

Frishkopf, L. S., and L. D. Harmon. Machine reading of cursive script. In C. Cherry (Editor), *Proceedings of the 4th London Symposium on Information Theory*. London: Butterworth, 1961. Pp. 287–299.

Halle, M., and K. Stevens. Speech recognition: A model and a program for research. *IRE Trans. on Information Theory,* IT–8, 1962, 155–159.

Helmig, R. G. Generation of time sequence information from non-time-sequential handwritten data points. S.B. Thesis, Department of Electrical Engineering, M.I.T., 1962.

MacDonald, J. S. Experimental studies of handwriting signals. Sc.D. Thesis, Department of Electrical Engineering, M.I.T., 1964.

Mermelstein, P. Computer recognition of connected handwritten words. Sc.D. Thesis, Department of Electrical Engineering, M.I.T., 1964.

Mermelstein, P., and M. Eden. Experiments on computer recognition of connected handwritten words. *Information and Control,* 1964, *7,* 255–270.

Mermelstein, P. Study of the handwriting movement. Quart. Prog. Rep. No. 69, Res. Lab. Electronics, M.I.T., April 15, 1963, pp. 229–232.

Tripp, C. A., F. A. Fluckinger, and G. H. Weinberg. Measurement of handwriting variables. *Perception and Motor Skills,* 1957, *7,* 279–294.

Van der Gon, J. M. D., J. Ph. Thuring, and J. Strackee. A handwriting simulator. *Phys. Med. Biol.,* 1962, *6,* 407–414.

*How very difficult it can be to get a machine to perform a task that skilled humans perform readily is illustrated in the next paper. Motivated to construct a machine that would make printed text easily available to the blind, the authors developed a procedure for recognizing printed characters. This procedure is to be used with an output of spelled speech in one model, and with artificially generated spoken speech in a later one. The present paper, however, describes only the front end of the system, the techniques developed for recognizing printed characters.*

*Samuel J. Mason and Jon K. Clemens are electrical engineers much concerned with developing machines to perform "interesting" tasks, especially machines that can compensate for human handicaps or impairments. Mason is a professor of electrical engineering and Associate Director of the Research Laboratory of Electronics at M.I.T. Clemens worked with Mason at M.I.T. and is now on the technical staff of RCA Princeton Research Laboratories.*

# 6. Character Recognition in an Experimental Reading Machine for the Blind

*Samuel J. Mason and Jon K. Clemens*

The design of a sensory-aid device or system for use by blind people poses general problems of pattern recognition. If the device were capable of performing sophisticated feats of pattern recognition, then communication of the abstracted information to the blind person would be relatively simple; if the device were merely a pickup or scanner, then the blind person would have to perform difficult feats of pattern recognition and abstraction upon the mass of redundant (and irrelevant) data that had been transcribed into tactile or auditory form. The best sensory aid is another human being, a reader and a guide who can perceive, interact, and report in the language of perception. We do not know how to build an artificial human being at the present state of the art. For the near future, at least, practical devices will be compromises between the sophisticated pattern recognition of human beings and the unselective performance of a scanning device.

This chapter is concerned with details of automatic character recognition in an experimental reading-machine system and bears only remotely upon the ultimate problem of devising sensory-aids, that is, developing or discovering an appropriate "language of meaning" for visual patterns. We do not imply a connection between human visual perception and the character-recognition process to be described. We do, however, provide an example of the artificial accomplishment of a task that is a simple one for the human visual system but nontrivial in engineering terms. Perhaps the contribution of this paper to a collection of papers under the heading of "Pattern Recognition" is that it may enhance the appreciation of the reader for the power of the human visual and cognitive system that we all tend to take so much for granted.

## The Basic Machine

The Cognitive Information Processing Group of the M.I.T. Research Laboratory of Electronics is working on experimental reading-machine systems, with the eventual aim of providing useful sensory aids for people who are blind, or blind and deaf. The present experimental system was not intended as a prototype of a practical reading aid, but rather as a real-time research facility for experimental investigation of the human information requirements and human learning capabilities upon which prototype design must be based. The experimental system development has involved, and will facilitate, continuing component research on print scanning, character recognition, and auditory and tactile displays.[1]

In this chapter, attention will be restricted to the "front end" of the system, where a printed page is scanned to acquire the raw data and these data are processed to accomplish identification of the printed characters.

A huge variety of schemes and systems for character recognition can be found in the literature (Automatic Character Recognition, 1961). The particular scheme to be described here is an example of that subclass in which automatic edge-tracing is the fundamental scanner operation (Greanias, et al., 1963). By tracing around the outer black-white edge of a printed character, we can tell something about its shape. Any scheme of character recognition based on edge-tracing is of course subject to serious disturbance when it encounters broken characters or touching characters. However, broken and touching characters are not a serious problem in most book print and magazine print, and there are, in fact, ways of preprocessing for correction of some breaks and touchings. For example, optical defocusing and proper adjustment of the black-white threshold decision level could weld a broken character, and a knowledge of typical letter widths would permit touching letters to be sliced apart at the right place. Some newsprint will require special processing, but book print and magazine print look good at this point.

More-general character-recognition schemes based on two-dimensional correlation techniques (basically template-matching) are theoretically more powerful than edge-tracing, but also much more expensive at the present state of the art. For the purposes of a reading machine for the blind, microscopic error rates and astronomical speeds are not required and relative simplicity of the character-recognition processing is highly desirable. Although we are not committed to the present scheme of character recognition, it has nevertheless permitted us to get

[1] For his doctoral thesis, Clemens demonstrated the feasibility of the character-recognition system by simulating it on a computer. The smoothing operation was one of his important contributions. Mason was leader of the research group and advisor on Clemens' thesis. Professors F. F. Lee and D. E. Troxel were members of the research group and coleaders of the project that developed the present experimental system, operating in real time. Professor Murray Eden was also instrumental in developing the system.

a real-time experimental system into operation and the system is performing quite well enough for the man-machine studies that we want to carry out.

## The Scanner

The scanner consists of a cathode-ray tube, together with a digital-deflection system. Upon reception of two binary words, the scanner positions a bright spot at the corresponding *xy* coordinates on the face of the tube. A lens images this bright spot upon the surface of the printed matter to be scanned, and a pair of photomultiplier tubes measure the reflected light and permit a threshold decision between "black" and "white" at the designated point on the page of printing. The field of the scanner is approximately ¼-inch high and ½-inch wide. A mechanical carriage, also under the control of digital input signals, moves the printed material to locate the scanner field in any desired neighborhood of the printed page. Within its field, the scanner can interrogate neighboring points on the printed page lying on a square grid, with a point-to-point spacing of approximately 0.002 inch. For the book print with which we have been working, this resolution corresponds to several dozen grid points per letter height. Such resolution is relatively high in comparison with most character recognizers that have been proposed or built. The high resolution permits the edge-tracing routine to find its way safely along a letter boundary that lies quite close to the boundary of another letter. Our philosophy is to employ high resolution at the outset, for raw data acquisition, after which much of the data may be safely discarded in subsequent smoothing and recoding operations.

## Character Acquisition

The scanner is positioned near the beginning of a line of print by manual control, after which an automatic "line-finding" mode of operation is initiated. For line-finding, the scanner moves to the right along a horizontal line for a distance of several letter widths, and the number of black points along that line is stored. By repeating the process at each of a succession of different vertical positions, the system obtains a "horizontal histogram" for that portion of that line of print. As shown in Fig. 6.1, the histogram, or black-density function, contains sharp level changes indicative of the principal vertical coordinates of the type font, which are designated A, B, C, D in the figure. A threshold decision on the histogram, such as the slice X — X in this figure, dependably locates vertical coordinates B and C, after which coordinates A and D can be computed, or, alternatively, obtained from another threshold decision on the histogram. The existence of a fully capitalized word or two would throw an ambiguity into the line-finding procedure, because it would tend to locate lines B and C at the bottom and top of

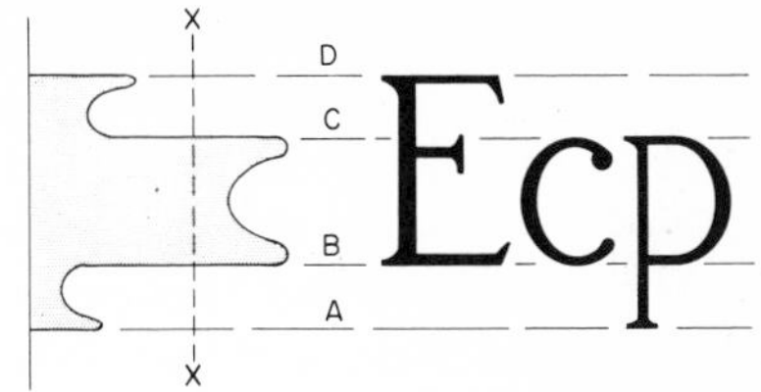


**Fig. 6.1** Line finding.

the capital letters, but a human user of the system presumably could recognize the difficulty and correctly assign lines B and D. For the usual flow of book print, the line-finding works quite dependably without ambiguity.

Once the zone lines are located, the program control shifts to character acquisition, in which mode of operation the scanner searches for the leftmost extremity of the first letter. The acquisition scan consists of successive interrogation of points along a vertical line segment lying between two of the previously determined horizontal zone lines. If no black is encountered, the vertical line shifts to the right and the process repeats until black is located.

Most operations are under the program control of a small general-purpose digital computer, but the edge-tracing procedure next to be described and some other basic operations are under the control of a small special-purpose digital system that we have built for the specific purpose of relieving the data-transfer burden on the computer.

## Edge-Tracing

The example shown in Fig. 6.2 illustrates the basic edge-tracing algorithm. Very simply, the scanner proceeds by moving from one grid point to a neighboring grid point, turning right after it encounters white and turning left when it encounters black. The succession of movements indicated by arrows 1 through 16 in Fig. 6.2 follows the turn rule and accomplishes the identification of black "edge points" A through F. The process continues until the entire outer black-white boundary of the printed character has been traced and terminates when the captive scan returns to the original starting point or within some threshold distance of that starting point. The coordinates of the black edge points are transmitted to the computer in preparation for the next stage of processing.

Figure 6.2 is a much expanded picture. When the edge points are viewed in the context of the entire letter, they appear visually as a curve that is a good approximation to the outer black-white boundary of the printed character.

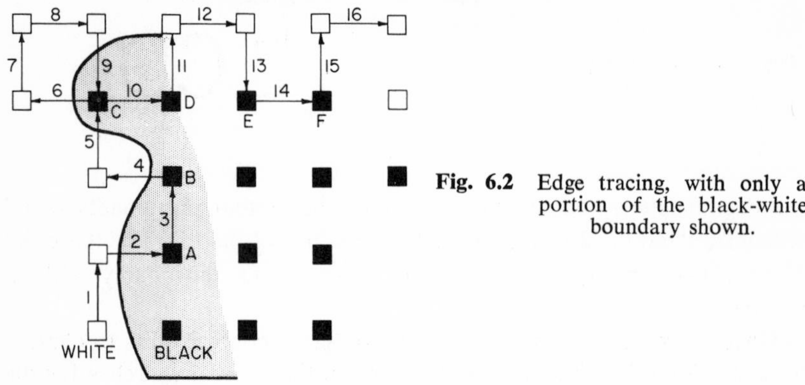


**Fig. 6.2** Edge tracing, with only a portion of the black-white boundary shown.

In Fig. 6.2, the succession of steps 6, 7, 8, and 9 causes the scanner to return to point C for a second interrogation. Between the two interrogations of point C, it is entirely possible that mechanical jitter, optical shimmer, or other noise in the system may cause the black-white boundary to shift in such a way that point C will be detected as a white point the second time that it is interrogated. In that event, the scanner would hang up in a square loop consisting of cyclic repetition of steps 6, 7, 8, and 9. In order to avoid this practical difficulty, the edge-tracing algorithm has been augmented by the additional rule that three successive right turns must be followed by a left turn, and three successive left turns must be followed by a right turn, and this rule is substituted for the black-white interrogation that would otherwise take place. This particular anti-jitter algorithm yields entirely satisfactory performance in practice.

## Smoothing

As the computer receives the numerical coordinates of the successive edge points, it proceeds to smooth the data in the following way. Let $x_k$ and $y_k$ be the horizontal and vertical coordinates, respectively, of the $k$th edge point. Now let $\overline{X}_k$ and $\overline{Y}_k$ stand for the "smoothed" coordinate values into which the original coordinates will be transformed. Let $A$ be the value of a preassigned threshold parameter. Let us start with

$\bar{X}_1$ and $\bar{Y}_1$ set equal, respectively, to $x_1$ and $y_1$. The smoothing process then proceeds through successively larger values of the subscript $k$, according to the recursion rules or algorithm given in Table 1. This algorithm is the digital equivalent of the familiar analogue mechanical

**Table 6.1** The Smoothing Algorithm.

| IF | THEN |
|---|---|
| $\bar{Y}_k < y_{k+1} - A$ | $\bar{Y}_{k+1} = y_{k+1} - A$ |
| $y_{k+1} - A \leq \bar{Y}_k \leq y_{k+1} + A$ | $\bar{Y}_{k+1} = \bar{Y}_k$ |
| $y_{k+1} + A < \bar{Y}_k$ | $\bar{Y}_{k+1} = y_{k+1} + A$ |

process known as gear backlash. Table 6.1 applies to vertical coordinates of the edge points. Exactly the same algorithm applies to the smoothing of the successive horizontal coordinates $x_k$ to obtain the smoothed values $\bar{X}_k$.

Figure 6.3 illustrates the way in which the smoothing process eliminates reversals of small amplitude, thereby retaining only the principal

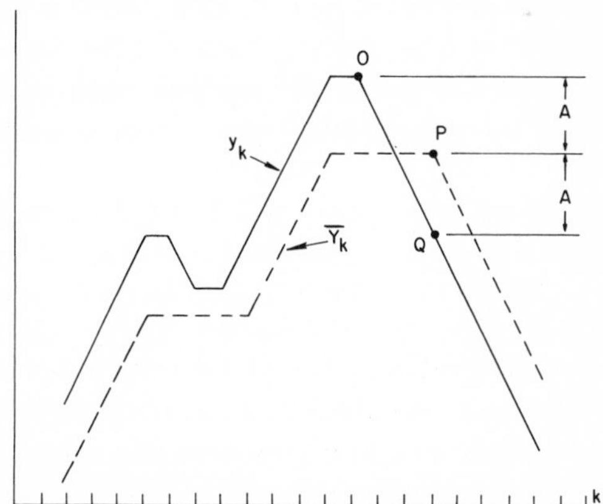


**Fig. 6.3** "Backlash" smoothing.

features of the shape of the character that has been traced. Thus we are able to identify principal extrema, such as point O, as those extrema which are followed by a reversal of direction that persists for at least a distance $2A$. Only such a reversal of direction of motion will produce an accompanying reversal in the smoothed coordinate sequence, as at point $P$ in Fig. 6.3. In practice, we have found that a value of $A$ approximately equal to one-eighth of a typical letter height produces helpful smoothing and at the same time retains sufficient information to permit character recognition. The "smoothing threshold" should be thought of as $2A$, rather than $A$, because $2A$ is the amount of reversal of the original coordinate sequence required in order to produce identification of an extremum.

The horizontal and vertical coordinates of each extremum so identified are stored for use in the next step of processing. Incidentally, we might choose to store the coordinate of any one of the three points O, P, or Q in Fig. 6.3, together with the corresponding horizontal coordinate. The system is presently operating on the basis of storage of Q-type coordinates.

## Code Generation

Figure 6.4 shows the set of horizontal and vertical extrema that might be identified upon tracing the letter *S*. If we agree to start at the lower left horizontal extremum, then a clockwise tracing of the character will produce the sequence 1 0 0 1 1 0 1 0 0 1 1 0. Vertical and hori-

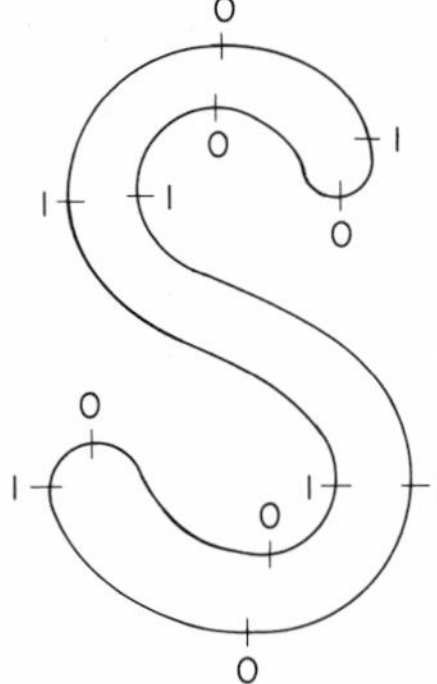

**Fig. 6.4** Vertical and horizontal extrema on the letter S.

zontal extrema are designated by 0 and 1, respectively. If we start at a left-horizontal extremum and then trace in a clockwise direction, the next event must be either a vertical maximum or a horizontal maximum. Similarly, after a vertical maximum, the next event must be either a vertical minimum or a horizontal maximum. In short, each succeeding event is one of only two possibilities, so that a one-bit designation of each event, as in Fig. 6.4, contains all of the qualitative information about the succession of extrema.

The binary word (the succession of ones and zeros) describing the succession of extrema is called the code word. To the code word is appended a coordinate word, consisting of crude information about the spatial locations at which the extrema occurred. In particular, the rectangle circumscribing the printed character may be divided into four quadrants, in general not equal in area, whereupon two bits of information are sufficient to locate each of the extrema in one of the quadrants. A few additional bits of information are then appended to provide information on whether or not the character extends below zone line B or above zone line C, on the basis of two spatial thresholds, one lying somewhere between zone lines C and D and the other somewhere between zone lines A and B in Fig. 6.1. Finally two additional bits are attached to indicate, very roughly, the height-to-width ratio of the character. The complete binary word so assembled is called the signature of the character. In practice the space reserved for the binary signature is thirty-one bits of storage. If a generated signature is too long, the coordinate word is simply truncated to fit.

The signature, representative of the encountered character, is not unique. Because of random variations in different printings of the same letter, a number of different signatures need to be generated and stored in order to prepare for identification of a newly traced character from previously stored data. We come next to the business of "training" or "learning," a process by which the machine acquires the necessary stored information for subsequent automatic recognition.

## "Training"

In its normal mode of operation, the scanner first acquires a printed character by means of a systematic vertical raster-scan search, after which its edge-traces that character, transmits the edge-point coordinates to the computer, and awaits further instructions from the computer that tell it to begin searching for the next character on that line. Small black specks, incidentally, are automatically discarded if the (normalized) number of black points around their periphery is less than some preassigned number. The computer smoothes the coordinates, generates the signature word, and identifies the character by finding a match in a stored table of previously acquired signature words. To build up this stored table of words, we put the machine through a training process, using samples of the print that contain all of the characters. During training, the scanner is allowed to trace the same printed character many times. Because of shimmer, jitter, and other noise in the system, a set of different signature words will be generated from successive tracings of the very same printed character. Moreover, the statistical distribution of this set of different signature words appears in practice to be representative of the set generated by single tracings of each of a number of different printed appearances of the same character. On the face of it, this may perhaps suggest that the system, or the signature-generating algorithm, or both, are simply too noisy. However, such randomness results in the generation of only a few different highly probable signature words per character, on the average, and, as we shall see later, the randomness can be exploited to decrease the error rate of the operating system.

To train the machine, the experimenter locates a character and allows the scanner to trace that character again and again. Starting with a vacant memory of signature words, the machine will, of course, not recognize the character on the first tracing. If the character is not recognized, the machine is programmed to stop and await character designation by the experimenter. The experimenter then types the appropriate character on the console typewriter, the machine stores the signature word under the appropriate character label, and then proceeds to retrace the same character. If the newly generated signature is different from the one in storage, the machine again requests identification and the experimenter complies. If, however, a retrace of the character produces a previously generated signature, then the machine types the identified character on the console typewriter, and proceeds immediately to trace the character again. When the machine is able to identify the character about two hundred times in succession, the experimenter decides that the machine has learned that character, whereupon he relocates the scanner upon a new character and continues with the training. The process is actually somewhat less tedious than it may sound from the detailed description. In the final stages of training, of course, the experimenter may try out the memory thus far acquired by testing the machine on some additional randomly selected samples of the same text, supplying additional identifications when the machine fails to accomplish recognition.

As training proceeds, the stored table of signature words increases in length. Too short a table results in more frequent nonidentifications when the machine is switched to the normal mode of operation. Too long a table, that is, overtraining, may eventually lead to an increasing frequency of substitution errors, that is, identification of one letter as another, in the normal mode of operation. Fortunately there appears to be a useful range of memory size within which the rates for nonidentification and ambiguity of identification are both acceptably small.

## Character Identification

In the normal mode of operation, the machine proceeds through cyclic repetition of the three steps of character acquisition, edge tracing, and character identification. Character identification is, of course, followed by activation of the auditory or tactile output display that supplies the information to the sightless subject. In the present experimental version of the machine, the auditory display is "spelled speech" and the alternative tactile display is braille. If character identification fails, the machine is instructed to retrace that same character again, a process that will most likely generate a new signature word, different from that produced by the first tracing. By allowing as many as three such tracings of the same character, we can greatly reduce the chances of nonidentification of the character, with negligible increase in average processing time. For example, if the probability of generating a signature word that matches one in the stored list is 90 per cent, and if successive tracings of the same character are assumed to be statistically independent (which is, no doubt, only partially true), then allowance for three tracings would reduce the chance of nonidentification from 10 per cent to 0.1 per cent. In practice, the experimental system is operating on Roman book print with nonidentification and misidentification rates both at levels less than one-third of 1 per cent. A sample of the book print is shown in Fig. 6.5. For these tests the memory contained approximately

> If you look closely at his fur coat, you will see that it is very thick. It may be that he takes in his stride even the coldest weather and the iciest water because he is so well protected.
>
> Watch him jump from one rock to another or

**Fig. 6.5** A sample of the Roman bookprint.

500 stored signature words. The performance figures include identification of capital letters, lower-case letters, numerals, and all punctuation marks. The latest test that we have run covered approximately 1000 characters on one page of book print and resulted in no nonidentifications and two ambiguities. In one of the ambiguities, a broken lower-case "r" was identified as a lower-case "i." In the other, the letter-pair "fi" was identified as a lower-case "h." It should be mentioned that the line-finding procedure (Fig. 6.1) is supplemented by incremental adjustments after each letter identification so that the zone-boundary lines are continually updated and the necessity for accurate horizontal alignment of a line of print is therefore eliminated.

### Special Ambiguities

There exist certain pairs or small sets of characters that the basic algorithm finds some difficulty in separating. The performance figures cited earlier are based on the inclusion of a small number of special subroutines that go into action when one of these latent ambiguities is encountered. In particular, the four ambiguous sets are (O, D, B), (V, Y), (ff, A), (r, z). The character pair "ff" is treated as a single character, as are the other ligatures. In each of these ambiguous cases the subroutine consists simply of a black-point count along an appropriate vertical trace, to detect the presence of a vertical stroke. To separate D and B, an additional vertical trace is made through the center of the letter to detect the number of black-white transitions. Thus far, ambiguities do not appear to be a serious problem.

## Concluding Remarks

This discussion of a particular experimental character-recognition system is an interim report. There remain many parameters and features of the system to be studied, changed, or optimized. For example, the choice of vertical and horizontal axes for extremum identification is, in fact, suspect. We have already looked at the two 45-degree axes and it appears that their use will result in the generation of a smaller number of different signature words per character. Extremum identification on the basis of both vertical-horizontal and 45-degree axes also looks interesting and might permit us to acquire enough information about the shape so that the coordinate portion of the signature word could be eliminated. It also remains for us to acquire extensive statistics on a variety of other fonts of type. Although the character-recognition algorithm is inherently somewhat font-independent because of the smoothing procedure utilized, preliminary investigation shows that some additional ambiguities may be expected. However, it does not appear that an appreciably larger list of signature words would be needed to handle many additional fonts, provided such fonts are not wildly different in character shape. There is also the reasonable possibility of font identification.

Our parallel studies of error rates acceptable to human readers of braille and auditory spelled-speech indicate that error rates much higher than those we are now obtaining would be quite acceptable in practice, especially if the errors involve systematic substitutions among small subsets of characters. However, for a projected version of the system, in which the recognized characters are translated into phoneme character strings which are then used to control an artificial-speech generator, maintenance of a low error rate is highly desirable.

When this system was first planned — in vague outline a few years ago and then sharply as a crash project in January of 1966 — we decided upon the use of digital logic wherever possible, for flexibility and modularity. We did not foresee at the earlier time the subsequent phenomenal drop in the cost of commercially available integrated logic components. Some of our designs for experimental research equipment may yet turn out to be the most economical realizations of desired functions in a practical reading machine for the blind. In all aspects of the work, we hope to contribute toward the eventual existence of useful systems that will provide better access to graphical material for those people afflicted with sensory deprivation.

## Acknowledgment

This work was supported principally by the National Institutes of Health (Grant 1 PO1 GM-14940-01), and in part by the Joint Services Electronics Program (Contract DA 28-043-AMC-02536(E)).

## References

Automatic Character Recognition, a State-of-the-Art Report. National Bureau of Standards Technical Note No. 112, May 1961.

Greanias, E. C., P. F. Meagher, R. J. Norman, and P. Essinger. The recognition of handwritten numerals by contour analysis. *IBM J.*, 1963, *7*, 14–21.

*It is an astonishing experience to engage a typewriter in a dialogue, especially a therapeutic dialogue. One types in his point of view and the typewriter types back its comments, questions, or interpretations. Of course it is not just a typewriter that does this, but a typewriter tied to a computer. Getting the computer to recognize the import of what has been typed, and the typewriter to generate sensible remarks in turn, is the feat described in the next paper.*

*Of particular and profound importance in this paper is the fact that the mechanisms which generate the complex production are themselves quite simple. Behavioral scientists sometimes fail to realize that one does not need complexity to describe complexity, that complex productions may actually be the result of simple mechanisms. This paper reveals how two mechanisms, each fairly simple, can be combined to produce rather complex-looking results.*

*Joseph Weizenbaum was trained in mathematics but is now an associate professor of electrical engineering and political science at M.I.T. His current work is done largely at Project MAC, but in the past he designed the popular and powerful symmetric list processor SLIP.*

# 7. Contextual Understanding by Computers

*Joseph Weizenbaum*

We are here concerned with the recognition of semantic patterns in text.

I compose my sentences and paragraphs in the belief that I shall be understood — perhaps even that what I write here will prove persuasive. For this faith to be at all meaningful, I must hypothesize at least one reader other than myself. I speak of *understanding*. What I must suppose is clearly that my reader will recognize patterns in these sentences and, on the basis of this recognition, be able to re-create my present thought for himself. Notice the very structure of the word "RECOGNIZE," that is, know again! I also use the word "re-create." This suggests that the reader is an active participant in the two-person communication. He brings something of himself to it. His understanding is a function of that something as well as of what is written here. I shall return to this point later.

Much of the motivation for the work to be discussed here derives from attempts to program a computer to understand what a human might say to it. Lest it be misunderstood, let me state right away that the input to the computer is in the form of typewritten messages — certainly not human speech. This restriction has the effect of establishing a narrower channel of communication than that available to humans in face-to-face conversations. In the latter, many ideas that potentially aid understanding are communicated by gestures, intonations, pauses, and so on. All of these are unavailable to readers of telegrams, be they computers or humans.

Further, what I wish to report here should not be confused with what is generally called content analysis. In the present situation we are concerned with the fragments of natural language that occur in conversations, not with complete texts. Consequently, we cannot rely on the texts we are analyzing to be grammatically complete or correct. Hence, no theory that depends on parsing of what linguists term well-

The cooperation of the editors of the *COMMUNICATIONS of the ACM* in permitting the extensive quotations from the article "ELIZA," Vol. 9, No. 1, January 1966, by the present author is hereby gratefully acknowledged.

formed sentences can be of much help. We must use heuristics and other such impure devices instead.

The first program I wish to discuss is a particular member of a family of programs that has come to be known as DOCTOR. The family name of these programs is ELIZA. This name was chosen because these programs, like the Eliza of *Pygmalion* fame, can be taught to speak increasingly well. DOCTOR causes ELIZA to respond roughly as would certain psychotherapists (Rogers, 1951). ELIZA performs best when its human correspondent is initially instructed to "talk" to it, via the typewriter, of course, just as one would to a psychiatrist.

This mode of conversation was chosen because the psychiatric interview is one of the few examples of categorized dyadic natural language communication in which one of the participating pair is free to assume the pose of knowing almost nothing of the real world. If, for example, one were to tell a psychiatrist "I went for a long boat ride" and he responded "Tell me about boats," one would not assume that he knew nothing about boats, but that he had some purpose in so directing the subsequent conversation. It is important to note that this assumption is one made by the speaker. Whether it is valid or not is an altogether separate question. In any case, it has a crucial psychological utility in that it serves the speaker to maintain his sense of being heard and understood. The speaker further defends his impression (which even in real life may be illusory) by attributing to his conversational partner all sorts of background knowledge, insights, and reasoning ability. But again, these are the speaker's contribution to the conversation. They manifest themselves inferentially in the interpretations he makes of the offered responses. From the purely technical programming point of view, the psychiatric interview has the advantage that it eliminates the need of storing explicit information about the real world.

The human speaker will contribute much to clothe ELIZA's responses in vestments of plausibility. However, he will not defend his illusion (that he is being understood) against all odds. In human conversation a speaker will make certain, perhaps generous, assumptions about his conversational partner. As long as it remains possible to interpret the latter's responses to be consistent with those assumptions, the speaker's image of his partner remains undamaged. Responses that are difficult to interpret in this way may well result in an enhancement of the image of the partner, by additional rationalizations that then make more complicated interpretations of his responses reasonable. When, however, such rationalizations become too massive and even self-contradictory, the entire image may crumble and be replaced by another ("He is not, after all, as smart as I thought he was"). When the conversational partner is a machine (the distinction between machine and program is not useful here), then the idea of credibility may well be substituted for that of plausibility.

When in conversation with ELIZA, the user types in some statement or set of statements in natural language using normal punctuation and sentence structures. The user's statement is terminated by a double carriage return which serves to turn control over to ELIZA. ELIZA then analyzes the user's statement and generates some response which it types out. Control is then again with the user.

A typical conversation is the following, the machine responses appearing in capitals:

Men are all alike.

IN WHAT WAY

They're always bugging us about something or other.

CAN YOU THINK OF A SPECIFIC EXAMPLE

Well, my boyfriend made me come here.

YOUR BOYFRIEND MADE YOU COME HERE

He says I'm depressed much of the time.

I AM SORRY TO HEAR YOU ARE DEPRESSED

It's true. I am unhappy.

DO YOU THINK COMING HERE WILL HELP YOU NOT TO BE UNHAPPY

I need some help, that much seems certain.

WHAT WOULD IT MEAN TO YOU IF YOU GOT SOME HELP

Perhaps I could learn to get along with my mother.

TELL ME MORE ABOUT YOUR FAMILY

My mother takes care of me.

WHO ELSE IN YOUR FAMILY TAKES CARE OF YOU

My father.

YOUR FATHER

You are like my father in some ways.

WHAT RESEMBLANCE DO YOU SEE

You are not very aggressive but I think you don't want me to notice that.

WHAT MAKES YOU THINK I AM NOT VERY AGGRESSIVE

You don't argue with me.

WHY DO YOU THINK I DON'T ARGUE WITH YOU

You are afraid of me.

DOES IT PLEASE YOU TO BELIEVE I AM AFRAID OF YOU

My father is afraid of everybody.

WHAT ELSE COMES TO MIND WHEN YOU THINK OF YOUR FATHER

Bullies.

DOES THAT HAVE ANYTHING TO DO WITH THE FACT THAT YOUR BOYFRIEND MADE YOU COME HERE

The gross procedure of the program is quite simple; the text is read and inspected for the presence of a key word. If such a word is found, the sentence is transformed according to a rule associated with the key word, if not, a content-free remark or, under certain conditions, an earlier transformation is retrieved. The text so computed or retrieved is then printed out.

In detail, of course, the procedure sketched above is considerably more complex. Key words, for example, may have a RANK or precedence number. The procedure is sensitive to such numbers in that it will abandon a key word already found in the left-to-right scan of the text in favor of one having a higher rank. Also, the procedure recognizes a comma or a period as a delimiter. Whenever either one is encountered and a key word has already been found, all subsequent text is deleted from the input message. If no key had yet been found, the phrase or sentence to the left of the delimiter, as well as the delimiter itself, is deleted. As a result, only single phrases or sentences are ever transformed.

Key words and their associated transformation[2] rules constitute the SCRIPT for a particular class of conversation. An important property of ELIZA is that a script is data; that is, it is not part of the program itself. Hence, ELIZA is not restricted to a particular set of recognition patterns or responses, indeed not even to any specific language. At this writing, ELIZA scripts exist in Welsh and German as well as in English.

The fundamental technical problems with which ELIZA must be preoccupied are the following:

1. The identification of the "most important" key word occurring in the input message.

2. The identification of some minimal context within which the chosen key word appears; for example, if the key word is "you," it is followed by the word "are" (in which case an assertion is probably being made).

3. The choice of an appropriate transformation rule and, of course, the making of the transformation itself.

4. The provision of a mechanism that will permit ELIZA to respond "intelligently" when the input text contains no key words.

[2] The word "transformation" is used in its generic sense rather than that given it by Harris (1957) and Chomsky (1965) in linguistic contexts.

5. The provision of machinery that facilitates editing, particularly extension, of the script on the script-writing level.

There are, of course, the usual constraints dictated by the need to be economical in the use of computer time and storage space.

The central issue is clearly one of text manipulation, and at the heart of that issue is the concept of the transformation rule which has been said to be associated with certain key words. The mechanisms subsumed under the slogan "transformation rule" are a number of functions which serve to (1) decompose a data string according to certain criteria, hence to test the string as to whether it satisfies these criteria or not, and (2) to reassemble a decomposed string according to certain assembly specifications.

While this is not the place to discuss these functions in all their detail (or even to reveal their full power and generality), it is important to the understanding of the operation of ELIZA to describe them in some detail.

Consider the sentence "I am very unhappy these days." Suppose a foreigner with only a limited knowledge of English but with a very good ear heard that sentence spoken but understood only the first two words "I am." Wishing to appear interested, perhaps even sympathetic, he may reply "How long have you been very unhappy these days?" What he might have done is to apply a kind of template to the original sentence, one part of which matched the two words "I am" and the remainder isolated the words "very unhappy these days." He must also have a reassembly kit specifically associated with that template, one that specifies that any sentence of the form "I am BLAH" can be transformed to "How long have you been BLAH," independently of the meaning of BLAH. A somewhat more complicated example is given by the sentence "It seems that you hate me." Here the foreigner understands only the words "you" and "me;" that is, he applies a template that decomposes the sentence into four parts:

(1) It seems that (2) you (3) hate (4) me

of which only the second and fourth parts are understood. The reassembly rule might then be "What makes you think I hate you"; that is, it might throw away the first component, translate the two known words ("you" to "I" and "me" to "you"), and tack on a stock phrase (What makes you think) to the front of the reconstruction. A formal notation in which to represent the decomposition template is

(0 YOU 0 ME)

and the reassembly rule

(WHAT MAKES YOU THINK I 3 YOU).

The "0" in the decomposition rule stands for "an indefinite number of words" (analogous to the indefinite dollar sign of Comit; see Yngve, 1961) while the "3" in the reassembly rule indicates that the third component of the subject decomposition is to be inserted in its place. The decomposition rule

(0 YOU 1 ME)

would have worked just as well in this specific example. A nonzero integer *n* appearing in a decomposition rule indicates that the component in question should consist of exactly *n* words. However, of the two rules shown, only the first would have matched the sentence, "It seems you hate and love me"; the second would fail because there is more than one word between "you" and "me."

In ELIZA the question of which decomposition rules to apply to an input text is, of course, a crucial one. The input sentence might have been, for example, "It seems that you hate"; in this case the decomposition rule (0 YOU 0 ME) would have failed in that the word "ME" would not have been found at all, let alone in its assigned place. Some other decomposition rule would then have to be tried and, failing that, still another, until a match could be made or a total failure reported. ELIZA must therefore have a mechanism to delimit sharply the set of decomposition rules which are potentially applicable to a currently active input sentence. This is the key-word mechanism.

An input sentence is scanned from left to right. Each word is looked up in a dictionary of key words. If a word is identified as a key word, then (apart from the issue of precedence of key words), only decomposition rules containing that key word need be tried. The trial sequence can even be partially ordered. For example, the decomposition rule (0 YOU 0) associated with the key word "YOU" (and decomposing an input sentence into (1) all words in front of "YOU," (2) the word "YOU," and (3) all words following "YOU") should be the last one tried since it is bound to succeed.

Two problems now arise. One arises from the fact that almost none of the words in any given sentence are represented in the key word dictionary. The other is the "associating" of both decomposition and reassembly rules with key words. The first is serious in that the determination that a word is not in a dictionary may well require more computation (that is, time) than the location of a word that is represented. The attack on both problems begins by placing both a key word and its associated rules on a list. The format of a typical key list is the following:

$$
\begin{array}{l}
(K\ ((D_1)(R_{1,1})(R_{1,2}) \cdots (R_{1,m_1})) \\
\quad ((D_2)(R_{2,1})(R_{2,2}) \cdots (R_{2,m_2})) \\
\quad \vdots \\
\quad ((D_n)(R_{n,1})(R_{n,2}) \cdots (R_{n,m_n})))
\end{array}
$$

where $K$ is the key word, $D_i$ the $i$th decomposition rule associated with $K$ and $R_{i,j}$ the $j$th reassembly rule associated with the $i$th decomposition rule.

A common pictorial representation of such a structure is the tree diagram shown in Fig. 7.1. The top level of this structure contains the

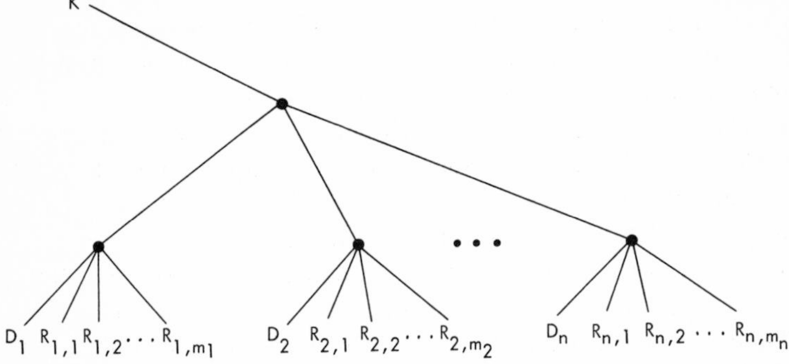


**Fig. 7.1** Key-word and rule-list structures.

key word followed by the names of lists, each one of which is again a list structure beginning with a decomposition rule and followed by reassembly rules. Since list structures of this type have no predetermined dimensionality limitations, any number of decomposition rules may be associated with a given key word and any number of reassembly rules with any specific decomposition rule.

An ELIZA script consists mainly of a set of list structures of the type shown. The actual key-word dictionary is constructed when such a script is first read into the hitherto empty program. At present the basic structural component of the key-word dictionary is a vector KEY of 128 contiguous computer words. As a particular key-list structure is read the key word $K$ at its top is randomized (hashed) by a procedure that produces a 7-bit integer $i$. The word "always," for example, yields the integer 14. Key ($i$), that is, the $i$th word of the vector KEY, is then examined to determine whether it contains a list name. If it does not, then an empty list is created, its name placed in KEY ($i$), and the key-list structure in question placed on that list. If KEY ($i$) already contains a list name, then the name of the key-list structure is placed on the bottom of the list named in KEY ($i$). The largest dictionary so far attempted contains about 50 key words. No list named in any of the words of the KEY vector contains more than two key-list structures.

Every word encountered in the scan of an input text, that is, during the actual operations of ELIZA, is randomized by the same hashing algorithm as was originally applied to the incoming key words, hence yields an integer that points to the only possible list structure which could potentially contain that word as a key word. Even then only the tops of any key-list structures that may be found there need be interrogated to determine whether or not a key word has been found. By virtue of the various list-sequencing operations, the actual identification of a key word leaves as its principal product a pointer to the list of decomposition (and hence reassembly) rules associated with the identified key word. One result of this strategy is that often less time is required to discover that a given word is not in the key-word dictionary than to locate it if it is there. However, the location of a key word yields pointers to all information associated with that word.

The conversation displayed in this paper requires that first person pronouns be exchanged for second person pronouns and vice versa throughout the input text. There may be further transformations but these minimal substitutions are unconditional. Simple substitution rules ought not to be elevated to the level of transformations, nor should the words involved be forced to carry with them all the structure required for the fully complex case. Furthermore, unconditional substitutions of single words for single words can be accomplished during the text scan itself, not as a transformation of the entire text subsequent to scanning. To facilitate the realization of these desiderata, any word in the key dictionary, that is, at the top of a key-list structure, may be followed by an equal sign followed by whatever word is to be its substitute. Transformation rules may, but need not, follow. If none do follow such a substitution rule, then the substitution is made on the fly, that is, during text scanning, but the word in question is not identified as a key word for subsequent purposes. Of course, a word may be substituted and be a key word as well. An example of a simple substitution is

(YOURSELF = MYSELF).

Neither "yourself" nor "myself" is a key word in the particular script from which this example was chosen.

The fact that key words can have ranks or precedences has already been mentioned. The need of a ranking mechanism may be established by an example. Suppose an input sentence is "I know everybody laughed at me." A script may tag the word "I" as well as the word "everybody" as a key word. Without differential ranking, "I" occurring first would determine the transformation to be applied. A typical response might be "You say you know everybody laughed at you." But the important message in the input sentence begins with the word "everybody." It is very often true that when a person speaks in terms of universals such as "everybody," "always," and "nobody" he is really referring to some quite specific event or person. By giving "everybody" a higher rank than "I," the response "Who in particular are you thinking of" may be generated.

The specific mechanism employed in ranking is that the rank of every key word encountered (absence of rank implies rank equals 0) is compared with the rank of the highest ranked key word already seen. If the rank of the new word is higher than that of any previously encountered word, the pointer to the transformation rules associated with the new word is placed on top of a list called the keystack, otherwise it is placed on the bottom of the keystack. When the text scan terminates, the keystack has at its top a pointer associated with the highest ranked key word encountered in the scan. The remaining pointers in the stack may not be monotonically ordered with respect to the ranks of the words from which they were derived, but they are nearly so — in any event they are in a useful and interesting order. Figure 7.2 is a simplified flow diagram of key-word detection. The rank of a key word must, of course, also be associated with the key word. Therefore, it must appear on the key-word list structure. It may be found, if at all, just in front of the list of transformation rules associated with the key word. As an example, consider the word "MY" in a particular script. Its key-word list may be as follows:

(MY = YOUR 5 (transformation rules)).

Such a list would mean that whenever the word "MY" is encountered in any text, it would be replaced by the word "YOUR." Its rank would be 5.

Upon completion of a given text scan, the keystack is either empty or contains pointers derived from the key words found in the text. Each of these pointers is actually a sequence reader — a mechanism that facilitates scanning of lists — pointing into its particular key list in such a way that one sequencing operation to the right will sequence it to the first set of transformation rules associated with its key word, that is, to the list

$$((D_1)(R_{1,1})(R_{1,2}) \cdots (R_1,R_{m_1})).$$

The top of that list, of course, is a list which serves a decomposition rule for the subject text. The top of the keystack contains the first pointer to be activated.

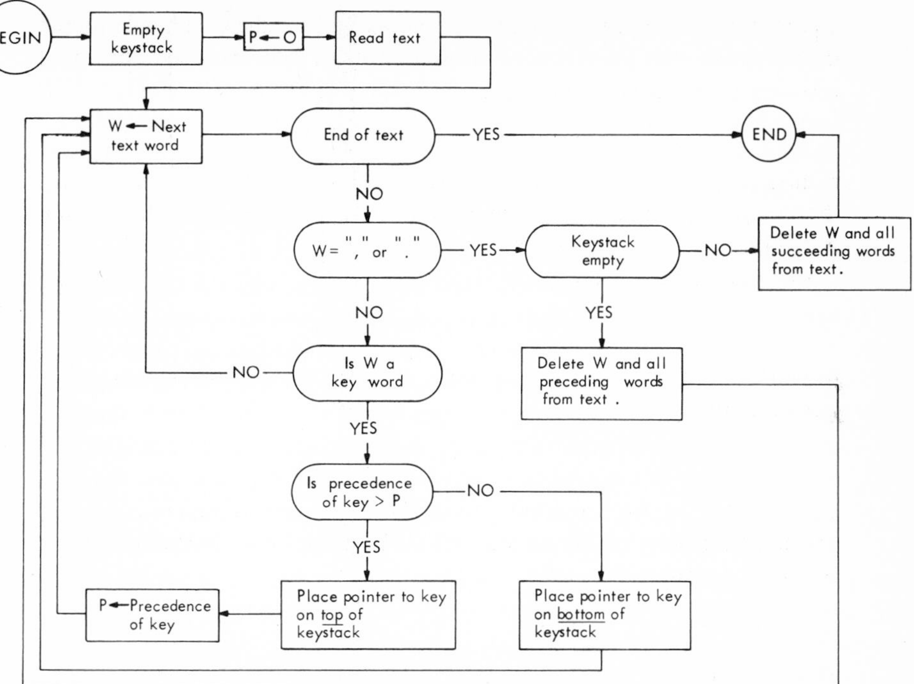


**Fig. 7.2** Basic flow diagram of key-word detection.

The decomposition rule $D_1$ associated with the key word $K$, that is, $\{(D_1), K\}$, is now tried. It may fail however. For example, suppose the input text was

You are very helpful.

The key word, say, is "you," and $\{(D_1), \text{you}\}$ is

(0 I remind you of 0).

(Recall that the "you" in the original sentence has already been replaced by "I" in the text now analyzed.) This decomposition rule obviously fails to match the input sentence. Should $\{(D_1), K\}$ fail to find a match, then $\{(D_2), K\}$ is tried. Should that too fail, $\{(D_3), K\}$ is attempted, and so on. Of course, the set of transformation rules can be guaranteed to terminate with a decomposition rule which must match. The decomposition rule

(0 $K$ 0)

will match any text in which the word $K$ appears while

(0)

will match any text whatever. However, there are other ways to leave a particular set of transformation rules, as will be shown later. Suppose that some particular decomposition rule $(D_i)$ has matched the input text. $(D_i)$, of course, was found on a list of the form

$$((D_i)(R_{i,1})(R_{i,2}) \cdots (R_{i,m_i})).$$

Sequencing the reader which is presently pointing at $(D_i)$ will retrieve the reassembly rule $(R_{i,1})$, which may then be applied to the decomposed input text to yield the output message.

Consider again the input text

You are very helpful

in which "you" is the only key word. The sentence is transformed during scanning to

I are very helpful

$\{(D_1)$, you$\}$ is "(0 I remind you of 0)" and fails to match as already discussed. However, $\{(D_2)$, you$\}$ is "(0 I are 0)" and obviously matches the text, decomposing it into the constituents

(1) empty (2) I (3) are (4) very helpful

$\{(R_{2,1})$, you$\}$ is

(What makes you think I am 4).

Hence, it produces the output text

What makes you think I am very helpful.

Having produced it, the integer 1 is put in front of $(R_{2,1})$ so that the transformation-rule list in question now appears as

$$((D_2)1(R_{2,1})(R_{2,2}) \cdots (R_{2,m_2})).$$

Next time $\{(D_2),K\}$ matches an input text, the reassembly rule $(R_{2,2})$ will be applied and the integer 2 will replace the 1. After $(R_{2,m_2})$ has been exercised, $(R_{2,1})$ will again be invoked. Thus, after the system has been in use for a time, every decomposition rule which has matched some input text has associated with it an integer which corresponds to the last reassembly rule used in connection with that decomposition rule. This mechanism insures that the complete set of reassembly rules associated with a given decomposition rule is cycled through before any repetitions occur.

That considerable care is taken to delay any repetition of previous output is evidence to the effect that one of the principal aims of the DOCTOR program is to keep the conversation going — even at the price of having to conceal any misunderstandings on its own part. We shall see how more ambitious objectives are realized subsequently. In the meanwhile, our discussion has already provided a framework within which a number of useful points may be illuminated.

Most important is the crucial role *context* plays in all conversations. The subject who is about to engage in his first conversation with the DOCTOR is told to put himself in a role-playing frame of mind. He is to imagine that he has some problem of the kind one might normally discuss with a psychiatrist, to pretend he is actually conversing with a psychiatrist, and under no circumstances to deviate from that role. While some of the responses produced by the program are not very spectacular even when the subject follows his instructions, it is remarkable how quickly they deteriorate when he leaves his role. In this respect, the program mirrors life. Real two-person conversations also degenerate when the contextual assumptions one participant is making with respect to his partner's statements cease to be valid. This phenomenon is, for example, the basis on which many comedies of error are built.

These remarks are about the *global* context in which the conversation takes place. No understanding is possible in the absence of an established global context. To be sure, strangers do meet, converse, and immediately understand one another (or at least I believe they do). But they operate in a shared culture — provided partially by the very language they speak — and, under any but the most trivial circumstances, engage in a kind of hunting behavior which has as its object the creation of a contextual framework. Conversation flows smoothly only after these preliminaries are completed. The situation is no different with respect to visual pattern recognition; a visual pattern may appear utterly senseless until a context within which it may be recognized (known again, that is, understood) is provided. Very often, of course, a solitary observer arrives at an appropriate context by forming and testing a number of hypotheses. He may later discover that the pattern he "recognized" was not the one he was intended to "see," that is, that he hypothesized the "wrong" context. He may see the "correct" pattern when given the "correct" context. It does not mean much to say that the pattern "is" such and such. We might, for example, find a string of Chinese characters beautiful as long as we do not know what they spell. This, an apparent impoverishment, that is, really a broadening, of context will enhance the esthetic appeal of a pattern. Similarly, many people think anything said in French is charming and romantic precisely *because* they do not understand the language.

In real conversations global context assigns meaning to what is being said in only the most general way. The conversation proceeds by establishing subcontexts, sub-subcontexts within these, and so on. It generates and, so to speak, traverses a contextual tree. Beginning with the topmost or initial node, a new node representing a subcontext is generated, and from this one a new node still, and so on to many levels. Occasionally the currently regnant node is abandoned; that is, the conversation ascends to a previously established node, perhaps skipping many intermediate ones in the process. New branches are established and old ones abandoned. It is my conjecture that an analysis of the pattern traced by a given conversation through such a directed graph may yield a measure of what one might call the consequential richness of the conversation. Cocktail party chatter, for example, has a rather straight-line character. Context is constantly being changed — there is considerable chaining of nodes — but there is hardly any reversal of direction along already established structure. The conversation is inconsequential in that nothing being said has any effect on any questions raised to a higher level. Contrast this with a discussion between, say, two physicists trying to come to understand the results of some experiment. Their conversation tree would be not only deep but broad as well; that is, they would ascend to an earlier contextual level in order to generate new nodes from there. The signal that their conversation terminated successfully might well be that they ascended (back to) the original node, that is, that they are again talking about what they started to discuss.

For an individual the analogue of a conversation tree is what the social psychologist Abelson (Abelson and Carroll, 1965) calls a *belief structure*. In some areas of the individual's intellectual life, this structure may be very logically organized, for example, in the area of his own profession. In more emotionally loaded areas, the structure may be very loosely organized and even contain many contradictions. When a person enters a conversation, he brings his belief structures with him as a kind of agenda.

A person's belief structure is a product of his entire life experience. All people have some common formative experiences, for example, they were all born of mothers. There is consequently some basis of understanding between any two humans simply because they are human. But, even humans living in the same culture will have difficulty in understanding one another where their respective lives differed radically. Since, in the last analysis, each of our lives is unique, there is a limit to what we can bring another person to understand. There is an ultimate privacy about each of us that precludes full communication of any of our ideas to the universe outside ourselves and which thus isolates each one of us from every other poetic object in the world.

There can be no total understanding and no absolutely reliable test of understanding.

To know with certainty that a person understood what has been said to him is to perceive his entire belief structure and *that* is equivalent to sharing his entire life experience. It is precisely barriers of this kind that artists, especially poets, struggle against.

This issue must be confronted if there is to be any agreement as to what machine "understanding" might mean. This argument is intended to make clear that it is too much to insist that a machine understands a sentence (or a symphony or a poem) only if that sentence evokes the same imagery in the machine as was present in the speaker of the sentence at the time he uttered it. For by that criterion no human understands any other human. Yet, we agree that humans do understand one another *within acceptable tolerances*. The operative word is "acceptable" for it implies *purpose*. When, therefore, we speak of a machine understanding, we must mean understanding as limited by some objective. He who asserts that there are certain ideas no machines will ever understand can mean at most that the machine will not understand these ideas tolerably well because they relate to objectives that are, in his judgment, inappropriate with respect to machines. Of course, the machine can still deal with such ideas symbolically, that is, in ways which are reflections — however pale — of the ways organisms to whom such objectives are appropriate deal with them. In such cases the machine is no more handicapped than I am, being a man, in trying to understand, say, female jealousy.

A two-person conversation may be said to click along as long as both participants keep discovering (in the sense of uncovering) identical nodes in their respective belief structures. Under such circumstances the conversation tree is merely a set of linearly connected nodes corresponding to the commonly held parts of the participants' belief structures. If such a conversation is interesting to either participant, it is probably because the part of the belief structure being made explicit has not been consciously verbalized before, or has never before been attached to the higher level node to which it is then coupled in that conversation, that is, seen in that context, or because of the implicit support it is getting by being found to coexist in someone else.

Backtracking over the conversation tree takes place when a new context is introduced and an attempt is made to integrate it into the ongoing conversation, or when a new connection between the present and a previous context is suggested. In either case, there is a need to reorganize the conversation tree. Clearly the kind of psychotherapist imitated by the DOCTOR program restricts himself to pointing out new connectivity opportunities to his patients. I suppose his hope is that any reorganization of the conversation tree generated in the therapy session will ultimately reflect itself in corresponding modifications of his patients' belief structures.

I now turn back to the program reproduced earlier. I hope the reader found the conversation quoted there to be smooth and natural. If he did, he has gone a long way toward verifying what I said earlier about the investment a human will make in a conversation. Any continuity the reader may have perceived in that dialogue — excepting only the last machine response — is entirely illusory. A careful analysis will reveal that each machine response is a response to the immediately preceding subject input. Again with the exception of the last sentence, the quoted conversation has no subcontextual structure at all. Nor does the description of the program given so far offer any clues as to how subcontexts might be recognized or established or maintained by the machine.

To get at the subcontext issue, I want to restate the over-all strategy in terms somewhat different from those already used. We may think of the ELIZA script as establishing the global context in which subsequent conversations will be played out. The DOCTOR script establishes the Rogerian psychiatric context. The list of key words are guesses about what significant words might appear in the subject's utterances. The appearance of any of these words in an actual input tentatively directs the system's attention to decomposition rules associated with the identified word. These rules are hypotheses about what an input containing such words might mean. An important property of the system is that, just as the entire set of key words need not be searched in the analysis of every input sentence, neither does the whole list of hypotheses about what *any* input might mean have to be tested in order to generate a response to a specific sentence. Should the set of hypotheses associated with the currently regnant key word be exhausted without success, there is a way (although not described here) to go to decomposition rules associated with lower ranking key words that may have appeared in the input string.

Much is known about an input sentence once it matches a decomposition rule. If, for example, the rule

(0 MY (/FAMILY) DRINKS 0)

matches a sentence, then we know that the subject matter is a family member, and that this person drinks. (The notation "(/ABC)" means that in that position a word "tagged" with any of the symbols A or B or C is looked for. Words are tagged as part of the script. This mechanism is not further discussed here.) A reassembly rule can subsequently identify the family member in question, for example, father. The successful matching of a decomposition rule — hence, the verification of a hypothesis — is therefore an opportunity not only to generate a plausible response but also to establish a subcontextual node. The laying down of such a node does not mean merely remembering what is now being talked about, but what is more important, making hypotheses about what is likely to be said next within the new contextual framework.

The realization of such a mechanism in an ELIZA script involves attaching a substructure to decomposition rules which says, in effect, that if a so-modified decomposition rule matches an input sentence and a suitable subcontext exists, then control is transferred to a set of decomposition and reassembly rules appropriate to that subcontext. The details of mechanization are not important here. I will, however, show its effect by exhibiting the following conversational fragment from the DOCTOR program:

Because you are so stubborn.

IS THAT THE REAL REASON

Maybe.

WHAT IS A BETTER REASON THEN

My stomach hurts.

TELL ME ABOUT YOUR PAINS IN GENERAL

My head bothers me, too.

YOU SEE SOME PSYCHOLOGICAL REASON WHY YOUR HEAD SHOULD PAIN YOU

Maybe.

YOU THINK COMING HERE MIGHT HELP ALLEVIATE YOUR HEAD PAIN

Certainly.

LET'S TALK ABOUT YOUR FEELINGS WHEN YOU THINK OF YOUR HEAD AND ITS PAINS

We are here in the middle of a dialogue. The first sentence is an input to the program, the next a machine response and so on in alternation.

The word "because" was the key that triggered the first machine response. At the same time the reason subcontext was established. Notice that the next subject input, the word "maybe," was interpreted as meaning "no," as is appropriate in that particular context, and that a contextually correct machine response was produced. The next input serves to establish a "hurt" subcontext. I believe the conversation is self-explanatory from that point on. Notice, however, that in the new subcontext the word "maybe" which was earlier interpreted to mean "no" is now seen as meaning "yes." Under still other circumstances it would be understood as indicating uncertainty.

My secretary watched me work on this program over a long period of time. One day she asked to be permitted to talk with the system. Of course, she knew she was talking to a machine. Yet, after I watched her type in a few sentences she turned to me and said, "Would you mind leaving the room, please?" I believe this anecdote testifies to the success with which the program maintains the illusion of understanding. However, it does so, as I have already said, at the price of concealing its own misunderstandings. We all do this now and then, perhaps in the service of politeness or for other reasons. But we cannot afford to elevate this occasional tactic to a universal strategy. Thus, while the DOCTOR program may be useful as an instrument for the analysis of two-person conversations, and while it is certainly fun, its aim must be changed from that of concealment of misunderstanding to its explication.

Another difficulty with the system currently under discussion is that it can do very little other than generate plausible responses. To be sure, there are facilities for keeping and testing various tallies as well as other such relatively primitive devices, but the system can do no generalized computation in either the logical or numerical sense. In order to meet this deficiency and others of the original ELIZA system, I wrote a new program, also called ELIZA, which has now replaced its ancestor.

The new ELIZA differs from the old one in two main respects. First, it contains an *evaluator* capable of accepting expressions (programs) of unlimited complexity and evaluating (executing) them. It is, of course, also capable of storing the results of such evaluations for subsequent retrieval and use. Second, the idea of the script has been generalized so that now it is possible for the program to contain three different scripts simultaneously and to fetch new scripts from among an unlimited supply stored on a disc storage unit; intercommunication among coexisting scripts is also possible.

The major reason for wishing to have several scripts available in the core (that is, high-speed) memory of the computer derives from the arguments about contexts previously made. The script defines a global context within which all of the subsegment conversation is to be understood. We have seen that it is possible for a single script to establish and maintain subcontexts. But what is a subcontext from one point of view is a major (not to say global) one as seen from another perspective. For example, a conversation may have as its over-all framework the health of one of the participants but spend much time under the heading of stomach disorders and headache remedies.

In principle one large, monolithic ELIZA script could deal with this. However, such a script would be very long and extremely difficult to modify and maintain. Besides, long exposure to computer programming should at least instill a healthy respect for subroutines, their power and utility. In the new ELIZA system, scripts are in fact very much like subroutines. One script plays the role of the so-called "main program"; that is, it is the one for calling in and replacing subscripts. This is the one that, in an important sense, governs the computer's role in the conversation. Such a script may, for example, play the role of an initial interviewer in a hospital, that is, a person who knows just enough about the field of medicine and the organization of the hospital to be able to determine, by means of appropriate questions, to whom the incoming patient is to be directed. A more highly specialized script then plays the role of that person. It may call on still further levels of scripts — and each script, except for the "main" one, can return the issue up one or more levels with information "explaining" that action.

We saw earlier how the word "maybe" was differentially interpreted in what might be called different microcontexts. The hierarchy of scripts now under discussion makes much more nearly global contextual distinctions possible. For example, the word "tone" probably means muscle tone to the internist but audio tone to the ear specialist. The occurrence of that word as a key word would establish an entirely different contextual mode, or call in a different subscript, depending on whether it was identified in an internist or an ear-specialist script.

Of course, another important advantage of this kind of subscripting is that scripts (sub- or otherwise) can presumably be written by specialists in a very narrow field. The fact that scripts now tend to be rather short means that a specialist might actually find the time to produce one as part of a larger cooperative effort.

The following conversations were governed by a script in the new ELIZA system. This script was designed to illustrate the power of the evaluator to which ELIZA has access. The key word and other such mechanisms are not very different from those already described. The important departure is that expressions can be turned over to the evaluator, evaluated, and the results displayed and stored.

The area of a circle is pi times the radius of the circle squared. The radius of a dish is 10. A dish is a circle. What is the area of the dish?

IT'S 314.158996

The area of a sphere is pi times the diameter of the sphere squared, also the area of a square is a side of the square squared. The diameter of an object is twice the radius of the object. The radius of a ball is 10.

What is the area of the ball?

IS BALL A KIND OF CIRCLE? no

IS BALL A KIND OF SPHERE? yes

IS BALL A KIND OF OBJECT? yes

IT'S 1256.635986

When I say AS I mean area of sphere. Whenever I say RS I mean radius of sphere. Let volume (sphere) = AS*RS/3. Whenever I say globe I mean ball. What is the volume of the globe.

IT'S 4188.786621

Please tell me how much that/(5/3) is.

IT'S 2513.271972

And how much is that divided by 2.

IT'S 1256.635986

What is the difference between that and (area of ball).

IT'S 0

Compute area of dish. Call it x. Compute sqrt (x/3.14159).

IT'S 9.999999

Please tell me what the value of x is.

IT'S 314.158996

I'm now going to teach you some German, so listen carefully.

Whenever I say ICH SAGE I mean I SAY.

Whenever ich sage MEINE ICH I mean I MEAN.

When ich sage WENN meine ich WHEN.

Wenn ich sage QUADRAT meine ich squared.

Wenn ich sage WIEVIEL IST meine ich WHAT IS.

Und wenn ich sage DAS meine ich THAT.

Nun, mein guter Herr, wieviel ist 3 quadrat.

IT'S 9.000000

Sehr gut, und wieviel est das plus 8.

I DIDN'T UNDERSTAND YOU

Ja, tut mir leid. Ich frage gerade wieviel ist das plus 8.

IT'S 17.000000

Jetzt wenn ich sage NENNEN SIE DAS meine ich CALL THAT. Bitte nennen sie das x. Sagen sie mir wieviel ist x quadrat.

IT'S 289.000000

Und wieviel ist x + x.

IT'S 34.000000

Wenn ich sage DANKE meine ich THANK YOU. Also danke und auf-wiedersehen.

YOU'RE QUITE WELCOME, COME AGAIN

The particular example shown here is one in which the system is asked not merely to entertain but to perform some useful service. The script is one which establishes a context in which a few terms can be interpreted as giving directions about the evaluation of certain expressions. The number of keys that actually lead to decomposition rules is very small. They are as follows:

I mean
Is (* a an)
Of (* a an the)

What (* the is)
Where
Call
Let
Define
Compute
=
Also
Thanks

(A key of the form "Is (* a an)" will match either "Is a" or "Is an.") In addition, there are 17 substitution keys like "Twice = 2 *." The effect of that particular one is to substitute the symbols "2 *" whereever the word "twice" appeared in the input text. Of course, the evaluator sitting behind ELIZA, so to speak, recognizes words like "SQRT," "LOG," and so on. The function of this script is to interpret the user's wishes with respect to the evaluation of expressions, perform certain translation functions on these expressions, and control the traffic between the input/output system of ELIZA and that of the evaluator.

Consider the dozen keys just shown. The sentence "*Let* me try to *define what the call of the* sea means" contains five of these keys. It could perhaps be understood by the DOCTOR but not by the program we are now considering. It would reply "I didn't understand you."

I call attention to this contextual matter once more to underline the thesis that, while a computer program that "understands" natural language in the most general sense is for the present beyond our means, the granting of even a quite broad contextual framework allows us to construct practical language recognition procedures.

The present script is designed to *reveal,* as opposed to *conceal,* lack of understanding and misunderstanding. Notice, for example, that when the program is asked to compute the area of the ball, it does not yet know that a ball is a sphere and that when the diameter of the ball needs to be computed the fact that a ball is an object has also not yet been established. Appropriate questions are therefore asked. But when, later on, the volume of the globe (that is, ball) is required, all the parameters are known and no questions are asked. The transcript also makes clear that the program now has memory and, of course, that it can compute. The definition of the volume of a sphere, by the way, was included to show that the long-windedness of the first few definitions, while permitted, is not required.

I can imagine at least two questions that might have arisen in the mind of the reader in response to this material. First but less important is, What role does the kind of psychiatric program shown here play in serious psychotherapy. My answer to that must be that psychotherapy is not my field and that I have no intention of pursuing any therapeutic implications of this work. It is clear that there is considerable psychological material to be exploited here, material that may conceivably lead to some therapeutic developments. There may also be some use in this kind of technique in simulation of the neurotic processes. K. M. Colby (1967), a practicing psychoanalyst, does propose to use conversational programs as psychotherapeutic tools vis-à-vis real patients. I believe the unsolved technical problems in the computer realm alone are so enormous as to insure the postponement of the realization of such a goal for a very long time yet.

The second question concerns itself with the implications of this work on so-called teaching machines. Here I feel on much firmer ground. It is my belief that the kind of programmed teaching that is based on multiple choice testing of the student is best done without the use of computers. With the techniques described here, it becomes possible to instruct the student in a corner of some field and then, the contextual framework having been established, to have the student interact with the machine in natural language.

The following conversation, based on a script written by Dr. Edwin Taylor of the Center for Research in Teaching and Learning of M.I.T., makes the point very well.

PLEASE CONSIDER HOW WE MIGHT SYNCHRONIZE TWO CLOCKS TO READ THE 'SAME TIME'. ONE OF THESE CLOCKS IS IN SAN FRANCISCO, THE OTHER IS IN NEW YORK. AS YOU THINK ABOUT THE PROBLEM, ASK ME ANY QUESTIONS THAT OCCUR TO YOU. WHEN YOU ARE READY TO PROPOSE A SYNCHRONIZATION METHOD, TYPE 'READY' THEN I WILL QUIZ YOU ABOUT YOUR PROPOSED METHOD.

what do you mean by synchronize

FOR THE PRESENT MAKE USE OF THE EVERYDAY MEANINGS OF SUCH PHRASES AS 'SAME TIME' AND 'SYNCHRONIZE.' LATER WE WILL DISCUSS THE MEANING OF THESE TERMS MORE CAREFULLY

may i use telegraph signals

CERTAINLY, FEEL FREE TO USE TELEGRAPH

ready

NOW I WILL QUIZ YOU ON YOUR SYNCHRONIZATION METHOD DOES YOUR METHOD OF SYNCHRONIZATION INVOLVE THE PROPAGATION OF SOME SIGNAL — OR MATERIAL OBJECT — FROM ONE PLACE TO ANOTHER

yes

WHAT KIND OF PROPAGATING SIGNAL OR TRAVELING OBJECT DO YOU PROPOSE TO USE a watch

WILL YOUR WATCH MOVE AT A SPEED VERY MUCH SMALLER THAN THE SPEED OF LIGHT

of course

GOOD. TRAVELING CLOCKS CAN BE USED TO SYNCHRONIZE DISTANT CLOCKS TO ARBITRARILY HIGH ACCURACY IF THEY TRAVEL SLOWLY ENOUGH. YOU MAY LEAVE THE PROBLEM BY PUSHING THE 'QUIT' BUTTON TWICE. IF YOU WOULD LIKE TO EXPLORE FURTHER THE MATTERS OF PRINCIPLE ASSOCIATED WITH OTHER METHODS, CHOOSE ANOTHER WAY TO COMMUNICATE BETWEEN THE DISTANT CLOCKS. WHAT KIND OF PROPAGATING SIGNAL OR TRAVELING OBJECT DO YOU PROPOSE TO USE

light

WELL, OF COURSE THE LIGHT SIGNAL WILL NOT FOLLOW THE CURVATURE OF THE EARTH. SO LET US ASSUME THAT SOME SYSTEM OF RELAY TOWERS IS USED. NOW LET ME ASK, WILL THE LIGHT SIGNAL TRAVEL DIRECTLY BETWEEN NEW YORK AND SAN FRANCISCO OR WILL THE LIGHT SIGNAL TRAVEL TO OR FROM SOME INTERMEDIATE POINT

it will travel from st louis in both directions

IS YOUR INTERMEDIATE POINT EQUIDISTANT FROM NEW YORK AND SAN FRANCISCO

let's say it is, yes

MY UNDERSTANDING IS THAT YOU EXPECT TO USE TWO SIGNALS AND THAT THESE SIGNALS WILL EITHER CONVERGE ON OR BE SENT OUT FROM A POINT EQUIDISTANT FROM NEW YORK AND SAN FRANCISCO. IS MY UNDERSTANDING ON THIS POINT CORRECT

yes

WILL THIS PAIR OF SIGNALS CONVERGE ON THE INTERMEDIATE POINT OR BE SENT OUT FROM THIS POINT

they will be sent from the point

WILL THE TWO SIGNALS LEAVE THE INTERMEDIATE POINT AT THE SAME TIME

certainly

AHA, I'VE GOT YOU. YOU ARE TRYING TO SYNCHRONIZE THE NEW YORK AND SAN FRANCISCO CLOCKS TO READ THE 'SAME TIME' HOW CAN IT BE VALID TO ASSUME A 'SAME TIME' FOR THE DEPARTURE OF A PAIR OF SIGNALS FROM THE MIDPOINT

because the pair of signals leave from the same point

RIGHT

THE PHRASE 'SAME TIME' HAS AN UNAMBIGUOUS MEANING WHEN APPLIED TO EVENTS THAT OCCUR NEAR THE SAME POINT IN SPACE. NOW YOU ARE GOING TO CONTINUE YOUR ARGUMENT BY SAYING THAT THE TWO SIGNALS THAT START FROM THE MIDPOINT AT THE SAME TIME WILL PRESUMABLY REACH NEW YORK AND SAN FRANCISCO AT THE SAME TIME. THESE SIGNALS CAN THUS BE USED TO SYNCHRONIZE THE NEW YORK AND SAN FRANCISCO CLOCKS. IS THIS THE WAY YOUR ARGUMENT WILL CONTINUE

yes

ONE FINAL QUESTION. WHAT ASSUMPTION ARE YOU MAKING ABOUT THE SPEEDS OF THE TWO SIGNALS THAT TRAVEL IN OPPOSITE DIRECTIONS

that these speeds are equal

VERY GOOD. YOU HAVE DEVISED A VALID METHOD FOR SYNCHRONIZING TWO CLOCKS, ONE IN NEW YORK AND ONE IN SAN FRANCISCO. I AM NOW RETURNING YOU TO THE CTSS SYSTEM

I have chosen to skew this discussion in the direction of "understanding" and have used that difficult word almost as if it were synonymous with "recognition." Actually, recognition is a prerequisite to understanding. The latter provides a test of the former. Even though no test of understanding can be defined with rigor, we do feel we are understood when the person we are talking to asks what we believe to be relevant questions and when he finally answers our question or solves the problem we posed. By such criteria, the conversations displayed justify the assertion that the programs that produced the responses recognized textual patterns and understood what they were being told.

## Acknowledgment

Work reported herein was supported (in part) by Project MAC, an M.I.T. research program sponsored by the Advanced Research Projects Agency, Department of Defense, under Office of Naval Research Contract Number Nonr-4102(01).

## References

Abelson, R. P., and J. C. Carroll. Computer simulation of individual belief systems. *Amer. Behav. Sci.,* May 1965, *9,* 24–30.

Chomsky, N. *Aspects of the Theory of Syntax.* Cambridge, Mass.: M.I.T. Press, 1965.

Colby, K. M. Computer simulation of change in personal belief systems. Paper delivered in Section $L_2$, The Psychiatric Sciences, General Systems

Research, AAAS Berkeley Meeting, December 29, 1965. *Behavioral Science,* 1967, *12,* 248–253.

Colby, K. M., J. B. Watt, and J. P. Gilbert. A computer method of psychotherapy: preliminary communication. *J. nerv. ment. Dis.,* 1966, *142,* 148–152.

Harris, Z. S. Co-occurrence and transformation in linguistic structure. *Language,* 1957, *33,* 293–340.

Rogers, C. *Client Centered Therapy: Current Practice, Implications and Theory*. Boston: Houghton Mifflin, 1951.

Yngve, J. *COMIT Programming Manual.* Cambridge, Mass.: M.I.T. Press, 1961.

*We began our collection with a description and end it with a description — here a description of a classification scheme for patterns and of some general areas we have not explored in more detail. As we began with the assertion that a study of living systems can aid the designer of automatic ones, and vice versa, we conclude with the assertion that, this study notwithstanding, there is no necessary comparability between the performance of the two. In Nature, to this day we still very much must take what we get, and, in fact, the variance is often illuminating. With our machines, we specify goals and design operations that attempt to achieve them. The execution of the operations need not be the same in a machine and in a living system, but any successful machine will ultimately use principles derived from or relevant to the operation of living systems.*

# 8. Other Pattern Recognition Problems and Some Generalizations

*Murray Eden*

Only a very small number of the problems in pattern recognition that are currently receiving attention can be considered within the compass of this collection. The specific problems treated in some detail in the preceding papers are obviously only illustrative of the whole. Many important and interesting problems are not touched upon, so it seems worth while to describe some of them briefly here. At the same time, I shall attempt to expose certain features that are common to many pattern-recognition problems.

When writing on a well-structured and well-studied field of learning, it is customary to begin with its theoretical framework and then to proceed to discussions of applications and specific problems. We have chosen to reserve most of our generalizations for the last chapter of the collection, however, because there are relatively few strong generalizations that one can make, and those few can only be made by inference and conjecture. Pattern recognition has been the subject of an extensive series of papers by many authors who purport to set the problems into a general framework. But the predictive value of current formulations of pattern-recognition theory is near zero and the validation of some of the claims, by any objective criterion, has been meager; therefore we proceed tentatively.

The study of pattern recognition as a human activity, and as a pragmatic tool to facilitate communication, and release human beings from the tedium of some iterative task, has begun only recently. Where there have been successes in performing pattern-recognition tasks by mechanical means, the successes have rested on rules that were prescribed *ad hoc,* in the literal sense of that phrase; that is to say, the successful methods classify *reliably* that particular set of patterns for which the methods were designed, but are likely to lack any significant value for classifying any other set of patterns. By this we mean, for example, that the rules for recognizing handwritten words, however successful, are by and large useless for recognizing printed characters or speech sounds. The converse is equally true.

Nevertheless, if pattern recognition has any claim to being a coherent subject of study, attempts to synthesize a theory of pattern recognition will continue. But no serious synthesis will be proposed here. Rather, in this chapter we have set ourselves the more modest task of examining some of the successes and drawing attention to their similarities and differences, so that at the very least a beginning can be made in classifying the pattern-recognition problems themselves.

## The Classification of Pattern Recognition

The obvious criterion for partitioning the class of pattern-recognition problems is the sensory mode by which patterns enter into human consciousness; sight, hearing, and touch represent quite different qualities to humans and presumably to other organisms as well. As was pointed out in Chapter 5, patterns that can be seen are much more tractable objects of study than the ephemeral objects of hearing or of touch. Even a rapidly changing visual sequence can be frozen by photography to be looked at in detail or over-all as suits the observer. It is no wonder therefore that most of the problems in pattern recognition that are currently under study deal with visual, and usually two-dimensional, objects. Nevertheless, the criterion of sense mode does not specify a crucial difference between patterns so far as the recognition problem is concerned. The same underlying patterns can be recognized in all three modalities that we have mentioned; natural language, for example, can be spoken, written, and even felt (by a braille reader). The means of acquiring the patterns are different and some of the preprocessing is different in the three modes, but these two preliminary steps by no means distinguish the recognition problem.

A more fruitful criterion for dividing the pattern problems distinguishes between patterns represented by a symbol in some conventional symbol system, and patterns represented by a classificatory label applied to a set of natural objects. In the first instance the problem is to make a correct identification of a symbol; in the second instance, it is to make a correct identification of an object of the real world. It is intrinsic to conventional symbol systems that the *tokens,* the characters in an alphabet, for example, are designed and produced by humans. "Natural" patterns on the other hand are assigned to categories by certain man-made rules or criteria. The objects which we wish to categorize in this case are not the product of man's creation.

## Man-made and Natural Patterns

I shall discuss two different types of patterns, things that may be called man-made patterns and things found in nature to which man assigns names. Chemical symbols and musical notation will be used to illustrate the man-made patterns; clouds and diseases will exemplify the natural patterns. Let me begin by presenting the reasons for considering these two pattern types separately.

All communication between humans involves one form or another of conventionalized patterns.[1] Special attention will be given in this chapter to the systems in wide use for scoring music and for recording the structure of organic molecules.[2] Of course many other conventionalized systems exist; for example, notation for dance movements, road signs for traffic control, sign language, maps, architect's plans or blueprints, and instructions for knitting or crocheting. I choose music and chemistry only as illustrations of this whole class of conventionalized symbol systems.

In order that communication between humans take place, it is necessary that there be an agreed-upon interpretation of the signals passing between them. In other words, it is a minimal requirement that there exist a set of conventions which prescribe the interpretation of the primitive symbols of the system. The characters of written language have just such an agreed-upon interpretation. It is also clear that the alphabetic characters are arbitrarily assigned; they bear no canonical relation (geometrical, topological, or otherwise) either to the objects that they are used to name or to the sounds that they represent in the spoken language. It is obvious that one can choose a different set of conventional symbols to write any language. Many examples of such relatively arbitrary substitutions exist. Yiddish, for instance, is essentially a dialect of middle German, but it is written with Hebrew characters. While it is true that both the Roman characters and the Hebrew ones have a common historical origin, they are by now so far apart in their geometric forms and the way they are scanned that it is pointless to consider them

[1] The ability to create conventional patterns appears to be an attribute peculiar to humans. While animals undoubtedly communicate with one another, there is little reason to believe that they have procedures for creating symbols for communication and the rules for manipulating the symbols.

[2] Note that the chemical notation for identifying the structure of an organic molecule is a conventional and not a natural pattern class. It does not deal with the problem of classifying the organic compound in question by any sense data such as sight, smell, taste, touch, and so on. Rather, it is intended to communicate a certain set of abstract properties associated with a compound. It is no different in this sense from the symbol system of printed characters that represent natural language. No amount of study of the brown and friendly beast who habitually occupies my easy chair would lead me to the conclusion that the symbol "dog" is appropriate to this creature. This identification is made by way of a rule of English and not a rule of biology. But there *is* a problem in finding the chemical name from a study of certain properties of a particular crystalline powder, or yellow, pungent oil. In our terms, such a problem would be called natural pattern recognition. People whose profession it is to solve this kind of pattern-recognition problem usually refer to it as "qualitative organic chemical analysis."

as other than entirely different conventions. Many other symbol systems have been derived directly from speech or, more often, from written language: braille, semaphore signals, telegraphic code, hand sign language are all of this type. Missionaries, explorers, and colonial administrators have frequently made transliterations of the spoken languages of the indigenous people with whom they were in contact; usually, the transliterations were made in the Roman alphabet, although in some cases the Western observer followed his own fancies in inventing symbols. In one case, the Seminole chief Sequoyah, having observed that Europeans communicated with written symbols that he thought were isomorphic to the spoken sound, invented his own set of symbols that corresponded to syllables of his native language.

Speech sounds themselves are conventional. It is easily possible to change many — and in principle all — of the speech sounds of a language, and still have the same language. One simple and relevant example of such a modification is Pig Latin (which should with better justice be called "Pig English"). A more interesting example can be found in the private language referred to by Keyser and Halle in Chapter 2 of this collection.

Several other symbol systems were referred to earlier that are not simple translations of natural language, such as musical or chemical notations. Nevertheless, each of the symbol systems that have been considered worthy of serious study as problems of pattern recognition, partakes of many of the properties of a natural language. Only the very simplest pattern classes, so far as I know, fail to exhibit the common attributes to be described in the following paragraphs. Each of these attributes will be considered briefly because it is our contention that pattern classes that share so many properties will be easier to study in the light of the procedures and principles that have contributed in some measure to the successes in linguistic studies.

## Properties of Conventional Pattern Classes

### *Finiteness of the alphabet of primitive symbols*

The number of primitive symbols is finite for any conventional symbol system of which I am aware. It may be argued that in some very special cases, the primitive symbol itself can be varied in shape or form; for example, nothing prescribes the exact orientation and length of a timing bar or phrase mark in music. Even in these rather bizarre examples it is possible to describe the infinite set of such symbols in terms of a few simple formation rules.

Note that this property of finiteness of the set of symbols is not necessarily true for problems of natural pattern recognition. For example, it is a crucial feature of medical diagnosis that the set of possible disease entities, as well as the set of properties of the patients that are relevant to diagnosis, is unbounded. There is no end to the number of possible diseases or symptoms.

### *Underlying abstract structure of the symbol set*

The existence of an underlying abstract structure in language has been amply demonstrated by linguists. One can imagine a device which could take any of the various representations of English — spoken, printed, handwritten, stenotyped, in braille, or in Pig Latin — convert it into some "machine language" and produce any one of the other forms as an equivalent output. Clearly, every one of these representations is converted into a common currency by means of the abstract representation.

The same can be said of musical notation, representing as it does relations between sounds that are independent of the instrument which is used to produce the sound. And the same is true of chemical notation, which symbolizes certain adjacency relations between atoms in a molecule. Thus it is not enough merely to identify the primitive symbols in such systems. The correct identification requires, in addition, that the relations between the symbols be represented.

Many natural pattern classes do not have a known underlying abstract structure. In many cases the goal of scientific theory is to find such structures, but the task of recognizing natural pattern classes is readily accomplished by humans although no sufficiently precise scientific theory is available.

### *A finite set of formation rules*

Each symbol system has a finite set of formation or syntax rules that prescribe the ways in which the primitive symbols are put together. In large measure these rules are hierarchically ordered; that is, some must be applied before certain others can be applied.

This is another property that has been firmly established for linguistic tasks. Its relevance to the nonlinguistic pattern classes is not nearly so clear-cut. Perhaps this is merely because the nonlinguistic systems have received much less attention and their formalization is not so advanced. It is certainly clear that there are rules for putting music down on paper or drawing benzene rings in a chemical structure. It appears that an order for the application of the rules is helpful to the analysis. Whether a strict ordering for the application of rules is essential (as is claimed for grammatical analysis) remains to be seen.

*Context sensitivity*

It is well known that the syntactic analysis of natural language requires techniques that go beyond those required to parse a context-free language. Context sensitivity is easily shown in both of the illustrative classes we have been considering simultaneously. In music, for instance, the key signature establishes the value of all subsequent notes until the signature is changed. Further, the occurrence of an accidental in a measure supersedes the specification of the key signature, not only for the note immediately following the accidental but for every note in the measure at that position on the staff.

In musical scores there is often an intrusion of verbal instructions. However, they should not be strictly interpreted as language, and frequently a nonverbal symbol of equivalent meaning is used. Thus a musician will come across the Italian word "Fine" ("End") in the text, but he should not interpret that as a mandatory rule to stop playing. Rather, he should continue until he has played to a special symbol (usually a set of double vertical lines). At this point he will usually find the Italian words "Da capo al fine" which he will interpret to mean: "Return to the beginning of the piece of music and play to the point designated by the symbol 'Fine.' "

In chemistry, one accepted procedure is to use the letter "R" as a variable whose value is another chemical structure ordinarily specified explicitly by a verbal statement, that is, by the names of the structures or their structural representations. If the text contains a sequence of chemical structures, as in a sequence of chemical reactions, then the variable symbol R will range over the same set of structures, no matter how long the sequence. The same concept of the range of a variable exists, of course, in algebra, as for the specification of any $x$ in an equation.

*Extensive redundancy*

The role of redundancy in natural language has been considered in several of the preceding chapters. Redundancy is essential to error correction and to recognition in the presence of noise. Redundancy in natural language is so great that whereas the alphabet of English can in principle encode about 4.5 bits per symbol, in actual use in natural language the information is probably not much more than 1.5 bits per symbol.

Equivalent estimates are difficult to make for either musical or chemical notation. For one thing these patterns are intrinsically two-dimensional, while language is only one-dimensional; therefore, they are more difficult to analyze. Nevertheless, it will be obvious to even an inexpert reader of music that much of the symbolism is redundant. For example, the lines that mark the measures are redundant because the time is specified at the beginning of the piece. However, there are many more subtle dependencies: the tonality, the melodic line, the dynamics, the tempo can in large measure be inferred by a good musician from what has gone before, by his knowledge of the composer, of the instrument, and so on.

In chemistry, the principal redundancy in the structural formulas is the fixed valence of virtually all elements that one would expect to find in an organic molecule. In a carefully drawn structural formula, the abbreviations of the names of the elements are used to label the nodes of the formula, even though sometimes, as when the chemist is in a hurry, the nodes are not labeled at all; and sometimes, the nodes for hydrogen are simply eliminated, since all this information can be inferred from the reduced symbol alone.

### *Introduction of new symbols and new rules*

Another way in which many conventional symbol systems resemble natural language is that they can continue to grow and change to suit the needs of the users. As with language, changes in other systems also occur primarily in the rules of the lowest level. Musical notation has been fairly well standardized for perhaps two hundred and fifty years, but it is not unusual to find a score with a more or less novel symbol and, usually, a prefatory note describing the interpretation of that symbol.

Chemical notation is more fluid, perhaps because chemical theory is still developing. Even within the last three decades there have been significant modifications in chemical notation, as in the representation of the coordinate covalent bond, the hydrogen bond, bridge structures, chelation, and so on. Many aspects of the chemical symbol system are not yet satisfactorily resolved. It is well known that chemical structural formulas cannot be completely modeled by mathematical structures as simple as labeled, ordered graphs. Many features of the underlying molecular entity are three-dimensional, but the chemist wants to record them on a two-dimensional page and, consequently, he will invent a convention to do so, usually in a way which he believes to be unambiguous in interpretation.

Some symbol systems are either so simple or so stereotyped that they need not be considered as interesting problems in pattern recognition.

These systems have little or no redundancy and are hardly open to more than one interpretation. Typical examples would be traffic and road signs, letter grades for academic performance, natural numbers in decimal notation, and so on. When for practical reasons it becomes desirable to recognize such symbols automatically, then the most efficient procedure designed so far has been to make the convention suit the machine. For example, check-reading machines work on highly specialized characters designed so that their differences from each other are relatively easy for a machine to register.

Mathematics makes use of a symbol system of especial interest. There is virtually no redundancy in a mathematical expression and only rarely may it be interpreted in more than one way in a given context. Mathematical notations are sometimes very complicated and can in principle be arbitrarily long. At the same time, mathematics is the "language" of computers; consequently, great efforts are being expended to write computer programs that will "recognize" and execute mathematical instructions written in the conventional symbolism of algebra or analysis. In this rather special sense, languages such as Fortran are the most successful pattern recognition schemes that exist today. But even here the success is not unalloyed. Fortran (or any of the other similar computer languages) cannot always interpret mathematical expressions in the sense intended by the writer.

The foregoing discussion may be summarized as follows. The conventional symbol systems have a number of abstract properties in common, but the fact that they are *conventional* implies that the rules for recognizing the symbols of one system are irrelevant for any other. We are concerned in this collection specifically with the problem of pattern recognition rather than pattern description, although the two are intimately related. In Chapters 5 and 6, we have described machine recognition of man-made patterns of language. I shall present an additional illustration of machine recognition, but in this case the man-made patterns are not patterns of natural language.

## The Recognition of Musical Notation

I have referred several times to the pattern-recognition problem of music. Here we can regard the over-all task as equivalent to that of inserting a page of sheet music into the "music reader" and having the machine play the music so that it is indistinguishable from human performance. In this problem, as in all other conventional pattern-recognition problems, the first task is to provide an abstract form for the patterns that are recognized; the second is to use the abstract representation to generate the output.[3] The second half of this problem is of considerable interest for music because the interpretation of the composition by a human performer imbues the music with more than appears on the printed page. Most computer programs which "play" the music from an abstract representation have no interpretative variations; tempo, intonation, dynamics are all metronomic. (In every case so far they have been prepared by humans; for example, by typing out a paper tape according to some straightforward and obvious rules.) However, only a highly qualified musician would be able to make a meaningful attack on such a subtle pattern-recognition problem. On the other hand, the first half of the problem is approachable, since one need not be a very good musician in order to read the music, and one need not have any ability to play it. Some aspects of the problem of machine recognition of music which were investigated by Dennis Pruslin (1966) in our laboratory are well worth my describing here.

Musical notation differs from most symbol systems, in particular from natural language, in that it is two-dimensional; that is, recognition proceeds for a variety of events which occur simultaneously. Certain of these events, for example, the notes, have their tonal values established by their relative vertical position in the pattern; other events, such as phrase marks and dynamic marks are not modified by their vertical position but by the horizontal place. In orchestral scores, a dozen or more staves, referring to different instruments, must all be interpreted so as to preserve in performance the temporal order of the notes played by the several instruments. In any case, the symbols are overlaid on a pattern of horizontal lines which serve as a kind of tonal "metric." Music score recognition is a difficult problem even though as a symbol system it is quite specific and rarely ambiguous. The work on score recognition is presented in some detail in order to reveal the many problems that must be solved in order to achieve machine recognition starting from the same artefact — the printed score — which a human would use in recognizing the same patterns.

So far only a fraction of the information in a musical score has been recognized by the computer program; certainly too little to permit "playing" the music by machine. Pruslin, who, so far as I know, was the first to attempt the problem, limited his concern to a small number of the symbols in the score. He attempted to identify solid-body notes,

[3] This division is recognized by linguistic theory as well. Linguists refer to their studies as being related to the knowledge available to anyone "competent" in a given natural language. Competence, for language, is the ability to recognize and understand grammatical sentences, but not necessarily to produce them. Production is not essential for competence; a mute is competent in his language. Further, it is unquestionably true that the competence of children in language, and in music, outstrips their performance.

that is, quarter notes, eighth notes, and so on, and the general timing-bar complexes, that is, the duration of each note cluster. He found the relations between these symbols in a way that enabled him to assign both time and tone value to each of the notes or note clusters that he identified. Pruslin studied double stave piano music, by no means the simplest music to read. In fact, the two staves of piano music are likely to require many more symbols than the orchestral score of the same composition because they contain a significant part of the information distributed over perhaps a dozen staves of an orchestral score.

The task of pattern recognition of musical notation can be divided into several subtasks.

*Identification of a unit in the unbounded text*

Such a unit is comparable to a word of a natural language. Many of the properties of the unit are independent of context, so that they can be discovered without reference to the other units in the text. The "natural" unit in music is the measure, measures being separated from one another by a vertical line. Pruslin assumed that the task of dividing the score into distinct measures had been done, in much the same way that we had assumed in the work on handwriting (Chap. 5) that the boundaries between words were easy to recognize. Whether the assumption of easy separability is justified remains to be seen, but a practical way to begin is to assume machine recognition of the boundaries to be easy.[4]

*Isolation of discrete picture elements*

Since all the symbols of musical notation are overlaid on the pattern of horizontal lines, one cannot analyze the elements by a simple search for geometric properties. Many of the geometric properties that are exploited in pattern recognition, for example, angles and intersections, occur accidentally in music all over the picture. It is obvious that the horizontal lines of the staff must first be removed.

The staff lines were eliminated by Pruslin by a procedure analogous to defocusing horizontally. The staff lines in most sheet music are very narrow, so any operation that is equivalent to low-pass filtering will tend to erase them. The musical measure was analyzed by a raster scan with the rapid sweep in a vertical direction. A black point is retained only

[4] The comparable problem in speech recognition is by no means easy to solve. In ordinary speech, the speaker does not separate every word by a pause; but in this task as well it is recognized that progress in identifying segments of speech sound which have been chosen to begin and end at word boundaries is essential before the more general problem of utterance recognition can be approached.

if its immediate predecessor in the vertical sweep is also a black point. In other words, the new array will contain fewer black points than the original. In particular, the thin horizontal segments in the original will be eliminated, leaving the rest of the picture relatively unchanged. Care must be taken, however, not to eliminate or to fragment other symbols of the music, for example, phrase marks, sharps, and naturals. One obvious step is to subtract, that is, erase, the identified features from the original picture and reprocess the remaining picture for elements such as accidentals, rests, and so on. In fact Pruslin used this procedure as a preliminary step in locating the staff line positions.

However, Pruslin had set himself the task of identifying only the solid-body notes and the relatively thick timing bars, so that fragmentation of the other symbols was not of concern to him.

### *Staff line location*

While the staff lines can be eliminated, it is essential to determine their positions, since the note values are defined by their relation to the staff lines. Pruslin chose to determine the staff line locations by a procedure that is analogous to cross correlation, that is, by looking for stretches of narrow lines more or less horizontally extended in the image; the horizontal lines were recovered by retaining precisely those points eliminated in the erasure operation. Note that the horizontal histogram technique that is used so effectively to locate field boundaries in handwriting or characters would be inapplicable here. The thinness of the staff lines is such that the histogram would be too sensitive to slight changes in the orientation of the picture.

Pruslin simplified the pattern further by repeating the filtering procedure in the vertical direction as well. In this way the stem, which is associated with all notes other than the whole notes, is eliminated and the note or note cluster is separated from its timing-bar complex. At this point in the analysis the pattern has been reduced to a collection of disconnected symbols which were designated "traces."

### *Contour tracing and intratrace operations*

Each of the disjoint traces must be examined to determine whether it is a note cluster or a timing marker or neither. Pruslin used the contour tracing algorithm, described earlier in connection with character recognition, as the first criterion for determining whether a given trace was in one of the two categories of interest. Certain traces can be eliminated because they are too small or too narrow. In the main, if the trace is neither too large in horizontal extent nor too small in vertical extent, an attempt is made to identify it as a note cluster or chord.

Although the conventions concerning note clusters do not appear to be given explicitly in descriptions of musical notation, they are nevertheless quite regular. Pruslin was able to identify twenty-three distinct note-cluster types, each referring to a completely determined chord, once the note cluster as a whole is located relative to the staff. For example, a vertical configuration of four notes must all be spaced two units apart — either all on the staff lines or all between the lines. On the other hand, a cluster of four notes with the second and fourth from the bottom displaced to the right can only be a chord of notes one unit apart. The exact values and the size of the tonal differences — half-steps or whole-steps — can only be determined after the relative position on the staff and the key signature are determined.

Note clusters can be named by listing the displacement of the note bodies (beginning arbitrarily at the lowest note) relative to a vertical fiducial line computed to lie on the center of the lowest note. As a result a code word is generated in much the same way as for the printed characters described by Mason (Chap. 6). In this instance the correctness of the identification was verified by matching the original trace against a template, the template being constructed from a set of criterial points found within the trace.

### *Timing complexes*

If a trace is not identified as a note cluster, it may be a timing-bar complex. A timing-bar complex is a pattern that a human would certainly not confuse with a note; the computer program would presumably be able to tell one from the other easily. However, pattern-recognition specialists have learned by experience that the relative ease with which humans discriminate patterns is a poor indicator of the difficulty or complexity of a computer program designed to perform an analogous task. The interpretation of the musical significance of timing-bar complexes is a problem quite different from that of note identification. Pruslin comments on these two tasks. There are

> two basic types of forms in the material to be recognized. One type, the clusters of notes, can be considered as characters, because a given note cluster is the same form every time it appears, to within printing noise variations. The second type, the timing complexes, cannot be considered as characters. This is so because there is essentially a continuum of forms which can represent timing complexes, despite the fact that these forms are far from arbitrary. This is in contrast to the character recognition problem, where all forms are characters once the size and type font have been set (1966, p. 19).

The timing complexes are assemblages each of whose elements can be thought of as a parallelogram with two vertical sides. However, the orientation and length of the sloping sides are dependent upon the note clusters to which the complexes refer. Pruslin noted that the relation between the elements of the timing complex are far from arbitrary, and that these relations could be formalized in a way that permits one to write generation rules for the complexes. A detailed description of the timing-complex recognition cannot be given here. It is not a simple procedure, for it entails a rather complicated series of steps. Three sequential operations are required. First, the "traces" or "blobs" that are potential candidates for consideration as elements of a timing complex need to be examined and a decision made as to whether or not they are timing-bar components. This can be regarded as an intratrace procedure. Before time values can be assigned to note clusters, the separate components of a timing complex must be interrelated. It is at this juncture that the generation rules play a key role. Finally, the timing complexes must be related to the notes and note clusters in the correct way so that the timing values of the chords are correct.

Pruslin was able to devise a computer program to execute the variety of tasks described above, tasks that are appropriate to at least a few of the essential aspects of reading sheet music.

### *Experimental results*

The experimental results are neither more nor less meaningful in this pattern-recognition problem than in the other conventional symbol-recognition tasks described in this collection. Percentage success in a task has meaning only for the particular sample studied and the particular task which was to be performed. Ultimately, it is meaningful only in terms of the subjective judgment of the reader who might compare the accuracy of the device with the accuracy he might expect of a human interpreter of the same symbols *under the same constraints,* in particular, with no wider contextual information than would be available explicitly to the computer program.

Pruslin examined one hundred and fifty-three note clusters. They were all correctly identified by the contour-trace code word but one, a single note, which would have been rejected by the template-match check routine. The timing-bar characterization procedures were tested on thirty-four timing-bar components, corresponding to twenty-two timing complexes. No errors occurred in either the intratrace operations or the component-merging operations. The procedure for resolving ambiguities between note cluster and timing base was correct in the fifteen cases where it was used. The procedure for determining note sequence made no errors while determining thirty-five subsets of note clusters. The procedure for time value assignment made no errors in assigning time values to fifty-seven note clusters.

The reader may be able to make a judgment of the significance of such apparently excellent results after he has examined Fig. 8.1. It displays one of the bars of music that Pruslin's program interpreted.

```
                         FINAL RECOGNITION RESULTS
NOTES STRUCK AT TIME 1 OF SEQUENCE ARE:   NOTES STRUCK AT TIME 6 OF SEQUENCE ARE:
NOTE CODE    0/1                          NOTE CODE    0/1
TIME VALUE   1/16                         TIME VALUE   1/8
NOTE CODE    2:2/1                        NOTE CODE    2:1/1
TIME VALUE   1/4                          TIME VALUE   1/8
```

**Fig. 8.1** An instance of machine recognition of music.

The encircled note values and the timing-bar complexes were recognized by the machine. The heading is a copy of the computer print-out and indicates the number and timing values of the first and sixth items of the upper and lower staves. The first item of the upper staff is a single note, the first item of the lower, a chord.

A few summary comments on music recognition are appropriate. Again we find that one of the tasks which humans can perform with great skill and speed, albeit only after a very great investment in learning time, a machine can, at least at present, perform only in a rudimentary and halting fashion. The technical problems are multitudinous. The general-purpose computer, for all its flexibility, seems to be singularly mismatched to the task. It is clear that a great deal more work needs to be done before the complete task of sheet music recognition may be considered solved; the variety of other symbols on the musical page must also be recognized, and the symbols interrelated. Pruslin's recognition was done on a single musical score. This, at least so far as the notes are concerned, is equivalent to character recognition of a single type font. Therefore it cannot be regarded as a solution to the more general problem of reading any printed sheet music following the same conventions. Finally, it should be pointed out that even this partial recognition of sheet music is several orders of magnitude slower than a proficient pianist would be who was playing the same score *a tempo.*

## Natural Pattern Classes

In an earlier section I listed some of the characteristics of conventional symbol systems and suggested how these characteristics enter into the task of recognizing the patterns that are meaningful for them. Although much of the work on pattern recognition has been directed toward conventional symbol systems, there is also considerable interest in the recognition of natural patterns. (Sometimes the investigator will distinguish between the two categories by referring to the task of classifying natural objects as signal detection.)

The "natural objects" that have been referred to for recognition are remarkably diverse: fingerprints, electrocardiograms, radar echoes from celestial bodies, engine noises, seismic events, white blood cells, clouds, diseases, nuclear events (in bubble chamber photographs or spark chamber tracks), leaves, insects, psychopathies, faces, and so on.[5]

If the tasks just cited are considered to be legitimate subjects of concern to workers in pattern recognition, it should be clear that it is fruitless to look for a single theory of pattern recognition. Above all, the search for regularities in the description of natural objects is *the* principal concern of science. These pattern-recognition tasks may share a need for the statistical techniques that are associated with the concepts of sensitivity, reliability, reproducibility, measurability, and so on, but they have little else in common that can be dignified by the appelation "theory."

There is no common methodology for the recognition of natural objects, but there appears to be a unifying objective. To put it somewhat differently, what unifies these problems and justifies their being considered together is the kind of question that categorizers of natural objects are obliged to ask and, hopefully, to answer.

[5] Sometimes the tokens of the conventional pattern classes are studied for their own sakes, as in the study of handwriting as a reflector of personality, or the recognition of a person from an analysis of his speech. In these cases the physical signal is produced by an individual who intends it to be the representation of a symbol in a specified language; but the signal is categorized by the investigator, usually without reference to its symbolic meaning.

*Motivation of natural pattern recognition*

To begin with, the motivation for performing the pattern recognition needs to be specified. In many cases the object of the study is to assign to a particular natural object a name that designates a class already defined, to which the object belongs. However, much of science is concerned with a prior problem. Scientists are presented with a set of natural objects and are required to categorize or partition the set in a conceptually useful way into mutually exclusive classes. But first, of course, the classes must be defined, and it is this problem that presents the serious difficulties. When a satisfactory solution is found for it, the application of an assignment procedure to an actual set of objects may well become a logical triviality even though a number of technical difficulties remain.

*Pragmatic pattern recognition*

How does one set up a classification of sets of objects? Clearly one must first know the purpose for which the classification is required. In many cases the pattern-recognition problem is set with a pragmatic end in view. The categories established and the rules for determining class membership are likely to be equally pragmatic. The goal of a law enforcement agency insofar as fingerprints are concerned is to identify an individual by a particular characteristic. No strong theory is required. It is sufficient to note that certain geometric and topologic features of a fingerprint are so variable that the determination of a modest number of such features in a particular set of fingerprints is enough to establish a correlation with a unique individual, or at most with a small number of individuals, even though the file of fingerprints to which the match is attempted may contain many millions. No theory of the formation of fingerprints or of the genetic characteristics of fingerprints is used. It may well be that none is required for this purpose.

On the other hand, the purpose of pattern recognition of electrocardiograms is to establish the likelihood of a normal or abnormal heart in the patient or, more specifically, the disease likely to be found in the patient with an abnormality.[6] Some of this work has proceeded on a

[6] A surprisingly large number of pattern-recognition problems relate to medical use. In particular, electrocardiography has been approached from many points of view. Discussions of several of the medically oriented pattern-recognition problems will be found in *The Diagnostic Process,* Proceedings of a Conference sponsored by the Biomedical Data Processing Training Program of the University of Michigan; held at the University of Michigan Medical School, May 9–11, 1963, John A. Jacquez, M.D., Editor.

purely empirical basis. Intentionally arbitrary properties of the waveform are measured on a sample of normals and on samples of abnormals of various disease types.[7] These measurements are combined in such a way as to achieve an optimal separation of disease types. Usually an attempt is made to use only a single statistic or to minimize the number of statistics that are needed. Another approach begins with the particular properties that competent cardiologists use or that are to be found in textbooks on electrocardiography. The pattern-recognition program can then be written so as to measure these particular properties. Then a comparison is made between the diagnoses made by the physicians who provided the original information upon which the program was prepared, and the computer program. In a sense this approach simply tests whether or not the physician has been able to make explicit his criteria of recognition, and also whether the computer programmer was able to translate these criteria into machine terms. In general, it is not easy to decide whether the imprecision lies with the physician or with the programmer.

Finally, another group who are studying the waveforms of electrocardiography are content to hold the problem of recognition in abeyance until the physical theory underlying the electric events that constitute the electrocardiogram is better understood. In effect, they hold to the view that a theory for the generation, and hence for the description, of the electrocardiogram must precede any systematic attempt to categorize it. It may well be that a theory of the electric sources and their distribution will make the electrocardiogram a more meaningful and useful signal; but physicians find it to be of use even though the signals have not been given a complete physical interpretation, especially since human beings require treatment for heart disease now.

### *A scientific basis for recognition*

There are many examples of the importance of a scientific basis for classification. In chemistry, the classification of inorganic substances was made on an empirical basis until the discovery of the elements, the concept of valence, and the formulation of Mendeleev's Table. Although analytical chemistry still uses some of the chemical procedures that were known prior to these discoveries, the categories of classification used are entirely different. In a similar manner, in organic chemistry, compounds were named and compound classes defined during the early

[7] Among the properties that have been used are arbitrary sampling at fixed time intervals measured from the peak of the R wave; Fourier coefficients, and coefficients of orthonormal exponentials. In this class, too, are the adaptive filter procedures and learning networks such as Madaline (Widrow, 1962).

nineteenth century, but not until Kekulé's discovery of the cyclicity of benzene and the consequent revolution in the structural description of cyclic compounds was it possible to rationalize the classification of the millions of organic compounds we know of today. In another realm, the classification of living species and the subsequent identification of specimens are problems at least as old as Aristotle. The great appeal of Darwinian notions to taxonomists was that they provided the beginnings of a theory for establishing a rational structure for the categories of animals or plants. Nowadays the taxonomist looks to the developments of molecular biology, and particularly to the "dogma of the DNA code," to provide him with an even more rigorously defined theory for the basis of his classifications. It is conceivable that the membership of an organism in a species or variety can be determined uniquely from the sequence of nucleotide residues in the DNA chains of its cells. If this were true and the DNA sequence capable of determination, then categorization of species might be reduced to defining degrees of similarity between DNA code words.

### *Relating scientific theory to conventional symbol systems*

The advantage to having a quantitative and explicit scientific theory for the classification of a set of natural objects is very great, for having one makes it possible to construct a conventional symbol system with the scientific theory as its basis. Earlier we discussed chemical notation as a conventional symbol system. Clearly, the current notations for chemical structures could not be formalized until the chemical theory for identifying atomic adjacency relations within a molecule was available. Right now it does not appear feasible to identify the chemical entity itself by automatic pattern-recognition techniques. The difficulty is that the immediately accessible properties of chemicals — melting point, boiling point, dielectric constant, specific gravity, spectral absorption, mass spectra, and the like — are not predictable currently from chemical structure alone. If and when such a strong theory of organic chemistry is discovered, these physical properties could be deduced or computed by using the symbols of the conventional chemical notations within an algebra for chemistry. So far as I am aware, there is only one pattern-recognition task currently under study for which such a strong physical theory is available. Nuclear events as revealed by particle tracks in bubble chamber or ionization chamber photographs are interpretable within the theory of nuclear physics.

In this problem and in particular in bubble chamber photographs the practical difficulties have not been completely circumvented but there is every reason to believe that pattern-recognition specialists studying this problem will be able to make the identification of nuclear events an automatic process.

When a need arises for assigning natural objects to categories, particularly if the number of objects to be categorized is large, it is to be anticipated that the persons who are concerned with the problem at hand will seek automatic pattern-recognition techniques, even though it may turn out, as it frequently does, that a computer program will not perform as accurately or as critically as a human but may be able to perform very much faster. A typical study of this kind was undertaken in our laboratory by Wade Swoboda, who investigated a procedure for classifying cloud cover patterns (1966). I shall discuss his research in some detail since it illuminates a number of facets of the problem of categorizing natural objects.

## *The recognition of clouds*

The TIROS series of weather satellites has furnished the meteorologist with millions of photographs of the earth's surface. It is impossible, given the small number of specialists and the amount of time available to them, to examine more than a small fraction of these photographs by eye. There is an acute need for some degree of automatic processing. However, it is not at all clear which specific aspects of the photographs concern the meteorologist. As a matter of fact, it is highly likely that the feature that captures the meteorologist's interest in one picture will be quite unrelated to the features that interest him in another. Before embarking upon the design of his system, Swoboda made a number of arbitrary decisions regarding the nature of the task.[8]

Swoboda restricted his interest to the problem of classifying the cloud cover into six categories: cirroform, stratoform, cumuloform, cumulonimbus, total overcast, and no cloud cover. Meteorologists identify other cloud types and subdivisions of types. In addition, a meteorologist may be able to identify more than one type of cloud cover in a single photograph. Swoboda recognized that, so far as the simplicity of processing was concerned, a great saving could be achieved by restricting consideration to properties of the photograph as a whole, putting aside the extraction of local features within the picture. It is worth noting that the choice of global properties rather than local-feature extractors has also been attempted in printed-character and block-letter recognition.

[8] Decisions of a similar nature must always be made. There is always a strong relationship between cost and time on the one hand and flexibility and complexity on the other. The designer must decide when the task he intends to solve is sufficiently informative to be useful to the specialist, and yet not so complex that computer time or the cost of construction for the recognition device is out of all proportion to the benefit to be derived from the automatic recognition procedure.

The simplicity of the processing equipment makes this procedure attractive. However, it is not surprising that global operators have proven virtually useless in recognition of patterns of conventional symbols.[9] We have earlier indicated the importance of context in recognition tasks, that is, a consideration of the relations between the symbolic elements contained within a larger entity. Global operators look at forests rather than trees. They may be able to distinguish a hardwood forest from a coniferous forest, but they are not likely to find an apple tree in a birch grove.

The decision to process the picture as a whole, and not to look for specific properties or locations within the picture, made it possible for Swoboda to do virtually all of the processing with analogue techniques. Digital operations were not much more complicated than counting values and assembling histograms.

### *Photograph preprocessing*

In many visual pattern-recognition problems the photograph is scanned by a flying-spot scanner, the position and intensity of points in the picture are quantized, converted from analogue to digital form, and stored as a matrix in the core memory or on magnetic tape. Since Swoboda was concerned exclusively with global properties, his flying-spot scanner employed more or less conventional electronic video techniques and he did not quantize the signal. The scanning raster size was chosen to include as large an area of the picture as possible. Furthermore, since the TIROS pictures are not ordinary photographs but are themselves generated by a video scan of rather coarse texture, the resolution that Swoboda used needed to be even coarser; thus, rapid variations in the amplitude of the scan signal, that is, in the grayness of the picture, from one point to its neighbors, are meaningless. Indeed, such variations could be misleading because they might simply represent the variations of amplitude as Swoboda's scan traversed the scan lines of the TIROS raster.

One of the properties that is used to distinguish types of clouds is their texture. These textures are frequently inhomogeneous, that is, clouds may be organized into a more or less striated pattern of parallel

[9] Perhaps the best publicized devices of this sort have been the Perceptron (Rosenblatt, 1962), and a number of analogous constructions, in particular, the Italian development which has been given the acronym PAPA (Borsellino and Gamba, 1961). A discussion of the virtues, limitations, and theoretical implications of this class of devices goes beyond the scope of this paper. However, it is by now quite clear that whatever the capabilities of these devices may be, they do not have very much to offer as insights into the problems of conventional symbol recognition.

elements. Thus texture will depend on the orientation of the scan relative to the clouds. The cloud, in turn, will have an orientation that is certainly uncorrelated with the orientation of the photograph. Accordingly, the coordinate system of the square raster scan was rotated through a fixed angle and the scan repeated at the new angle. The process was repeated until the coordinate system had been rotated through 180 degrees in all. Since the scan repetition rate was 10 per sec and the rotation rate was 180 degrees in 10 sec, each raster scan corresponded to an angular rotation of 1.8 degrees.

### *Choice of global parameters*

Implicit in a parametric approach to pattern recognition is the tacit assumption that the parametric description is a description of a single class. The choice of appropriate parameters will insure this condition or at least serve to minimize the likelihood of confusion of two classes. With well-defined samples of one pattern class, the attribute vectors constructed from the parametric values of each element in the sample show a marked clustering in attribute space and distinct separation from clusters representing well-defined samples of any other pattern class. When samples are not so easily assigned by the human observer to a particular pattern class, the boundaries of the group clusters in attribute space are no longer so well defined and in extreme cases the overlap is extensive. Unfortunately such confusion is unavoidable in the classification of cloud forms. One cloud type merges imperceptibly into another. The situation is further obscured in the processing of TIROS photographs since two different cloud types may appear in the same photograph. Since Swoboda had fixed on the use of global parameters only, there was no way to partition the picture into two spatial regions. His result in such cases would necessarily fall in an intermediate region in attribute space.

Swoboda comments on the difficulty of cloud classification as follows:

> The problem of classifying clouds has some rather distinctive features. The generic grouping of clouds is very loosely defined. Within these groups, individual clouds seldom possess a definite physical descriptor that can be attributed to a specific group. Even worse, it is quite possible for a descriptor that is used to separate two different groups to be invariant over a different sample set of the same two groups. A large part of this rather contradictory behavior is due to the detailed structure of a cloud. Clouds, by their nature, are very amorphous structures. Bounding a set of shapes, sites, or boundary characteristics to a specific group is a virtual impossibility. There is too much variation within groups and too much overlap among them. Although these structural characteristics are certainly important in the determination of group membership, when taken on a cloud by cloud

basis the error introduced is extremely large. Visual examination of a broad sampling of TIROS imagery substantiated these arguments, but indicated that there was a significant similarity in the texture of large formations of clouds of the same group (pp. 7–8).

The choice of parameters always is conditioned by the particular problem to be solved. The pattern recognition specialist depends heavily on his intuition to decide which of the features that are distinctive when judged by human perceptual skills can be translated into properties that can be measured readily by electronic devices.

From a practical point of view two additional constraints are unavoidable: cost and implementability. All too frequently excellent and perceptually distinct parameters can be found which must be rejected because of the high cost of implementation or the lack of a suitable technical procedure.

The electric properties of the scans which Swoboda measured were all either average values of intensity and rate of change of intensity or else variance of these properties. In this way it is the detail of the individual clouds — an important property and a component in many of the parameters — that is measured. It is not the fine structure of the cloud but rather the presence and distribution of fine structure that serves to identify the cloud type. We are not concerned with the properties of any particular cloud in the ensemble of clouds in any given photograph but rather the properties of the ensemble as a whole.

The first two textural parameters Swoboda estimated were simply the mean value and the variance of the video signal for any orientation of the raster scan. (Obviously these quantities should be independent of the orientation of the scan.) The other parameters were designed to provide measures of texture as a function of orientation. In terms of the photograph, the use of intensity information is restricted to such distinctions as "cloud" or "no cloud." Let $a$ = cloud and $b$ = no cloud. Swoboda observed that the texture associated with the distribution of detail — the occurrence of closely spaced *aba* boundaries or *bab* boundaries — is a significant feature. Subsequent mathematical operations on these boundaries provided several additional parameters. One parameter measured the "amount" of detail present, another measured the "length" of the boundaries present in the photograph, and ten others corresponded to the relative length of the boundary which is separated from parallel boundaries adjacent to it by a certain fixed interval. The data for each picture were transformed by these operations to a set of functions relating each of the parameters to the angle of rotation of the photograph.

Of course, this procedure generates many data and it is not surprising that on well-chosen test photographs they are sufficient to make a clean-cut separation between the cloud categories. Swoboda performed this work as part of his undergraduate thesis, and he was unable to conduct a substantial number of tests of his method. In any case, the work he had completed was sufficient to demonstrate that when a circumscribed and pragmatic attitude is adopted, when the choice of criteria and techniques rests on the objects to be identified rather than on their relevance to a theory of pattern recognition, a remarkably simple and inexpensive solution to the given problem may be found.

## Statistical Approaches

Having discussed two major kinds of pattern classes, I turn now to a different aspect of categorization, the "recognition" or detection of patterns by probabilistic means. Although we have paid little attention to the decision-theoretic and statistical procedures that have been widely discussed under the heading of pattern recognition, it should not be thought that we regard such techniques as irrelevant. Actually, certain of these techniques have been applied in problems discussed in earlier sections of this volume, notably with reference to Mermelstein's recognition of handwritten words (1964). Nevertheless, we contend that the statistical procedures that relate to the partition of abstract spaces are tangential to the problem of pattern recognition. In a sense the techniques of decision theory can only be applied after the pattern-recognition problem has been completed, that is, *after* the class of patterns in the objects to be classified is so explicitly defined that statistics can be used. What is not sufficiently recognized by the user of statistics is that the application of a particular statistical procedure carries with it a number of assumptions about the population of objects under study. In practice, these assumptions are occasionally unjustified so that using them robs the statistical technique of its significant applications.

A detailed discussion of the variety of techniques that have been proposed for pattern recognition and the conditions under which their use is justified will not be given here. The subject is too subtle and intricate to be treated by a paragraph or two of comment. Instead, I shall comment upon the domain of objects which one might wish to categorize and the issues concerning the characteristics of the objects that are relevant to the choice of a statistical method.

### *The infinite nature of property space*

First, it is necessary to realize that the number of measurable properties of any natural object is infinite. Moreover, with the possible exception of the electron, there are no natural object classes that are so well defined as to permit a complete description of the properties and behavior of these objects from a finite set of their properties. In many cases, of course, properties are highly correlated. In humans, for example, height is strongly correlated with the sex of an individual. Nevertheless, the general principle remains that no complete description of an object can be provided. Object classes can be uniquely defined in terms of a single property or a finite set of "basic" properties chosen for the purpose. As this segregation is always possible, it is obvious that the recognition problem is reduced to measuring the particular set of properties in the domain of objects under study and making an assignment according to the values of the properties. In this case, errors in recognition can be attributed solely to errors in the measuring techniques.

Object classes defined in this manner have been proposed in recent years, particularly for the taxonomic classification of living things, which has come to be known as numerical taxonomy. But such an arbitrary procedure leaves one with an uneasy feeling. After all, human beings have established thousands of different categories by which objects are named. It seems reasonable to ask that any objective classification scheme, such as the one proposed by students of numerical taxonomy, agree as far as possible with the intuitions of the human observer.

### *The problem of weighting parameters*

The infinitude of properties of objects forces the classifier to adopt a theory of the classes he is prescribing whether he recognizes it explicitly or not. The dilemma is purely mathematical. Suppose one wished to choose properties from a set "at random." In order to do so there must be a list of properties that one can construct and arrange so that each property can be chosen arbitrarily with equal probability. For an infinite countable set, this assumption is equivalent to associating an integer with each property. However, we are now reduced to choosing an integer or a finite set of integers "at random." But this is a futile, indeed meaningless, gesture. It is elementary to the theory of probability that, if the notion of probability is to have a serious meaning, a distribution must be defined over a set of finite measure. In other words, a rule must be prescribed that will assign significant probabilities to the choice of a finite number of properties, and a vanishingly small probability of choosing a particular one of the infinite set of other properties. As soon as the classifier orders the properties according to their probabilities, he has created a theory of the object class willy-nilly. He has already assumed which properties are important and which are unimportant.

This being the case, it would seem that the most efficient use of one's time would be to think, if one can, of the set of important properties and not worry about the others, unless it should become apparent from empirical test that the initial choices were poorly made.

### *Sample bias*

Another concern for the classifier has to do with the finiteness of the sample of objects which he can study, although these objects are drawn from populations that are potentially infinite or, at the very least, are astronomically large. The manner in which the sample is chosen may be biased. Here, too, we are forced to consider a characterization, that is, a theory of the population from which the sample is drawn, before a test can verify whether or not the sample choice was biased. Sometimes the "theory" of the population required may be no more than a statement concerning certain characteristics of the distribution of the population; in any case it is an implicit constraint on the study. If one remembers that classes of certain objects that we find important to classify, for example, species membership for organisms which are themselves changing (as species change, according to the concepts of Darwinian evolution), then the sample drawn at one time and place and useful at that time and place will be biased with respect to a sample drawn at another time and elsewhere, because the definition of the class has changed.

Finally, one must have a theory concerning the distribution of the values of the measured properties. At the least one would require a central tendency for each parameter. In other words, it is almost invariably assumed that if the value of a parameter measured on a particular test pattern falls close to the mean value of that same parameter as determined on the sample of patterns that were used to define a particular pattern class, then the likelihood that the test pattern falls in this class is enhanced. This is not necessarily the case. There are well-known distributions — the Cauchy distribution is one — that fit certain empirical data and that do not have a mean, that is, the mean is infinite. Other distributions have finite means but are multimodal. For example, if one were counting flower petals, many more roses would be found with 5 or 10 or 20 petals than with, say, 7 or 13.

Despite these remarks on the limitations of the applicability of statistical procedures in pattern recognition their usefulness in many classificatory tasks cannot be denied. Earlier I referred to the eclectic attitude of physicians in the interpretation of electrocardiograms. There is no question that statistical estimates enhance the reliability of machine diagnosis based on this physiological measurement. The two kinds of pattern-recognition problems — the natural and the man-made — were presented here without reference to the role that statistical procedures might play in them. For it is our contention, after all, that the crucial problem in pattern recognition is the structural description of a pattern class. When the structural description is adequate, one may be able to search systematically for a property or parameter without recourse to statistics.

However, it may well be that the crucial properties are inaccessible. As an instance, the cardiologist might well be able to make an unambiguous diagnosis by looking at the heart directly. Nevertheless, he must make his best diagnosis without this information. I turn now to an example of pattern recognition in which certainty of correct identification can never be anticipated and in which probabilistic considerations must enter.

## Applications to Medical Diagnosis

We can examine some of these statistical problems in the context of medical diagnosis, viewed as a pattern-recognition problem. First, what is a disease? The experts differ. At one extreme, certain physicians maintain that "disease" is undefinable except when it refers to the totality of symptoms and the history of a patient. This definition reduces the concept of disease to a tautology. At the other extreme, a disease is defined only by the presence of necessary and sufficient symptoms. The physician will refer to such a symptom as "pathognomonic" since it names the disease. While this is a precise definition, it is unsatisfying because only very few of the diseases which a practicing physician or, for that matter, a layman, will recognize, can be characterized uniquely. As soon as we attempt a definition somewhere between these two extremes and try to apply it to a specific disease, we find elements of disagreement among the diagnosticians. One difficulty is that the manifestation of the disease is modified by environmental factors, by climate, nutrition, the emotional state of the patient, and even culture. The different training of different physicians introduces additional variation. Despite these difficulties, diseases are usually recognized by physicians, as judged by their ability to cure patients of their ills.

Practical help for the physician may be provided by automatic pattern-recognition programs; if the automatic diagnosis and a competent physician agree, one would anticipate that such a program would be of practical value to a less competent physician, even though the validity of the program be clouded by a number of theoretical issues.

For a period of several years, Dr. Osler Peterson, Dr. Ernest Barsamian, and I (1966) have cooperated in a study of the quality of medical care as it was revealed in cases of pelvic surgery. Care was taken to choose a sample of hospitals to eliminate bias due to size, training of the staff, the patients' economic strata, and so on. Within each hospital certain surgeons were chosen, again, with an eye to including physicians of different age groups, levels of training, and degrees of specialization. A great deal of time was spent in preparing the logical schema by which the computer was to make its diagnoses. Expert surgeons were questioned in regard to their explicit diagnostic criteria and a suitable synthesis of these ideas was embodied in the program.

An additional feature was present in this study. Since all the cases involved surgery, the findings of the pathologist were recorded. A comparison could be made therefore between the diagnosis of the surgeon, the diagnosis of the computer, and the pathologists' findings. The surgeon and the computer program made the same diagnosis a gratifying number of times although the agreement was substantially less then perfect. In addition, many cases were observed in which the pathologist's findings differed from the diagnosis of the physician or computer or both. It would appear that these mismatches resulted largely from the difficulties of evaluating a number of factors, some of which I will now discuss.

## *The terminology of disease*

For one thing, it is not at all clear that the terminology used by the surgeons and the pathologists was identical. Agreement here would hinge on the definition of a particular disease. There was no way in this study to ascertain that all participants used the same definitions, if for no reason other than that there are no unambiguous definitions available. Another consideration is that the surgeon is not interested in a perfect score. He weighs the potential risks of operating or not operating according to his judgment of the likelihood that a particular pathological condition exists, or perhaps that a different disease will yield to the same surgical treatment. Yet another consideration is that there is no reason to presume that pathologists are infallible. Since one of their problems is also that of pattern recognition, they will identify the "easy" diseased tissues with high reliability and miss many of the "hard" ones. In like manner, one cannot put too much blame on the computer program for its errors. There, too, there was a terminological problem. Not only are the names of diseases defined fuzzily, but the symptoms too are imprecisely defined in many instances. During the course of the study a large notebook was filled with the variants of terms which physicians use. This book listed the different terms which mean the same thing to a particular physician, solving the problem of that ambiguity, but it is of no use in the case where the same term means different things to different physicians. Natural language being what it is, there are such ambiguities even in the lexicon of medicine. Sometimes, too, we were able to verify that the computer made the wrong diagnosis because the surgeon who had generated the patient's record had neglected to write down facts that were obvious to him but were clearly not inferrable or observable by the computer. Finally, the physicians could have made some observational mistakes, or in their own diagnosis have forgotten salient features that the computer would not forget once the feature had been entered in the record. All of these sources of "error" were relevant to the study.

### *The certainty of error*

This study of medical pattern recognition suggests that the search for perfection in pattern recognition, or even for statistical optimization of performance, is something of a will-o'-the-wisp. For medicine, as for many other natural object classifications, even should there be a unique property set that established class membership unambiguously, there would be no guarantee that the pathognomonic property set was accessible for measurement. In the study described above we had assumed that the pathologist's finding was pathognomonic. But the diagnostician must make his diagnosis before operating on the patient. In like manner, the seismologist can recognize the presence or absence of oil in a certain rock stratum simply by digging a well down to it. The trick is to predict the presence of oil before the well is dug.

The search for appropriate properties and measurements to improve recognition is well worth pursuing. Many workers prefer to proceed by investigation of empirically chosen properties and testing the usefulness of these new parameters in the identification task, well aware of the difficulties of statistical verification mentioned above. Others will look for an underlying explanation, a description, or a theory of the phenomena with which the objects of recognition are associated. Even in medicine, some diagnosticians depend on empiricism, on their experience with large numbers of patients, on their previous diagnoses, and on the subsequent histories of their patients. Other diagnosticians look for physiological or biochemical systems to make "sense" out of the set of symptoms and signs they elicit from the patient. Although I incline toward the side of the theory builders, I do recognize that empirical solutions to problems, while perhaps not esthetically as pleasing, are often of great social worth.

## Overview

If there is one thread common to all pattern recognition, it is that it is a characteristically human activity. Animals obviously also recognize patterns. The experiments of the behavioral psychologists have provided ample demonstration of this, if indeed any was required; but neither the richness and variety of ways in which we humans categorize things nor the ease with which we invent new categories is manifest in the rest of the animal kingdom. Why do we categorize things the way we do? Why are some classifications grossly obvious, others exceedingly subtle (at least as we feel them to be gross or subtle)? How is it that the manifold transformations of size, shape, color, aspect, and so on, do not upset our ability to recognize things, even when the things themselves have never been seen before?

Through most of the essays in this collection, it has been asserted that there is no necessary connection between pattern recognition as humans perform it and as machines can perform it. Yet the fact remains that many students of pattern recognition are acutely interested in finding out the ways humans recognize patterns. At the present time the only resemblance that can be found between the two ways of performing the same task is that the machine is successful where the human is successful, and that the machine fails where the machine fails.[10] Very little can be claimed beyond this point.

It may be that when science has invented better models for the performance of complex cognitive tasks, and when a more detailed knowledge of the workings of the nervous system is available, the engineer who studies pattern recognition can make a model relating the animate to the inanimate. Until then a great deal remains to be done in the practical tasks of pattern recognition.

## Acknowledgment

Preparation of this paper was supported principally by the National Institutes of Health (Grant 1 PO1 GM-14940-01), and in part by the Joint Services Electronics Program (Contract DA 28-043-AMC-02536(E)).

## References

Borsellino, A., and A. Gamba. An outline of a mathematical theory of PAPA. *Nuovo Cimento Suppl.*, 1961, *20*, 221–231.

[10] If the machine is more successful than the man, that is, if it recognizes when the human cannot, such a result is as strong an argument against the existence of an analogy between human process and machine process as the more common case in which the human recognizes where the computer fails.

Ginsburg, S., and J. Ullian. Ambiguity in context-free languages. *J. Ass. Computing Machinery,* 1966, *13,* 62–89.

Hiz, H. A linearization of chemical graphs. *J. Chem. Documentation,* 1964, *4,* 173–180.

Mermelstein, P. Computer recognition of connected handwritten words. Sc.D. Thesis, Department of Electrical Engineering, M.I.T., 1964.

Parikh, R. J. Language generating devices. Quart. Prog. Rep. No. 60, Res. Lab. Electronics, M.I.T., Jan. 15, 1961, pp. 199–212.

Peterson, O. L., E. M. Barsamian, and M. Eden. A study of diagnostic performance: A preliminary report. *J. Med. Educ.,* 1966, *41,* 797–803.

Pruslin, D. H. Automatic recognition of sheet music. Sc.D. Thesis, Department of Electrical Engineering, M.I.T., 1966.

Rosenblatt, F. *Principles of Neurodynamics: Perceptrons and the Theory of Brain Mechanisms.* Washington, D.C.: Spartan Books, 1962.

Sadler, E., L. Stark, J. Dickson, I. Sobel, and G. Whipple. Modification of input parameters for electrocardiograph pattern recognition analysis. Quart. Prog. Rep. No. 70, Res. Lab. Electronics, M.I.T., July 15, 1963, pp. 351–353.

Sokal, R. R., and P. H. Smith. *The Principles of Numerical Taxonomy,* San Francisco: W. H. Freeman, 1963.

Swoboda, W. A system for the semi-automatic classification of cloud imagery. S.B. Thesis, Department of Electrical Engineering, M.I.T., 1966.

Widrow, B. *Generalization and Information Storage in Networks of Adaline Neurons.* Stanford, California: University Press, 1962.

# Selected Bibliography

The topic of automatic pattern recognition has evoked a large and still burgeoning literature. As a further aid to the student of the subject, we are appending a bibliography that samples that literature. Because most of the papers in the first part of this book are already well documented, this bibliography concentrates upon formal treatments, engineering applications, and simulations. We have further restricted it to articles in English and to articles available in the open literature. A very large number of articles, regrettably, are published only as project reports, technical notes, and in other parochial ways, seriously limiting access to them; because of the difficulty of access, articles of this kind are not included in the bibliography. While the greatest amount of published work on automatic pattern recognition has appeared in English, an increasing body of work is becoming available in Russian. Only some of this is regularly translated into English, and some of that has been included. The topical headings represent the editors' partitioning of the data space.

**Theoretical and General**

Aizerman, M. A., E. M. Braverman, and L. I. Rozonoer. The probability problem of pattern recognition learning and the method of potential functions. *Avtomatika i Telemekhanika,* 1964, 25, 1307–1323. Translated in *Automation & Remote Control,* 1964, *25,* 1175–1193.

Albert, A. A mathematical theory of pattern recognition. *Ann. Math. Stat.,* 1963, *34,* 282–299.

Fischler, M., R. L. Mattson, O. Firschein, and L. D. Healy. An approach to general pattern recognition. *IRE Trans. on Information Theory,* 1962, IT-8, S64–S73.

Lewis, P. M. The characteristic selection problem in recognition systems. *IRE Trans. on Information Theory,* 1962, IT-8, 171–178.

Minsky, M. L. Steps toward artificial intelligence. *Proc. IRE* 1961, *49,* 8–30.

Minsky, M. L. *Computation: Finite and Infinite Machines.* Englewood Cliffs, N.J.: Prentice-Hall, 1967.

Nilsson, N. J. *Learning Machines.* McGraw-Hill Series in Systems Science. New York: 1965.

Sebestyen, G. S. *Decision Making Processes in Pattern Recognition.* New York: Macmillan, 1962.

Selfridge, O. G., and U. Neisser. Pattern recognition by machine. In E. A. Feigenbaum and J. Feldman (Editors), *Computers and Thought.* New York: McGraw-Hill, 1963. Pp. 235–267.

Selin, I. *Detection Theory.* Princeton, N.J.: Princeton University Press, 1965.

Uhr, L. (Editor). *Pattern Recognition: Theory, Experiment, Computation, Simulations, and Dynamic Models of Form Perception and Discovery.* New York: Wiley, 1966.

## Specific Mathematical Methods

Alt, F. L. Digital pattern recognition by moments. *J. Assoc. Computing Machinery,* 1962, *2,* 240–258.

Blaydon, C. C. On a pattern classification result of Aizerman, Braverman, and Rozonoer. *IEEE Trans. on Information Theory,* 1966, IT-12, 82–83.

Bonner, R. E. On some clustering techniques. *IBM J. Res. and Dev.,* 1964, *8,* 22–32.

Capon, J. Hilbert space methods for detection theory and pattern recognition. *IEEE Trans. on Information Theory,* 1965, IT-11, 247–259.

Chow, C. K. A recognition method using neighbor dependence. *IRE Trans. on Elec. Comp.,* 1962, EC-11, 683–690.

Cooper, P. W. The hyperplane in pattern recognition. *Cybernetica,* 1962, *5,* 215–238.

Cooper, P. W. Quadratic discriminant functions in pattern recognition. *IEEE Trans. on Information Theory,* 1965, IT-11, 313–315.

Cover, T. M., and P. E. Hart. Nearest neighbor pattern classification. *IEEE Trans. on Information Theory,* 1967, IT-13, 21–27.

Duda, R. O., and H. Fossum. Pattern classification by iteratively determined linear and piecewise linear discriminant functions. *IEEE Trans. on Elec. Comp.,* 1966, EC-15, 220–232.

Highleyman, W. H. Linear decision functions, with application to pattern recognition. *Proc. IRE,* 1962, *50,* 1501–1514.

Horwitz, L. P., and G. L. Shelton, Jr. Pattern recognition using autocorrelation. *Proc. IRE,* 1961, *49,* 175–185.

Schwartz, M. Abstract vector spaces applied to problems in detection and estimation theory. *IEEE Trans. on Information Theory,* 1966, IT-12, 327–336.

Sebestyen, G., and J. Edie. An algorithm for non-parametric pattern recognition. *IEEE Trans. on Elec. Comp.,* 1966, EC-15, 908–915.

Specht, D. F. Generation of polynomial discriminant functions for pattern recognition. *IEEE Trans. on Elec. Comp.,* 1967, EC-16, 308–319.

## Design and Analysis of Pattern Recognizers

Chien, Y. T., and K. S. Fu. A modified sequential recognition machine using time-varying stopping boundaries. *IEEE Trans. on Information Theory,* 1966, IT-12, 206–214.

Fukunaga, K., and T. Ito. A design theory of recognition functions in self-organizing systems. *IEEE Trans. on Elec. Comp.,* 1965, EC-14, 44–52.

Highleyman, W. H. The design and analysis of pattern recognition experiments. *Bell System Tech. J.,* 1962, *41,* 723–744.

Koford, J. S., and G. F. Groner. The use of an adaptive threshold element to design a linear optimal pattern classifier. *IEEE Trans. on Information Theory,* 1966, IT-12, 42–50.

Marrill, T., and D. M. Green. On the effectiveness of receptors in recognition systems. *IEEE Trans. on Information Theory,* 1963, IT-9, 11–17.

Marill, T., and D. M. Green. Statistical recognition functions and the design of pattern recognizers. *IRE Trans. on Elec. Comp.,* 1960, EC-9, 472–477.

Saaty, T. L. A discrete search problem in pattern recognition. *IEEE Trans. on Information Theory,* 1966, IT-12, 69–70.

Sezaki, N., and H. Katagiri. Pattern recognition by follow method. *Proc. IEEE,* 1965, *53,* 510.

## Applications of Pattern Recognition Techniques

Casey, R., and G. Nagy. Recognition of printed Chinese characters. *IEEE Trans. on Elec. Comp.,* 1966, EC-15, 91–101.

Eden, M. Handwriting and pattern recognition. *IRE Trans. on Information Theory,* 1962, IT-8, 160–166.

Greanias, E. C., P. F. Meagher, R. J. Norman, and P. Essinger. The recognition of handwritten numerals by contour analysis. *IBM J. Res. and Dev.* 1963, *7,* 299–307.

Liu, C. N. A programmed algorithm for designing multifont character recognition logics. *IEEE Trans. on Elec. Comp.* 1964, EC-13, 586–593.

Lodwick, G. S., C. L. Haun, W. E. Smith, R. F. Keller, and E. D. Robertson. Computer diagnosis of primary bone tumors. *Radiology,* 1963, *80,* 273–275.

Lodwick, G. S., T. E. Keats, and J. P. Dorst. The coding of roentgen images for computer analysis as applied to lung cancer. *Radiology,* 1963, *81,* 185–200.

Marzocco, F. N. Computer recognition of handwritten first names. *IEEE Trans. on Elec. Comp.,* 1965, EC-14, 210–217.

Sakai, T., and S. Doshita. Automatic speech recognition system for conversational sound. *IEEE Trans. on Elec. Comp.,* 1963, EC-12, 835–846.

Specht, D. F. Vectorcardiographic diagnosis using the polynomial discriminant method of pattern recognition. *IEEE Trans. on Bio-med. Eng.,* 1967, BME-14, 90–95.

Turner, L. F. A system for the automatic recognition of moving patterns. *IEEE Trans. on Information Theory,* 1966, IT-12, 195–205.

## Adaptive Machines: Theoretical

Abramson, N., and D. Braverman. Learning to recognize patterns in a random environment. *IRE Trans. on Information Theory,* 1962, IT-8, S58–S63.

Amari, S. A theory of adaptive pattern classifiers. *IEEE Trans. on Elec. Comp.,* 1967, EC-16, 299–307.

Borsellino, A., and A. Gamba. An outline of a mathematical theory of PAPA. *Nuovo Cimento,* 1961, 20, *Suppl.* No. 2, 221–231.

Braverman, D. Learning filters for optimum pattern recognition. *IRE Trans. on Information Theory,* 1962, IT-8, 280–285.

Cooper, D. B., and P. W. Cooper. Non-supervised adaptive signal detection and pattern recognition. *Information and Control,* 1964, *7,* 416–444.

Fralick, S. C. Learning to recognize patterns without a teacher. *IEEE Trans. on Information Theory,* 1967, IT-13, 57–64.

Kazmierczak, H., and K. Steinbuch. Adaptive system in pattern recognition. *IEEE Trans. on Elec. Comp.,* 1963, EC-12, 822–835.

Keller, H. B. Finite automata, pattern recognition and perceptrons. *J. Assoc. Computing Machinery,* 1961, *8,* 1–20.

Patrick, E. A., and J. C. Hancock. Non-supervised sequential classification and recognition of patterns. *IEEE Trans. on Information Theory,* 1966, IT-12, 362–372.

Rosenblatt, F. *Principles of Neurodynamics.* Washington, D. C.: Spartan Books, 1962.

Sworder, D. *Optimal Adaptive Control Systems.* New York: Academic Press, 1966.

Widrow, B. Pattern recognition and adaptive control. *IEEE Trans. on Applications and Industry,* 1964, *83,* 269–277.

## Adaptive Machines: Empirical

Braverman, E. M. Experiments on machine learning to recognize visual patterns. *Avtomatika i Telemekhanika,* 1962, *23,* 349–364. Translated in *Automation & Remote Control,* 1962, *23,* 315–327.

Gagliardo, E. On the evaluation of a formula for the errors of a learning machine. *Nuovo Cimento,* 1961, *20, Suppl.* No. 2, 232–238.

Gamba, A., L. Gamberini, G. Palmieri, and R. Sanna. Further experiments with PAPA. *Nuovo Cimento,* 1961, *20, Suppl.* No. 2, 112–115.

Palmieri, G., and R. Sanna. Automatic probabilistic programmer/analyzer for pattern recognition. *Methodos,* 1960, *12,* 331–357.

Rosen, C. A. and D. J. Hall. A pattern recognition experiment with near optimum results. *IEEE Trans. on Elec. Comp.,* 1966, EC-15, 666–667.

Scudder, H. J., III. Probability of error of some adaptive pattern-recognition machines. *IEEE Trans. on Information Theory,* 1965, IT-11, 363–371.

## Neural Simulation

Farley, B. G., and W. A. Clark. Activity in networks of neuronlike elements. In C. Cherry (Editor), *Proceedings of the 4th London Symposium on Information Theory.* Washington, D. C.: Butterworth, 1961. Pp. 242–251.

Fehmi, L. G., and T. H. Bullock. Discrimination among temporal patterns of stimulation in a computer model of a coelenterate nerve net. *Kybernetik,* 1967, *3,* 240–249.

Glucksman, H. A. A parapropagation pattern classifier. *IEEE Trans. on Elec. Comp.,* 1965, EC-14, 434–443.

Reiss, R. F. A theory and simulation of rhythmic behavior due to reciprocal inhibition in small nerve nets. *Proc. Spring Joint Computer Conf.,* 1962, *21,* 171–194.

Rosenfeld, A. Perceptrons as "figure" detectors. *IEEE Trans. on Information Theory,* 1965, IT-11, 304–305.

Uhr, L., and C. Vossler. Suggestions for self-adapting computer models of brain functions. *Behavioral Science,* 1961, *6,* 91–97.

## Models of Some Human Recognition Capabilities

Bourne, L. E., and F. Restle. Mathematical theory of concept identification. *Psychol. Rev.,* 1959, *66,* 278–296.

Eden, M., On the formalization of handwriting. In R. Jakobson (Editor), *Structure of Language and its Mathematical Aspects.* Proceedings Symposia in Applied Math., *12,* 83–88. Providence, R.I.: Am. Math. Soc., 1961.

Gyr, J. W., J. S. Brown, R. Willey, and A. Zivian. Computer simulation and psychological theories of perception. *Psychol. Bull.,* 1966, *65,* 174–192.

Halle, M., and K. Stevens. Speech recognition: a model and a program for research. *IRE Trans. on Information Theory,* 1962, IT-8, 155–159.

Hoffman, W. C. The Lie algebra of visual perception. *J. Math. Psych.,* 1966, *3,* 65–98.

Matthews, G. H. Analysis by synthesis of sentences of natural languages. *1961 International Conf. on Machine Trans. and Applied Language Analysis.* London: H.M. Stationery Office, 1967, *2,* 531–540.

Wathen-Dunn, W. (Editor). *Models for the Perception of Speech and Visual Form.* Cambridge: M.I.T. Press, 1967.

Wiener, Norbert, and J. P. Schadé (Editors). *Symposium on Cybernetics of the Nervous System: Nerve, Brain and Memory Models.* Progress in Brain Research, *2.* New York: Elsevier, 1963.

# Index